A Panorama of Pure Mathematics

This is a volume in
PURE AND APPLIED MATHEMATICS
A Series of Monographs and Textbooks

Editors: SAMUEL EILENBERG AND HYMAN BASS

A list of recent titles in this series appears at the end of this volume.

A Panorama of Pure Mathematics

As Seen by N. Bourbaki

Jean Dieudonné
Membre de l'Institut

Translated by

I. G. Macdonald
Department of Pure Mathematics
Queen Mary College
University of London
London, England

1982

ACADEMIC PRESS
A Subsidiary of Harcourt Brace Jovanovich, Publishers
New York London
Paris San Diego San Francisco São Paulo Sydney Tokyo Toronto

ACADEMIC PRESS, INC.
111 Fifth Avenue, New York, New York 10003

United Kingdom Edition published by
ACADEMIC PRESS, INC. (LONDON) LTD.
24/28 Oval Road, London NW1 7DX

Library of Congress Cataloging in Publication Data

Dieudonné, Jean Alexandre, Date.
A panorama of pure mathematics (as seen by N. Bourbaki)

(Pure and applied mathematics)
Translation of: Panorama des mathématiques pures.
Bibliography: p.
Includes index.
1. Mathematics--1961- . I. Title. II. Series.
QA37.2.D5313 510 80-2330
ISBN 0-12-215560-2 AACR2

This is the English language translation of
Panorama des mathématiques pures. Le choix bourbachique

PRINTED IN THE UNITED STATES OF AMERICA

82 83 84 85 9 8 7 6 5 4 3 2 1

Contents

A IV. Ergodic theory

A V. Partial differential equations

A VI. Noncommutative harmonic analysis

A VII. Automorphic forms and modular forms

Introduction

This book is addressed to readers whose mathematical knowledge extends at least as far as the first two years of a university honors course. Its aim is to provide an *extremely sketchy* survey of a rather large area of modern mathematics, and a guide to the literature for those who wish to embark on a more serious study of any of the subjects surveyed.

By "Bourbaki mathematics" I mean, with very few exceptions, the set of topics covered in the exposés of the Séminaire Bourbaki. Since the beginning of their collective work, the collaborators of N. Bourbaki have taken a definite view of mathematics, inherited from the tradition of H. Poincaré and E. Cartan in France, and Dedekind and Hilbert in Germany. The "Eléments de Mathématique" have been written in order to provide solid foundations and convenient access to this aspect of mathematics, in a form sufficiently general for use in as many contexts as possible.

From 1948 onward, the Bourbaki group has organized a seminar, consisting in principle of 18 lectures each year. The purpose of these lectures is to describe those recent results that appear to the organizers to be of most interest and importance. These lectures, almost all of which have been published, now exceed 500 in number, and collectively constitute a veritable encyclopedia of these mathematical theories.

*

* *

No publication under the name of N. Bourbaki has ever described how the topics for exposition in the seminar have been chosen. One can therefore only attempt to discern common features by examining these choices from outside, and their relation to the totality of the mathematical literature of our age. I wish to make it clear that the conclusions I have drawn from this examination are my own, and do not claim in any way to represent the opinions of the collaborators of N. Bourbaki.

The history of mathematics shows that a theory almost always originates in efforts to solve a specific problem (for example, the duplication of the cube in Greek mathematics). It may happen that these efforts are fruitless, and we have our first category of problems:

(I) Stillborn problems (examples: the determination of Fermat primes, or the irrationality of Euler's constant).

A second possibility is that the problem is solved but does not lead to progress on any other problem. This gives a second class:

(II) Problems without issue (this class includes many problems arising from "combinatorics").

A more favorable situation is one in which an examination of the techniques used to solve the original problem enables one to apply them (perhaps by making them considerably more complicated) to other similar or more difficult problems, without necessarily feeling that one really understands why they work. We may call these

(III) Problems that beget a *method* (analytic number theory and the theory of finite groups provide many examples).

In a few rather rare cases the study of the problem ultimately (and perhaps only after a long time) reveals the existence of unsuspected underlying structures that not only illuminate the original question but also provide powerful general methods for elucidating a host of other problems in other areas; thus we have

(IV) Problems that belong to an active and fertile general *theory* (the theory of Lie groups and algebraic topology are typical examples at the present time).

However, as Hilbert emphasized, a mathematical theory cannot flourish without a constant influx of new problems. It has often happened that once the problems that are of the greatest importance for their consequences and their connections with other branches of mathematics have been solved, the theory tends to concentrate more and more on special and isolated questions (possibly very difficult ones). Hence we have yet another category:

(V) Theories in decline (at least for the time being: invariant theory, for example, has passed through this phase several times).

Finally, if a happy choice of axioms, motivated by specific problems, has led to the development of techniques of great efficacy in many areas of mathematics, it may happen that attempts are made with no apparent motive to modify these axioms somewhat arbitrarily, in the hope of repeating the success of the original theory. This hope is usually in vain, and thus we have, in the phrase of Pólya and Szegö†

† G. Pólya and G. Szegö, "Problems and Theorems in Analysis," Springer-Verlag, Berlin and New York, 1972.

(VI) Theories in a state of *dilution* (following the example of these authors, we shall cite no instances of this).

In terms of this classification, it appears to me that the majority of the topics expounded in the Séminaire Bourbaki belong to category (IV) and (to a lesser extent) category (III). This is, I believe, as objective an opinion as I can form, and I shall abstain from further comment.

*

* *

Since the number and variety of the lectures in the Séminaire make them difficult to use, I have grouped them into sections under a fairly small number of headings, each of which contains a closely related group of subjects. One of the characteristics of Bourbaki mathematics is its extraordinary *unity*: there is hardly any idea in one theory that does not have notable repercussions in several others, and it would therefore be absurd, and contrary to the very spirit of our science, to attempt to compartmentalize it with rigid boundaries, in the manner of the traditional division into algebra, analysis, geometry, etc. now completely obsolete. The reader should therefore attach no importance to this grouping, which is purely a matter of convenience; its aim is to provide a clear overall view, halfway between the chaos of the chronological order of the lectures, and fragmentation into a dust-cloud of minitheories. At the beginning of each section I have inserted an "organization chart" designed to illustrate graphically its connections with the others, with arrows to indicate the direction of influence.

Each section contains, to the extent that it is feasible, a rapid didactic exposition of the main questions to be considered. With a few exceptions, only those are mentioned that have been covered in the Séminaire Bourbaki; the order followed is not in general the historical order, and the infrequent historical indications make no pretence of being systematic. At the end of each section will be found a list of the mathematicians who have made significant contributions to the theories described, and a brief mention of the connections (where they exist) between these theories and the natural sciences.

Each section or heading is designated by a boldface capital letter followed by a Roman numeral. This designation refers to the place occupied by the heading in the *Table of subjects* (p. 5), the capital letter indicating the level at which the heading is placed. These levels range from top to bottom, roughly speaking in decreasing order of what might be called their "Bourbaki density," that is to say (without pretension to numerical accuracy, which would be absurd), the proportion of the topics covered by the Séminaire Bourbaki to the total mathematical literature relating to the heading concerned.

*

* *

The references have been organized in such a way as to serve as a guideline to readers who wish to learn more. References to the Séminaire Bourbaki are indicated by the letter B followed by the number of the exposé. They are augmented by references to:

(i) the Séminaires H. Cartan, denoted by the letter C followed by the year;

(ii) the expository lectures organized by the American Mathematical Society and published in its *Bulletin*; these are indicated by the letters BAMS followed by the volume number of the *Bulletin* and the name of the lecturer;

(iii) the *Symposia* organized by the American Mathematical Society, denoted by the letters SAMS followed by a roman numeral and (sometimes) the author's name;

(iv) the lectures given at the recent International Congresses of Mathematicians at Stockholm (1962), Nice (1970), and Vancouver (1974); these are indicated by the name of one of these cities and the lecturer's name (in the case of the Nice Congress, the figure I indicates a one-hour lecture, and an indication of the section of the Congress a half-hour lecture);

(v) the "Lecture Notes in Mathematics" published by Springer-Verlag, denoted by the letters LN followed by a number (and by an author's name, in the case of a colloquium or symposium);

(vi) various articles and books, denoted by the letter or the number in brackets under which they are listed in the bibliography.

No reference is given for mathematical terms currently used in the first two years of a university honors course. For others, either a brief explicit definition is given, or a reference to a textbook in the bibliography.

The headings at level **D** in the table of subjects are those of Bourbaki density zero. They refer to theories that have in part been fixed for a considerable time, and constitute, in the etymological sense of the word, the *classical* part of mathematics, which serves as a basis for the rest of the edifice. The reader will find these theories expounded in the volumes of the "Eléments de Mathématique" that have already been published. Research still continues in these various theories, about which I shall say nothing except to remark on the curious historical phenomenon of a science divided into two parts that in practice ignore each other, without apparently causing the least impediment to their respective developments.

I wish to thank readers whose comments enabled me to correct certain errors and omissions in the second (French) edition. At the end of each section I have appended a list of references given in the text, together with some additional ones for the reader's benefit.

TABLE OF SUBJECTS

Levels							
A	**A** I Algebraic and differential topology	**A** II Differential geometry	**A** III Ordinary differential equations	**A** IV Ergodic theory	**A** V Partial differential equations		
	A VI Noncommutative harmonic analysis	**A** VII Automorphic and modular forms	**A** VIII Analytic geometry	**A** IX Algebraic geometry	**A** X Theory of numbers		
B	**B** I Homological algebra	**B** II Lie groups	**B** III "Abstract" groups	**B** IV Commutative harmonic analysis	**B** V Von Neumann algebras	**B** VI Mathematical logic	**B** VII Probability theory
C	**C** I Categories and sheaves	**C** II Commutative algebra	**C** III Spectral theory of operators				
D	**D** I Set theory	**D** II General algebra	**D** III General topology	**D** IV Classical analysis	**D** V Topological vector spaces	**D** VI Integration	

A I

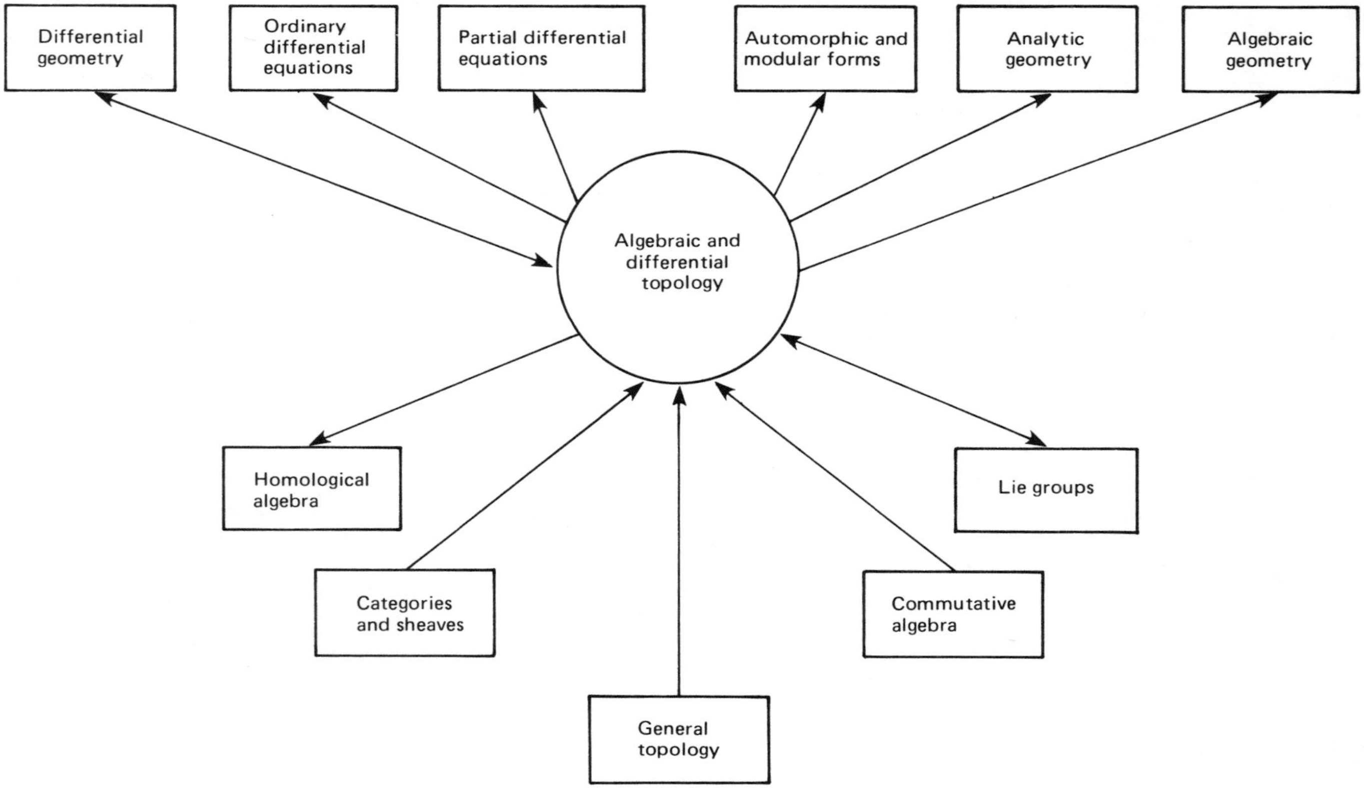

Differential geometry
Ordinary differential equations
Partial differential equations
Automorphic and modular forms
Analytic geometry
Algebraic geometry
Algebraic and differential topology
Homological algebra
Lie groups
Categories and sheaves
Commutative algebra
General topology

A I

Algebraic and differential topology

It may already be predicted without great likelihood of error that the 20th century will come to be known in the history of mathematics as the century of *topology*, and more precisely of what used to be called "combinatorial" topology, and which has developed in recent times into *algebraic topology* and *differential topology*. These disciplines were created in the last years of the 19th century by H. Poincaré, in order to provide a firm mathematical basis for the intuitive ideas of Riemann. At first they developed rather slowly, and it was not until the 1930s that they took wing. Since then they have multiplied, diversified, and refined their methods, and have progressively infiltrated all other parts of mathematics; and there is as yet no indication of any slowing down of this conquering march.

1. Techniques

The initial problem of algebraic topology, roughly speaking, is to "classify" topological spaces: two spaces are to be put in the same "class" if they are homeomorphic. The general idea is to attach to each topological space "invariants," which may be numbers, or objects endowed with algebraic structures (such as groups, rings, modules, etc.) in such a way that homeomorphic spaces have the same "invariants" (up to isomorphism, in the case of algebraic structures). The ideal would be to have enough "invariants" to be able to *characterize* a "class" of homeomorphic spaces, but this ambition has been realized in only a very small number of cases (for recent progress, see Vancouver (Sullivan) and T. Price, *Math. Chronicle* **7** (1978)).

This original problem may be reformulated as the study of continuous mappings that are bijective and bicontinuous. In this form it is merely one of a whole series of problems of existence of continuous mappings subjected to other conditions, such as to be injective, or surjective, or to be sections or retractions of given continuous mappings, or extensions of given continuous mappings, etc. [171 *bis*]. All these problems are amenable to the methods of algebraic topology.

The idea of homeomorphism is related to, but distinct from, the more intuitive notion of "deformation." In order to formulate mathematically the idea that a subspace Y_1 of a topological space X can be "deformed" into another subspace Y_2, one is led to the following definition: denoting by I the interval $[0, 1]$ in **R**, there exists a continuous mapping $(y, t) \mapsto F(y, t)$ of $Y_1 \times I$ into X such that (i) $F(y, 0) = y$ for all $y \in Y_1$, (ii) for each $t \in I$, the mapping $y \mapsto F(y, t)$ is a homeomorphism of Y_1 onto a subspace of X, and (iii) when $t = 1$, this subspace is Y_2. The mapping F is said to be an *isotopy* of Y_1 onto Y_2. The notion of isotopy is thus a *strengthening* of the notion of homeomorphism. The study of isotopy is difficult and has only recently led to substantial results (B 157, 245, 373; [86]).

Homotopy (C 1949, 1954; [50], [78], [170]). The notion that has become the most important in topology is a *weakening* of the notion of isotopy. Two continuous mappings g, h of a space X into a space Y are said to be *homotopic* if there exists a continuous mapping $F : X \times I \to Y$ such that $F(x, 0) = g(x)$ and $F(x, 1) = h(x)$, but with no conditions imposed on the mapping $x \mapsto F(x, t)$ for $t \neq 0, 1$. F is called a *homotopy* from g to h. The property of being homotopic is an equivalence relation on the set $\mathscr{C}(X, Y)$ of all continuous mappings of X into Y, and the set $[X, Y]$ of classes of homotopic mappings is evidently an "invariant" of the two spaces X, Y. It is *functorial* (**C** I) in X and Y: if $\alpha : X_1 \to X$ (resp. $\beta : Y \to Y_1$) is a continuous mapping, and if $g, h \in \mathscr{C}(X, Y)$ are homotopic, then so also are $g \circ \alpha$ and $h \circ \alpha$ (resp. $\beta \circ g$ and $\beta \circ h$); whence we have a mapping $\alpha^* : [X, Y] \to [X_1, Y]$ (resp. $\beta_* : [X, Y] \to [X, Y_1]$).

The notion of homotopy leads to a "classification" of topological spaces that is coarser than classification by homeomorphism, but is much easier to handle. A continuous mapping $f : X \to Y$ is called a *homotopy equivalence* if there exists a continuous mapping $g : Y \to X$ such that $g \circ f : X \to X$ is homotopic to the identity mapping of X and $f \circ g : Y \to Y$ homotopic to the identity mapping of Y. If there exists a homotopy equivalence $f : X \to Y$, the spaces X and Y are said to have the *same homotopy type*. Most of the "invariants" of algebraic topology are invariants of homotopy type (and not merely invariants under homeomorphisms). For example, $\mathbf{R}^n$ (or more generally any topological vector space over **R**) and a space consisting of a single point have the same homotopy type (spaces having the homotopy type of a single point are said to be *contractible*).

Besides the general notion of homotopy, there are more restrictive notions, such as the *simple* homotopy equivalence of J. H. C. Whitehead for spaces endowed with a "cellular" subdivision (such spaces are called CW-*complexes* or *cell-complexes* [170]; they are generalizations of polyhedra (B 392; LN 48; BAMS 72 (Milnor)). Another variant is to consider homotopies $(x, t) \mapsto F(x, t)$ that are *independent of t in a given subspace* A of X; this leads to the notion of homotopy relative to a subspace. The case in which A consists of a single point is the most common. It is convenient to define a new category (**C** I) in which the objects (called "pointed spaces") are pairs (X, x_0) consisting of a topological space X and a point $x_0 \in X$, the morphisms $(X, x_0) \to (Y, y_0)$ being continuous mappings $f : X \to Y$ such that $f(x_0) = y_0$. A homotopy $(x, t) \mapsto F(x, t)$ between two such morphisms is then required to satisfy $F(x_0, t) = y_0$ for all $t \in I$. In this way we obtain an equivalence relation, for which the set of equivalence classes is again denoted by [X, Y] if there is no risk of confusion.

Historically speaking, algebraic topology was at first mainly preoccupied with finite-dimensional spaces such as subspaces of $\mathbf{R}^n$. These are the spaces that arise most frequently in applications to other branches of mathematics. However, it is better to make no restrictive hypotheses on the dimension, because it is then possible to use with great advantage constructions that, when applied to finite-dimensional spaces, lead in general to spaces of infinite dimension: for example, for two spaces X and Y, the space $\mathscr{C}(X, Y)$ of all continuous mappings of X into Y, endowed with the "compact-open" topology (for each compact subset $K \subset X$ and each open subset U of Y, the sets $W(K, U) = \{f \in \mathscr{C}(X, Y) : f(K) \subset U\}$ form a basis of open sets for this topology). An important special case is the *space of paths* $\mathscr{C}(I, X)$. If (X, x_0) is a pointed space, $\mathscr{C}(I, X)$ is also a pointed space, the distinguished point being the constant mapping $\tilde{x}_0 : I \to x_0$. The *loop-space* of (X, x_0) is the pointed space $(\Omega(X, x_0), \tilde{x}_0)$ consisting of the paths $\gamma : I \to X$ such that $\gamma(0) = \gamma(1) = x_0$; it is usually denoted by ΩX if there is no risk of confusion.

All these definitions are functorial (**C** I). The functor $\mathscr{C}_0(X, Y)$ of morphisms $(X, x_0) \to (Y, y_0)$ of pointed spaces is the analog in this category of the Hom functor for modules (**C** I). There is also a construction that gives an analog of the tensor product: in the product space $X \times Y$, we consider the subspace $X \vee Y = (X \times \{y_0\}) \cup (\{x_0\} \times Y)$, and the quotient space $X \wedge Y = (X \times Y)/(X \vee Y)$, obtained by identifying all the points of $X \vee Y$ to a single point (which is the distinguished point of $X \wedge Y$). In particular, for each pointed space X, $\mathbf{S}_1 \wedge X$ is called the *suspension* of X, written SX. If X is a sphere $\mathbf{S}_n$, then $\mathbf{S}_1 \wedge \mathbf{S}_n$ is homeomorphic to $\mathbf{S}_{n+1}$.

In the category of pointed spaces, Ω and S are *adjoint functors* (**C** I); that is to say there exists a canonical functorial bijection

$$\mathscr{C}_0(SX, Y) \simeq \mathscr{C}_0(X, \Omega Y) \tag{1}$$

and therefore also a canonical bijection for the homotopy classes

$$[SX, Y] \simeq [X, \Omega Y]. \tag{2}$$

Homotopy groups. Juxtaposition of loops in the space ΩY is a law of composition, which gives rise to a group structure when we pass to the quotient by considering the homotopy classes of these loops. It follows that the set $[X, \Omega Y]$ (and hence also $[SX, Y]$) is canonically endowed with a group structure. The groups $[X, \Omega^k Y]$ are *commutative* for $k \geqslant 2$. For $n \geqslant 1$, the group $[S_0, \Omega^n X]$ is called the *nth homotopy group* of X and is denoted by $\pi_n(X)$. By virtue of (2), it can also be written $[S_k, \Omega^{n-k}X]$ for $0 \leqslant k \leqslant n$, and in particular as $[S_n, X]$. The group $\pi_1(X)$, which is the group of homotopy classes of loops on X, is also called the *fundamental group* of X; in general it is not commutative, whereas the $\pi_n(X)$ for $n \geqslant 2$ are commutative.

If we take $Y = SX$ in (1), the identity mapping $SX \to SX$ determines a canonical mapping $X \to \Omega SX$, hence a canonical mapping (the *suspension mapping*) $[X, Y] \to [X, \Omega SY] \cong [SX, SY]$. By iteration we obtain a sequence of mappings

$$[X, Y] \to [SX, SY] \to [S^2X, S^2Y] \to \cdots,$$

all of which except for the first are group homomorphisms. If Y is a polyhedron (see later) and X is finite-dimensional, these homomorphisms are isomorphisms from a certain point onward. In particular, we have suspension homomorphisms $\pi_n(X) \to \pi_{n+1}(SX)$.

Homotopy groups are difficult to calculate. The case most intensively studied is that of the homotopy groups of spheres $\pi_m(S_n)$. We have $\pi_m(S_n) = 0$ for $m < n$, and $\pi_n(S_n) = \mathbf{Z}$; but the groups $\pi_m(S_n)$ for $m > n$ are far from being completely known. In the sequence of suspension homomorphisms

$$\pi_{n+k}(S_n) \to \pi_{n+k+1}(S_{n+1}) \to \cdots,$$

the groups end by being isomorphic to $\pi_{2k+2}(S_{k+2})$ (called the *stable* groups). The groups $\pi_m(S_n)$ are known to be *finite* for $m > n$, with the single exception of the groups $\pi_{2n-1}(S_n)$, n even (Serre's theorem). The stable groups are known explicitly for the first 60 or so values of k, and so far do not appear to satisfy any simple general laws; on the other hand, there are general results for certain p-primary components of these groups (B 44; C 1954–5; [182]).

By contrast, for the homotopy groups of the (compact) *classical groups*, there is better information. For the unitary group $\mathbf{U}(n)$, the groups $\pi_i(\mathbf{U}(n))$ are known for $i \leqslant 2n + 2$; in particular, for $i < 2n$ we have $\pi_i(\mathbf{U}(n)) = \mathbf{Z}$ for i odd, and $\pi_i(\mathbf{U}(n)) = 0$ for i even (Bott's periodicity theorem). For the orthogonal group $\mathbf{O}(n)$, there are analogous results (with period 8) (B 172, 215, 259; C 1959–60).

Homotopy and cohomology [50]. Let n be an integer $\geqslant 1$ and let G be a group (commutative if $n \geq 2$). A space X is said to be an *Eilenberg–MacLane space* $K(G, n)$ if $\pi_i(X) = 0$ for $i \neq n$ and $\pi_n(X) = G$. Such spaces exist for all (G, n). If G, G_1 are two groups, $[K(G, n), K(G_1, n)]$ is in canonical one–one correspondence with the set $\mathrm{Hom}(G, G_1)$ of homomorphisms of G into G_1.

In particular, all the spaces K(G, n) for given G and n have the same homotopy type. For $n \geqslant 2$, ΩK(G, n) is a K(G, $n - 1$).

For a space X, the set [X, K(G, n)] is naturally endowed with a commutative group structure, by virtue of the homotopy equivalence

$$K(G, n) \to \Omega^m K(G, m + n).$$

This group is called the *nth cohomology group of* X *with coefficients in* G, and is denoted by $H^n(X, G)$.

There are canonical isomorphisms

$$[X, K(G, n)] \simeq [X, \Omega^m K(G, m + n)] \simeq [S^m X, K(G, m + n)].$$

Since the mapping $K(G, n) \to \Omega^m K(G, m + n)$ corresponds canonically to a mapping $S^m K(G, n) \to K(G, m + n)$, the isomorphism above is also the composition

$$[X, K(G, n)] \to [S^m X, S^m K(G, n)] \to [S^m X, K(G, m + n)].$$

This leads to a generalization of the groups $H^n(X, G)$. A *spectrum of spaces* is a sequence $\mathbf{B} = (B_m)_{m \in \mathbf{Z}}$ of pointed spaces and continuous mappings of pointed spaces $SB_m \to B_{m+1}$. For each space X, we have therefore a sequence of homomorphisms of commutative groups

$$\cdots \to [S^m X, B_{m+n}] \to [S^{m+1} X, B_{m+n+1}] \to \cdots$$

and the direct limit (**C** I) $H^n(X, \mathbf{B})$ of this sequence is called the *nth (generalized) cohomology group of* X relative to the spectrum **B** (LN 28, 99). The most important generalized cohomology groups come from K-theory (**B** I).

Homology and cohomology. The cohomology groups $H^n(X, \mathbf{Z})$ have an earlier history, and were originally defined in terms of other groups, the *homology groups* $H_n(X, \mathbf{Z})$. A space X is said to be a (generalized) *polyhedron* if it is homeomorphic to the geometric realization of a simplicial set (**B** I), and it is regarded as endowed with the additional structure consisting of the "n-simplexes" of this polyhedron, i.e., the images s_n in X of the $\{x_n\} \times \Delta(n)$, where x_n is an n-simplex of the simplicial object of which X is the geometric realization (n being any integer $\geqslant 0$). The classical notion is that of a *finite* polyhedron, the geometric realization of a simplicial set having only a finite number of simplexes. If X is a polyhedron and A is a commutative ring, we may consider for each integer $n \geqslant 0$ the A-module C_n of formal linear combinations of n-simplexes of X with coefficients in A. It is immediate that the C_n form a chain complex (**B** I) with respect to the boundary operator d_n defined by

$$d_n s_n = \sum_{i=0}^{n} (-1)^i F_i^n s_n,$$

where $F_i^n s_n$ is the image of $\{F_i^n x_n\} \times \Delta(n-1)$ in X. The *nth homology module* $H_n(X, A)$ is by definition the *n*th homology A-module of this complex of A-modules.

For an arbitrary topological space X, we define C_n to be the A-module of formal linear combinations of continuous mappings $\Delta(n) \to X$, and hence we obtain the *singular homology* A-modules $H_n(X, A)$. A space is said to be *triangulable* if it is homeomorphic to a polyhedron, and the images of the simplexes of this polyhedron are said to form a *triangulation* of the space. For a topological space homeomorphic to a finite polyhedron, the singular homology of the space is isomorphic to that of the polyhedron (defined in terms of the simplexes of the latter). Recently, Sullivan has shown how the homotopy of a polyhedron may be studied by generalizing the notion of differential form (B 475).

If we now consider, for a finite polyhedron X, the cochain complex (C_n^*) obtained by duality from (C_n) (**B** I), then the *n*th cohomology object of this complex is isomorphic to the A-module $H^n(X, A)$ defined above by means of homotopy.

The reason for these isomorphisms is to be found in the axiomatic characterization of cohomology (Eilenberg–Steenrod): the $H^n(X, G)$ satisfy a small number of properties that characterize them, in the sense that two systems of groups that satisfy these properties for finite polyhedra are necessarily isomorphic (C 1948–9; LN 12; [52], [170]). We remark also that the generalized cohomology groups $H^n(X, \mathbf{B})$ defined by a spectrum of spaces **B** satisfy the Eilenberg–Steenrod axioms, with the exception of the "dimension axiom," which fixes the cohomology of a space consisting of a single point (LN 28, 99). We can also define (generalized) homology groups relative to a spectrum **B**: for we have a sequence of homomorphisms of commutative groups

$$\cdots \to \pi_{n+k}(B_k \wedge X) \to \pi_{n+k+1}(B_{k+1} \wedge X) \to \cdots$$

arising from the mappings $SB_k \to B_{k+1}$, and $H_n(X, \mathbf{B})$ is defined to be the direct limit (**C** I) of this sequence. The groups $H^n(X, \mathbf{B})$ and $H_n(X, \mathbf{B})$ are related by *duality* properties that generalize the relations indicated above for the classical homology and cohomology of finite polyhedra (LN 28, 99; Nice (Mischenko); [194], [195]).

Cohomology and homology rings. For a space X and a commutative ring A, $H^{\cdot}(X, A) = \bigoplus_{n \geq 0} H^n(X, A)$ is a *graded* A-module (**C** II), and $X \mapsto H^{\cdot}(X, A)$ is a contravariant functor from the category of topological spaces into the category of graded A-modules. The diagonal mapping $\delta: X \to X \times X$ therefore defines a homomorphism of graded A-modules

$$H^{\cdot}(X \times X, A) \to H^{\cdot}(X, A).$$

On the other hand, under fairly weak conditions on X, Y, and A, $H^{\bullet}(X \times Y, A)$ is isomorphic to the graded tensor product A-module $H^{\bullet}(X, A) \otimes_A H^{\bullet}(Y, A)$ (Künneth theorem). The preceding homomorphism therefore defines on $H^{\bullet}(X, A)$ a structure of a graded A-*algebra*, which is *anticommutative* (i.e., $x_p x_q = (-1)^{pq} x_q x_p$ for $x_p \in H^p(X, A)$, $x_q \in H^q(X, A)$).

Likewise, we may consider the graded A-module $H_{\bullet}(X, A) = \bigoplus_{n \geqslant 0} H_n(X, A)$; but this time the functor $X \mapsto H_{\bullet}(X, A)$ is covariant, and we cannot define a "homology ring" in the same way as before. However, if X is a compact connected triangulable *manifold* of dimension n, and if C′ is a p-chain and C″ a q-chain (not necessarily belonging to the same triangulation), it is possible under certain conditions of "general position" to define an "intersection $(p + q - n)$-chain" $C' \cdot C''$ (provided that $p + q \geqslant n$) in such a way that $C' \cdot C''$ is a $(p + q - n)$-cycle if C′ and C″ are cycles, and that in this case the homology class of $C' \cdot C''$ depends only on those of C′ and C″. In this way we obtain on $H_{\bullet}(X, A)$ a structure of a graded anticommutative A-algebra, by reason of the fact that for any two given homology classes, it is always possible to find cycles in these classes that are in general position [152]. For a 0-cycle $C = \sum_j n_j P_j$, where the P_j are distinct points of X and the n_j are integers (of either sign), the number $\sum_j n_j$ is called the *degree* of C, denoted by deg(C); it depends only on the homology class of C. If C′ (resp. C″) is a p-cycle (resp. q-cycle) with $p + q = n$, and C′, C″ are in general position, the number $\deg(C' \cdot C'')$ is called the *intersection number* of C′ and C″, denoted by $(C' \cdot C'')$; it depends only on the homology classes of C′ and C″.

In particular, the intersection product determines a canonical bilinear mapping $H_p(X, \mathbf{R}) \times H_{n-p}(X, \mathbf{R}) \to \mathbf{R}$ that, for a *compact* manifold, puts $H_p(X, \mathbf{R})$ and $H_{n-p}(X, \mathbf{R})$ in duality ("Poincaré duality"). Hence we have a canonical isomorphism $H^p(X, \mathbf{R}) \xrightarrow{\sim} H_{n-p}(X, \mathbf{R})$ (which, however, is *not* valid for an arbitrary finite polyhedron).

Fibrations. Let $p: X \to B$ be a continuous mapping and let F be a topological space. The space X is said to be a *locally trivial fiber bundle* with *base* B, *fiber* F, and *projection* p if, for each point $b \in B$, there exists an open neighborhood U of b and a homeomorphism $\varphi: U \times F \to p^{-1}(U)$ such that $p(\varphi(y, z)) = y$ for all $y \in U$ and $z \in F$ (in other words, X is "locally" (over B) a *product*). For each $y \in U$, the "fibers" $p^{-1}(y)$ are all homeomorphic to F.

A *covering* X of B is a locally trivial bundle over B with discrete fibers. A *vector bundle* is such that in the above definition F and each fiber $p^{-1}(y)$ is a vector space over **R**, and for each $y \in U$ the mapping $z \mapsto \varphi(y, z)$ is a linear bijection of F onto $p^{-1}(y)$. The classic example is the tangent bundle T(B) of a differential manifold B, in which the fibers are the tangent spaces at the points of B [D, Chapter 16]. A *principal bundle* is a fiber bundle X with projection $p: X \to B$, endowed with the additional structure consisting of the action of a topological group G on X, such that this action is continuous, the orbits of G are the fibers $p^{-1}(y)$, and G acts simply transitively on each fiber ([D, Chapter 16], [87], [170], [171]).

When G acts continuously on a space E, we can associate canonically to a principal G-bundle X a bundle over B with fibers homeomorphic to E. The bundles obtained in this way are called *bundles with structure group* G. For example, a vector bundle over a differential manifold B may be regarded as a bundle with structure group the orthogonal group $\mathbf{O}(n)$, where n is the dimension of the fibers ([D, Chapter 16], [87]).

These definitions can be transposed into other categories, for example, categories of manifolds of various types (see below): we have simply to replace the continuous mappings by morphisms of the category in question.

An important property of fiber bundles is the *homotopy lifting property*: if P is a polyhedron, $g: P \to X$ a continuous mapping of P into a bundle X with base B and projection p, and if $F: P \times I \to B$ is a homotopy from $f = p \circ g$ to the mapping $z \mapsto F(z, 1)$, then there exists a homotopy $G: P \times I \to X$ such that $p \circ G = F$. More generally, a mapping $p: X \to B$ is called a *Serre fibration* (or simply a *fibration*) if it satisfies the homotopy lifting property. A typical example is the mapping $p: E(B) \to B$ where, for a pointed space (B, b_0), E(B) is the space of paths $I \to B$ with origin b_0, and p maps each path to its endpoint, so that $p^{-1}(b_0) = \Omega B$. It can be shown that every continuous mapping can be factorized into the composition of a fibration and a homotopy equivalence: this result often makes it possible to reduce the study of an arbitrary continuous mapping to that of a fibration.

If X is a fiber bundle with base B and projection p, and if $f: B' \to B$ is a continuous mapping, we define a fiber bundle X′ over B′ by taking X′ to be the set of points $(b', x) \in B' \times X$ such that $f(b') = p(x)$. The restriction $p': X' \to B'$ of the first projection defines X′ as a fiber bundle over B′; this bundle is denoted by $f^*(X)$ and is called the *inverse image* of X by f. At each point $b' \in B'$, the fiber $p'^{-1}(b')$ is canonically homeomorphic to $p^{-1}(f(b'))$. If X is a vector bundle (resp. a principal G-bundle), then so is X′. There is an analogous definition for Serre fibrations.

This construction leads in particular to a *classification* of principal bundles with given group G over the most familiar types of space. It can be shown that there exists a "classifying space" BG and a principal bundle E with base BG and group G, which is contractible and such that every principal bundle with group G and base B is isomorphic to a bundle $f^*(E)$ for some continuous mapping $f: B \to BG$; moreover, two such bundles are isomorphic if and only if the corresponding mappings of B into BG are *homotopic*. There is an analogous property for the classification of bundles with structure group G. This leads to the definition of cohomological invariants attached to the isomorphism classes of bundles over B: the mapping $f : \mathrm{B} \to \mathrm{BG}$ defines a homomorphism of cohomology rings

$$f^* : \mathrm{H}^\bullet(\mathrm{BG}, \mathrm{A}) \to \mathrm{H}^\bullet(\mathrm{B}, \mathrm{A}).$$

The elements of the image of f^* are called *characteristic classes* of the bundle $f^*(\mathrm{E})$; since they do not vary when f is replaced by a homotopic mapping, they are invariants of the isomorphism class of $f^*(\mathrm{E})$, which play a large role in numerous questions of differential topology, differential geometry, and global analysis (BAMS 75 (F. Peterson)). The most important are the Stiefel–Whitney classes, Pontrjagin classes, and Chern classes; the first two correspond to orthogonal groups, the third to the unitary group [126].

The notion of fibration also enables us to characterize homotopy types by a system of invariants. Given a sequence of groups $\mathrm{G}_1, \mathrm{G}_2, \ldots, \mathrm{G}_n, \ldots$, commutative for $n \geqslant 2$, we define a sequence of spaces $\mathrm{X}_1, \mathrm{X}_2, \ldots, \mathrm{X}_n, \ldots$, where $\mathrm{X}_1 = \mathrm{K}(\mathrm{G}_1, 1)$ and X_n for $n \geqslant 2$ is a bundle with base X_{n-1} and fiber $\mathrm{K}(\mathrm{G}_n, n)$. The inverse limit (**C** I) X of the sequence (X_n) is such that $\pi_n(\mathrm{X}) = \mathrm{G}_n$ for all n, and every space Y has the same homotopy type as such an inverse limit; this homotopy type is characterized by the G_n and, for each $n \geqslant 2$, the isomorphism class of the bundle X_n with base X_{n-1}; it can be shown that these isomorphism classes are in one–one correspondence with cohomology classes in $\mathrm{H}^{n+1}(\mathrm{X}_{n-1}, \mathrm{G}_n)$ (Postnikov's construction).

If $p : \mathrm{X} \to \mathrm{B}$ is a fibration of pointed spaces, and $\mathrm{F} = p^{-1}(b_0)$, where b_0 is the distinguished point of B, there is an exact sequence (**C** I) of homotopy groups

$$\pi_1(\mathrm{B}) \leftarrow \pi_1(\mathrm{X}) \leftarrow \pi_1(\mathrm{F}) \leftarrow \pi_2(\mathrm{B}) \leftarrow \cdots \leftarrow \pi_n(\mathrm{B}) \leftarrow \pi_n(\mathrm{X}) \leftarrow \pi_n(\mathrm{F}) \leftarrow \pi_{n+1}(\mathrm{B}) \leftarrow \cdots.$$

For cohomology, the relations between the cohomology groups of B, X, and F are more complex and are expressed by the *spectral sequence of a fibration* (B 44; C 1958–9; LN 2).

We remark that a space E (even if "very good," for example, a homogeneous space of a Lie group) may admit no "nontrivial" fibration (i.e., in which neither the base nor the fiber consists of a single point) (B 472).

These are the most fundamental basic notions of algebraic and differential topology. In addition there are a considerable number of auxiliary notions and various geometrical or topological constructions, in which all the techniques of homological algebra may be brought into play (B 54; C 1954–5, 1958–9; BAMS 74 (Heller), 77 (M. Curtis); SAMS XXII; LN 2, 12, 13, 157, 161, 168, 368) and more recently techniques inspired by commutative algebra and group theory, such as Galois theory, the theory of nilpotent groups, localization and completion of rings (Nice C 2 (Sullivan); LN 304, 418; [79]), or the theory of formal groups (B 408).

There exists also a purely combinatorial version of the notions of homotopy and of fibration, in which there is no longer any mention of continuous mappings, but only simplicial sets (**B** I); often it is more convenient to work in this category, and then pass back to topology by consideration of "geometric realizations" of these sets (Kan theory: B 199; C 1954–5, 1956–7; LN 43, 252, 271; [119]).

2. Results

We shall encounter applications of algebraic or differential topology in almost all the great mathematical theories of the present age. Here we shall restrict our survey to problems whose initial formulation has obvious topological aspects.

As a general rule, a *positive* solution of such a problem usually consists of an effective construction of the solution by geometrico-topological methods; on the other hand, a *negative* answer is generally obtained by showing that a *positive* solution, if it existed, would imply certain relations between topological invariants, and then by showing that these relations cannot be satisfied.

The different sorts of "manifolds." Riemann and Poincaré were led to develop topological notions in the context of the spaces most frequently encountered in classical analysis and geometry, namely, "manifolds." A *topological manifold* of dimension n is a metrizable space X in which each point admits a neighborhood U that is homeomorphic to an open subset of $\mathbf{R}^n$; an *atlas* of X is a family of such homeomorphisms $\varphi_\alpha : U_\alpha \to \varphi_\alpha(U_\alpha) \subset \mathbf{R}^n$, where the U_α form an open covering of X (observe that this definition makes sense only by virtue of the celebrated theorem of Brouwer on the *invariance of dimension*, namely, that there exists no homeomorphism of an open subset of $\mathbf{R}^m$ onto an open subset of $\mathbf{R}^n$ if $m \neq n$). We may impose additional structure on X by requiring the existence of an atlas with supplementary conditions on the *transition homeomorphisms* $\varphi_\beta \circ \varphi_\alpha^{-1} : \varphi_\alpha(U_\alpha \cap U_\beta) \to \varphi_\beta(U_\alpha \cap U_\beta)$ for each pair of indices such that $U_\alpha \cap U_\beta \neq \varnothing$. In particular we define in this way the notions of *piecewise-linear manifold*, *differential manifold*, *real-analytic manifold*, and *complex-analytic manifold* by requiring the $\varphi_\beta \circ \varphi_\alpha^{-1}$ to be respectively piecewise-linear, of class C^∞, real-analytic, or complex-analytic (in which case n must be even and $\mathbf{R}^n$ identified with $\mathbf{C}^{n/2}$). The topological manifolds form a category TOP, in which the morphisms are continuous mappings. The other types of manifold also form categories in which the morphisms are continuous mappings which, relative to the distinguished "charts" for the type of manifold in question, are "locally" piecewise-linear, of class C^∞, real-analytic, or complex-analytic, respectively; the first two of these categories are denoted by PL and DIFF. We shall see in (**A** II) and (**A** VIII) the consequences, for the topology of a space, of the existence of a differential or analytic manifold structure.

After the introduction of simplicial methods by Poincaré, the question naturally arose of whether a topological manifold necessarily admits a PL-manifold structure, and whether such a structure is unique ("Hauptvermutung"). Again, it can be shown that every DIFF-manifold can be "triangulated" and hence endowed with an essentially unique PL-structure; conversely, the question arises of whether every PL-manifold admits a DIFF-manifold structure, and whether such a structure is unique. Finally, there is the question of classifying TOP (or PL, or DIFF) manifolds having the same homotopy type, in terms of "concordance" (a weakened version of isotopy that takes account of the structures of manifold under consideration) [188].

These problems have been almost completely resolved.

The general idea is to work in the tangent bundle (for the category DIFF) or analogous constructs (microbundles, Spivak bundles) for the other categories. This introduces classifying spaces: for the category DIFF, it is the classifying bundle BO of the direct limit (**C** I) of the orthogonal groups $\mathbf{O}(n)$ as $n \to \infty$; for the other two categories, there are analogous spaces BPL, BTOP, with fibrations

$$\mathrm{BO} \to \mathrm{BPL} \to \mathrm{BTOP}$$

in which the fibers of the distinguished points are denoted by PL/O and TOP/PL. To a DIFF (resp. PL, TOP) structure on M there corresponds therefore a continuous mapping f of M into BO (resp. BPL, BTOP). For a PL-manifold to admit a DIFF-structure, it is necessary and sufficient that the mapping $f : \mathrm{M} \to \mathrm{BPL}$ should factorize into $\mathrm{M} \to \mathrm{BO} \to \mathrm{BPL}$, and the concordance classes of the DIFF-structures on M are then in one–one correspondence with [M, PL/O]. The first particular cases of these theorems were the celebrated example (Milnor) of an "exotic" DIFF-structure on the sphere $\mathbf{S}_7$ (not isomorphic to the usual structure), and an example due to Kervaire of a PL-manifold of dimension 10 that does not admit a DIFF-structure. When $\mathrm{M} = \mathbf{S}_n$, the set [M, PL/O] has a natural structure of a finite group Θ_n for $n > 4$ (Kervaire–Milnor): for example, Θ_{11} is cyclic of order 992. The passage from TOP structures to PL structures is more complex, but the set [M, TOP/PL] plays a preponderant role; an essential fact (Kirby–Siebenmann) is that TOP/PL has the homotopy type of the Eilenberg–MacLane space $\mathrm{K}(\mathbf{Z}/2\mathbf{Z}, 3)$. It follows that if M is a compact topological manifold of dimension $\geqslant 5$, there is an "obstruction" to the existence of a PL-structure on M that is a cohomology class in $\mathrm{H}^4(\mathrm{M}, \mathbf{Z}/2\mathbf{Z})$; if this class is zero, the classes of possible PL-structures are in one–one correspondence with $H^3(M, \mathbf{Z}/2\mathbf{Z})$. There are explicit examples of five-dimensional manifolds that have no PL-structure, and others having several nonisomorphic PL-structures (B 263, 280, 362; Nice I (W. Browder, C. T. C. Wall); Nice C 2 (Siebenmann); LN 197; [210]).

These results are the culmination of a whole series of researches pursued over a decade by many mathematicians. Besides the general techniques of algebraic topology, great use is made of cobordism and the theory of immersions (see below), and especially of the technique called "surgery," which comes from Morse theory. If $\mathbf{D}_n$ denotes the closed unit ball in $\mathbf{R}^n$, $\mathbf{D}_n$ is homeomorphic to $\mathbf{D}_k \times \mathbf{D}_{n-k}$, and its boundary is therefore the union of $\mathbf{S}_{k-1} \times \mathbf{D}_{n-k}$ and $\mathbf{D}_k \times \mathbf{S}_{n-k-1}$. A *handle* of type k in an n-dimensional manifold M is a closed subset A of M homeomorphic to $\mathbf{D}_k \times \mathbf{D}_{n-k}$, the intersection of A and $\overline{M - A}$ being the portion $\mathbf{S}_{k-1} \times \mathbf{D}_{n-k}$ of the boundary of A (the terminology is justified only when $k = 1$). Surgery on such a handle is a geometrical operation that results in replacing the k-handle by an $(n - k)$-handle (B 230, 397; BAMS 68 (A. Wallace); SAMS III (Milnor); [26], [188]).

Finally, we remark that a good proportion of the results on finite-dimensional manifolds become simpler for manifolds of infinite dimension (in which the "models" $\mathbf{R}^n$ are replaced by a Hilbert space); it is remarkable that this theory has led to a proof of a conjecture of J. H. C. Whitehead on *finite* cell-complexes, namely, that every homeomorphism of such complexes is a simple homotopy equivalence (B 428).

The Poincaré conjecture. Elementary algebraic topology shows that every compact, orientable, simply connected surface is homeomorphic to the sphere $\mathbf{S}_2$. Poincaré conjectured that the same is true for manifolds of dimension 3 and $\mathbf{S}_3$: at present, neither proof nor counterexample is known. The conjecture may be generalized to any dimension: if a compact, simply connected manifold of dimension n has the same homology (or cohomology) as $\mathbf{S}_n$, is it homeomorphic to $\mathbf{S}_n$? Surprisingly, this question has been answered affirmatively for $n \geqslant 5$, first by Smale for DIFF-manifolds, then by Stallings for PL-manifolds, and by M. H. A. Newman for TOP-manifolds; for $n = 4$, as for $n = 3$, the problem remains open (B 208, 230; BAMS 69 (Smale); C 1961–2).

Cobordism. The modern flowering of differential topology can be dated from Thom's solution (1954) of two problems posed earlier by Steenrod: in a differential manifold M, when is a homology class "represented" by a submanifold, and when is an n-dimensional manifold the boundary of an $(n + 1)$-dimensional manifold? Thom's principal idea was to reduce these problems to problems of homotopy of mappings into a "Thom complex" constructed from a ball bundle associated with a principal bundle over a classifying space BO(N), for N sufficiently large. Another of Thom's ideas was to introduce an equivalence relation in the set of oriented manifolds: two manifolds V, V′ are *cobordant* if the oriented manifold V′ − V, the disjoint union of V′ and the manifold −V with the opposite orientation to that of V, is the boundary of a manifold W. The set Ω^n of "cobordism classes" of dimension n is naturally endowed with a commutative group structure, the group operation being defined by disjoint union (B 78, 89, 180, 188). A remarkable fact is that certain invariants of the DIFF structure are also invariants for the relation of cobordism; and a knowledge of Ω^n leads to unsuspected relations between these invariants (B 88, [180]).

These ideas have been considerably developed and diversified in several directions (B 408; LN 178; [174]). An important variant is the notion of *h-cobordism*, which requires that in the definition above the injections $V \to W$ and $V' \to W$ should be homotopy equivalences. Smale deduced his theorem on the Poincaré conjecture from a fundamental result on h-cobordism: if $\dim V \geqslant 5$ and if V and V′ are simply connected, an h-cobordism W of V with V′ is diffeomorphic to $V \times I$. His method of proof consists of considering W as obtained by "attaching handles" to the manifold $V \times I$, and then showing that, under the given hypotheses, the handles can be removed one by one without changing W (up to diffeomorphism).

When V and V′ are no longer assumed to be simply connected, the h-cobordism theorem is no longer true; a supplementary condition is needed, which is related to the notion of "Whitehead torsion" (B 392; LN 48).

Let us note at this point a problem in some sense opposite to Steenrod's problem: given a noncompact manifold V without boundary, does there exist a manifold W with boundary such that V is the interior of W? This problem has been solved by Siebenmann by means of K-theory (B 304).

Immersions, embeddings, and knot theory. An *immersion* of a differential manifold M of dimension m in a differential manifold N of dimension $n > m$ is a C^∞-mapping $f: M \to N$ whose tangent mapping is everywhere injective. The mapping f itself need not be injective; an injective immersion is called an *embedding*. The classification problem for embeddings is the determination of the classes of embeddings for the following equivalence relation: "f and g are isotopic under a differential isotopy." For immersions, we must (since immersions are not in general injective) replace "isotopy" by "regular homotopy," which means a homotopy $(x, t) \mapsto F(x, t)$ such that $x \mapsto F(x, t)$ is an immersion for each $t \in I$.

The most interesting case is that in which $N = \mathbf{R}^n$ and M is compact; the classification of immersions was first achieved by Smale for $M = \mathbf{S}_m$, and then by M. Hirsch in the general case. The idea is to reduce to a homotopy problem by passing to the tangent bundles of M and N: for example, the immersions of $\mathbf{S}_m$ in $\mathbf{R}^n$ are classified by the elements of the homotopy group $\pi_m(\mathbf{S}_{n,m})$ of the Stiefel manifold $\mathbf{S}_{n,m}$ [D, Chapter 16] of orthogonal m-frames in $\mathbf{R}^n$. For embeddings, again the classification problem has been reduced to a problem of homotopy, provided that $n > 3(m + 1)/2$ (Haefliger) (B 157, 245; BAMS 69 (Smale)).

The classical theory of *knots* is the particular case of the classification of embeddings for $M = \mathbf{S}_1$ and $N = \mathbf{R}^3$; it is far from complete, so that the inequality $n > 3(m + 1)/2$ is essential (B 485). When $n > 3(m + 1)/2$ there are no "knotted m-spheres" in $\mathbf{R}^n$, and all embeddings of $\mathbf{S}_m$ in $\mathbf{R}^n$ are regularly isotopic; if $n \leqslant 3(m + 1)/2$, the theory of "knotted spheres" has hardly begun (B 280; [37]).

The whole of the preceding theory has its analogs in the categories PL and TOP ([71], [86]; SAMS XXII (Lashof)). But there are some rather surprising differences: for example, there are no knotted m-spheres in $\mathbf{R}^n$ (*in the* PL *sense*) as soon as $n \geqslant m + 3$, whereas for $3(m + 1)/2 \geqslant n \geqslant m + 3$ there may be m-spheres that are knotted in the DIFF sense but not in the PL sense.

For the case $M = \mathbf{S}_{n-1}$, $N = \mathbf{R}^n$, a problem which goes back to Jordan and Schoenflies is whether an embedding of $\mathbf{S}_{n-1}$ in $\mathbf{R}^n$ can be extended to an embedding of the ball $\mathbf{D}_n$ in $\mathbf{R}^n$; this is true in the category DIFF, and for $n = 2$ in the category TOP, but (in TOP) there is a counterexample of Alexander (the "horned sphere") when $n = 3$. Mazur and Morton Brown have proved that a homeomorphism $f : \mathbf{S}_{n-1} \to \mathbf{R}^n$ of $\mathbf{S}_{n-1}$ onto a closed subspace of $\mathbf{R}^n$ can be extended to a homeomorphism of $\mathbf{D}_n$ onto a closed subspace of $\mathbf{R}^n$, provided that f can be extended to a homeomorphism of an open neighborhood of $\mathbf{S}_{n-1}$ in $\mathbf{R}^n$ onto an open subset of $\mathbf{R}^n$ (B 205).

Finally, on the question of the *existence* of embeddings or immersions, a classical result of Whitney (for the category DIFF) is that there always exists an immersion of M in $\mathbf{R}^{2m-1}$ and an embedding in $\mathbf{R}^{2m}$; but it can be asked whether it is not possible in certain cases to reduce the number n. The theory of characteristic classes and K-theory provide answers to this question. The case in which M is a projective space $\mathbf{P}_m(\mathbf{R})$ has been studied the most. For example, it is known that Whitney's results are the best possible when $m = 2^r$; on the other hand, if $m = 2^r + 2$, we may take $n = 2m - 4$ for immersions and $n = 2m - 3$ for embeddings (LN 279; SAMS XXII (Gitler)).

Fixed points; spaces with group action. The property, for a continuous mapping $f : X \to X$ of a space into itself, of having a *fixed point*, i.e., a point $x \in X$ such that $f(x) = x$, is fundamental in existence proofs in functional analysis. One of the most famous theorems from the beginnings of algebraic topology is Brouwer's theorem, to the effect that every continuous mapping f of the closed ball $\mathbf{D}_n$ into itself has at least one fixed point. Another capital result is the *Lefschetz trace formula*, which, under certain conditions, expresses the number of fixed points of f in terms of cohomology: if X is a finite oriented polyhedron of dimension n, the mapping f determines endomorphisms f^i of the cohomology vector spaces $H^i(X, \mathbf{R})$ for $0 \leqslant i \leqslant n$; if $Tr(f^i)$ is the trace of the endomorphism f^i, the Lefschetz number $L(f) = \sum_{i=0}^{n} (-1)^i Tr(f^i)$ is equal to the sum, over all the fixed points of f, of the "indices" $\sigma(x)$, provided that the fixed points are isolated (and hence finite in number) and such that at each of them the diagonal of $X \times X$ and the graph of f intersect "transversally," so that their "intersection number" $\sigma(x) = \pm 1$ at this point is defined. (See (**A** V) for a generalization of this formula.)

If $f : X \to X$ is a homeomorphism, the positive and negative powers f^n form a group G acting on X, and the fixed points of f are the orbits of G that consist of a single point. We are thus led to the general study, from the topological point of view, of the orbits and the orbit space of a topological group G acting continuously on a space X. This study has many applications and ramifications, in diverse domains, such as the existence of fixed points or the topology of Lie groups and their homogeneous spaces (see **B** II) (B 45, 251; BAMS 66 (P. Smith, Conner-Floyd), 76 (Fadell); LN 34, 36, 46, 73, 298, 299; [20]).

3. Connections with the natural sciences

The majority are *indirect*, via other mathematical theories in which topology plays a part. Doubtless the reason for this is to be found in the fact that the theorems of algebraic topology are *qualitative* in nature, and affirm for example the existence (or the nonexistence) of an object, without in general providing any means of determining it explicitly. However, there is a very recent application of the calculation of homotopy groups of certain homogeneous spaces to the classification of "defects" of crystalline structures and liquid crystals (Poenaru, Toulouze, L. Michel, Bouligand).

4. The originators

The principal ideas in algebraic and differential topology are due to the following mathematicians:

Homology and cohomology. B. Riemann (1826–1866), H. Poincaré (1854–1912), L. E. J. Brouwer (1881–1966), S. Lefschetz (1884–1972), E. Noether (1882–1935), J. Alexander (1888–1971), H. Hopf (1894–1971), H. Whitney, H. Cartan, N. Steenrod (1910–1971), M. Atiyah, F. Hirzebruch, J. F. Adams, D. Sullivan.

Homotopy. W. Hurewicz (1904–1956), H. Hopf (1894–1971), J. H. C. Whitehead (1904–1960), S. Eilenberg, S. MacLane, H. Cartan, J.-P. Serre, D. Kan.

Fiber bundles, characteristic classes. H. Whitney, H. Hopf (1894–1971), S. Chern, L. Pontrjagin, N. Steenrod (1910–1971), J. Leray, A. Borel, F. Hirzebruch, J.-P. Serre, J. Milnor, D. Kan, S. Novikov.

Topology of manifolds. J. Milnor, M. Kervaire, S. Smale, J. Stallings, D. Sullivan, C. T. C. Wall, W. Browder, R. Kirby, L. Siebenmann, T. Chapman.

Cobordism. R. Thom, J. Milnor, C. T. C. Wall, D. Quillen, S. Novikov.

Immersions, embeddings, knots. C. Jordan (1838–1922), J. Alexander (1888–1971), H. Whitney, S. Smale, B. Mazur.

Fixed points, transformation groups P. Smith (1900–1980), A. Borel.

Topology of Lie groups and homogeneous spaces. E. Cartan (1869–1951), H. Hopf (1894–1971), L. Pontrjagin, J. Leray, A. Weil, A. Borel, R. Bott.

Topology in dimensions $\leqslant 3$. R. Bing, E. Moise, C. Papakyriakopoulos (1914–1976), W. Thurston.

The following have also made substantial contributions to these theories: J. Adem, P. Alexandroff, D. Barden, M. Barratt, J. Boardman, M. Bockstein, K. Borsuk, G. Bredon, E. H. Brown, Morton Brown, A. Bousfield, G. Brumfiel, S. Cairns, E. Čech (1893–1960), J. Cerf, A. Černavskii, P. Conner, M. Dehn (1878–1952), A. Dold, E. Dyer, B. Eckmann, R. D. Edwards, C. Ehresmann (1905–1979), F. Farrell, J. Feldbau (1914–1945), E. Floyd, R. Fox (1913–1973), H. Freudenthal, T. Ganea (1923–1971), H. Gluck, W. Gysin, A. Haefliger, P. Heegard (1871–1948), P. Hilton, G. Hirsch, M. Hirsch, W. C. Hsiang, W. Y. Hsiang, J. Hudson, I. James, H. Künneth (1892–1974), P. Landweber, R. Lashof, H. Lebesgue (1875–1941), J. Lees, J. Levine, E. Lima, A. Liulevicius, G. Livesay, L. Lusternik, M. Mahowald, W. Massey, P. May, R. Milgram, E. Mischenko, D. Montgomery, J. C. Moore, C. Morlet, J. Munkres, M. H. A. Newman, F. Peterson, V. Poenaru, M. Postnikov, D. Puppe, K. Reidemeister (1893–1971), V. Rohlin, J. Roitberg, M. Rothenberg, H. Samelson, L. Schnirelmann (1905–1938), A. Schoenflies (1853–1928), G. Segal, H. Seifert, J. Shaneson, A. Shapiro (1921–1962), W. Shih, L. Smith, E. Spanier, M. Spivak, J. Stasheff, E. Stiefel (1909–1978), A. Svarč, E. Thomas,

H. Tietze (1880–1964), H. Toda, T. tom Dieck, E. van Kampen (1908–1942), L. Vietoris, F. Waldhausen, A. Wallace, H. C. Wang (1919–1978), J. West, G. W. Whitehead, W. T. Wu, C. Yang, C. Zeeman, J. Zilber, W. Meeks, S. Yau.

References

B: 44, 45, 54, 78, 88, 89, 157, 172, 180, 188, 199, 205, 208, 215, 230, 245, 251, 259, 263, 280, 304, 362, 373, 392, 397, 408, 428, 472, 475, 485, 497, 509, 515, 516, 527, 574, 578.

LN: 2, 12, 13, 28, 34, 36, 43, 46, 48, 73, 99, 157, 161, 168, 178, 197, 249, 252, 271, 279, 298, 299, 304, 368, 422, 438, 473, 533, 540, 542, 557, 577, 591, 628, 657, 658, 664, 673, 722, 741, 763.

BAMS: 66 (Smith, Conner, Floyd), 68 (Wallace), 69 (Smale), 72 (Milnor), 74 (Heller), 75 (Peterson), 76 (Fadell), 81 (Burgess), 83 (Conner-Raymond, May, Lacher).

SAMS: III, XXII, XXXII.

Astérisque: 6, 12, 26, 32–33, 45.

[20], [26], [37], [50], [52], [71], [78], [79], [80], [86], [87], [119], [126], [152], [170], [171], [171 *bis*], [174], [181], [182], [188], [194], [195], [210], [212], [217], [226].

A II

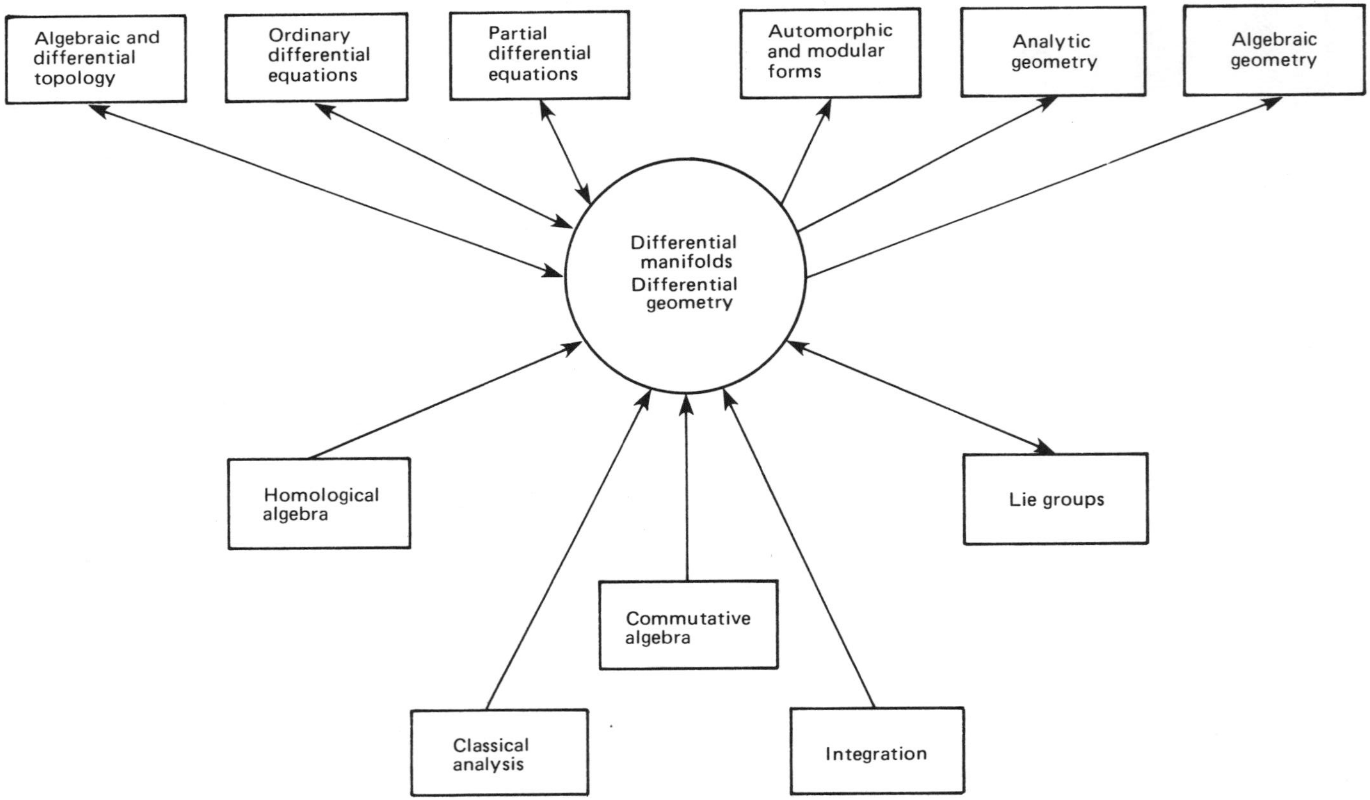

Algebraic and differential topology
Ordinary differential equations
Partial differential equations
Automorphic and modular forms
Analytic geometry
Algebraic geometry
Differential manifolds
Differential geometry
Homological algebra
Lie groups
Commutative algebra
Classical analysis
Integration

A II

Differential manifolds. Differential geometry

The study of problems in analysis such as the behavior of solutions of differential equations, partial differential equations, integral equations, etc., leads naturally to formulating these problems not only on open sets in $\mathbf{R}^n$, but on *differential manifolds*; this is particularly true of the problems of this nature that have arisen from mechanics or physics ever since the classical epoch, and they are joined nowadays by all those that inevitably arise in the theory of Lie groups and their homogeneous spaces (**B** II). Modern analysis, when it goes beyond "local" results (valid only in an unspecified neighborhood of a point or a subset) is therefore analysis on differential manifolds, also called *global* analysis: its methods and its principal results are described in (**A** III), (**A** IV), and (**A** V).

Of course, analysis on manifolds deals only with notions defined *intrinsically*, that is to say independently of all choices of charts (**A** I). The study of these notions constitutes the *general theory* of differential manifolds. On the other hand, differential manifolds can be endowed with richer structures, involving additional data (G-structures, connections, etc.) that originate from problems of geometry or mechanics, and the problems concerning these structures form the province of *differential geometry*. In both cases, the problems envisaged almost always involve the underlying topological properties of the manifolds under consideration.

1. The general theory

The main subjects studied concern the singularities of differentiable mappings and of vector fields.

Singularities of differentiable mappings. If f is a real-valued C^∞-function on a differential manifold V, the *critical points* of f are the points $x \in$ V at which the differential df vanishes. Simple examples show that the set of critical points of f can be an arbitrary closed set in V, and it appears therefore unrealistic to attempt a classification of C^∞-functions based on the nature of their critical points. A critical point is said to be *nondegenerate* if the polynomial formed by the second-degree terms in the Taylor expansion of f in a neighborhood of this point (with respect to any chart) is a nondegenerate quadratic form; the index of this form is by definition the *index* of the critical point. Functions that have only nondegenerate critical points and take distinct values at these points (which are necessarily isolated) are very special, being closely related to the topology of V (they are functions that determine a "presentation by handles" of V; see (**A** I)); but the remarkable fact is that, with respect to a suitable topology on the space $\mathscr{E}(V)$ of C^∞-mappings of V into **R**, these "Morse functions" form a dense open set in $\mathscr{E}(V)$.

These results, which constitute the beginnings of Morse theory (B 36; BAMS 64 (Pitcher); [124]), have provided the starting point of a vast program of study of the C^∞-mappings of a compact differential manifold M into a differential manifold N, inaugurated in about 1955 by Whitney and Thom. The fundamental ideas introduced by these authors are the following:

(a) Only "generic" mappings are considered: these are mappings characterized by conditions on the "jets"† of a certain order (depending on the dimensions m, n of M and N).

(b) Introduction of two equivalence relations on the set $\mathscr{E}(M, N)$ of C^∞-mappings $f : M \to N$: *differential equivalence*, which means that f and f' are equivalent if there exists a diffeomorphism g (resp. h) of M (resp. N) onto itself such that $f' = h \circ f \circ g$; and *topological equivalence*, in which g and h are only required to be homeomorphisms.

(c) Introduction of a natural topology on the set $\mathscr{E}(M, N)$. A mapping $f \in \mathscr{E}(M, N)$ is said to be differentiably (resp. topologically) *stable* if the mappings differentiably (resp. topologically) equivalent to f form a neighborhood of f.

These definitions make it plausible that a "generic" mapping should be stable in one or other of the two senses just defined, and that the generic mappings should be *dense* in $\mathscr{E}(M, N)$.

(d) A *singular* point $x \in M$ for $f : M \to N$ is a point at which the tangent linear mapping of f does not have maximum rank. For a generic mapping f, one expects that the singular points will form a submanifold $S(f)$; when restricted to $S(f)$, the mapping f will have a submanifold $S(S(f))$ of singular points, and so on. Moreover, from the homological point of view, the singular

† A *jet* of order k is an equivalence class of C^k-mappings that, at a point, have the same derivatives up to and including order k (with respect to any charts). The jets of order 1 may be identified with tangent linear mappings [D, Chapter 16].

loci S(f), S(S(f)), etc., are related to the Stiefel–Whitney classes of M (**A** I) and to the images under f^* of those of N, by universal polynomial formulas ("Thom polynomials") (B 134; C 1956–7).

The realization of this program is far advanced, primarily by the work of J. Mather. It is established that the topologically stable mappings always form a dense open subset of $\mathscr{E}$(M, N), but the same statement for differential stability is true only for certain explicitly determined pairs of dimensions (m, n) (the "good dimensions"). Generic mappings are always topologically stable, and in good dimensions, generic mappings are identical with differentiably stable mappings. There are regular methods for determining explicitly the germs of generic mappings, up to equivalence, for given m and n; finally, regular methods are now beginning to be developed for the calculation of the Thom polynomials. The techniques of proof consist in reducing questions of differential stability to analogous questions about the jets of the mappings under consideration, and then using the instruments of the theory of commutative *local rings* (**C** II), by virtue of a key result, namely, Malgrange's generalization to C^∞-functions of the Weierstrass "preparation theorem" (B 336, 424; BAMS 75 (Thom); LN 192, 197, 209, 371, 373; Vancouver (Arnol'd); [51], [204]).

Vector fields on differential manifolds. On a differential manifold M, the *critical points* at which a vector field X [D, Chapter 16] of class C^r ($r \geqslant 1$) vanishes play an important role in the study of the integral curves of the field, of which they are the singular points (**A** III). H. Poincaré was the first to discover a relation between the critical points of a vector field on a surface and the topological invariants of the surface, and the general form of this relation was given by H. Hopf. Suppose that M is compact, and that the critical points of X are finite in number; to each of these points there is intrinsically associated an integer, called the *index* of the point, and the sum of the indices (also called the index of X) is equal to the Euler–Poincaré characteristic of M. If $X_1, \ldots, X_k$ are k vector fields on M, the *singular points* of this system are the points $x \in$ M at which the vectors $X_1(x), \ldots, X_k(x)$ are linearly dependent; the notion of index can be generalized to such systems, and there are results on its relations with the homology of M when $k = 2$. A much studied problem is the determination of the largest integer k for which there exist k vector fields $X_1, \ldots, X_k$ with no singular points. If $k = n =$ dim(M), the manifold M is said to be *parallelizable*. This problem is completely solved in the case of spheres $\mathbf{S}_n$ (J. F. Adams): write $n + 1$ in the form $(2a + 1)2^{c+4d}$, where a, c, d are integers $\geqslant 0$, and $c \leqslant 3$; then it can be shown with the help of generalized cohomology based on K-theory that the number k is equal to $2^c + 8d - 1$ (B 233, BAMS 75 (Thomas), 76 (Baum)). In particular, the only parallelizable spheres are $\mathbf{S}_1, \mathbf{S}_3, \mathbf{S}_7$.

2. G-structures

The method of the moving trihedron was invented in the 19th century by Ribaucour and Darboux for the differential study of surfaces. E. Cartan was the first to perceive the much greater range of this method, and he applied it with virtuosity to many questions of differential geometry and the general theory of partial differential equations. C. Ehresmann clarified and systematized the ideas of E. Cartan, by setting them in the context of the theory of fiber bundles. With the tangent bundle T(M) of a manifold M of dimension n there is naturally associated a principal bundle R(M), called the *bundle of frames* of M. Its fiber at each point $x \in M$ is the set of bases of the tangent space $T_x(M)$, and the structure group is the general linear group $\mathbf{GL}(n, \mathbf{R})$; moreover, T(M) may be considered as the associated vector bundle with fiber $\mathbf{R}^n$ [D, Chapter 20]. If G is a closed subgroup of $\mathbf{GL}(n, \mathbf{R})$, a G-*structure* on M is a subspace $S_G(M)$ of R(M) that is a principal G-bundle over M (the action of G on the fibers being the restriction of the action of $\mathbf{GL}(n, \mathbf{R})$) [D, Chapter 20]. Then T(M) appears as a vector bundle with G as structure group, and the relation between $S_G(M)$ and T(M) is very analogous to that which exists between a group G and a homogeneous space G/H; and just as in this latter case it is better to work in G rather than in G/H, in order to benefit from the richer group structure, in the same way the essential idea of E. Cartan's "method of moving frames" consists in calculating in $S_G(M)$ rather than in T(M).

The most important cases are: (1) $G = \mathbf{O}(n)$, the orthogonal group, in which case the G-structures are called *Riemannian structures*; (2) $n = 2m$ is even, $G = \mathbf{Sp}(2m, \mathbf{R})$, the symplectic group, to which correspond the *almost-Hamiltonian* (or *symplectic*) structures; (3) $n = 2m$ is even, $G = \mathbf{GL}(m, \mathbf{C})$, the complex general linear group, in which case the G-structures are called *almost-complex* structures. Every complex-analytic manifold is canonically endowed with an almost-complex structure, but the converse is false: an almost-complex structure does not necessarily come from a complex-analytic structure on M, unless a supplementary condition of "integrability" is satisfied (B 166).

On any manifold it is always possible (in infinitely many ways) to define a Riemannian structure. On the other hand, for other subgroups G of $\mathbf{GL}(n, \mathbf{R})$, the existence of a G-structure on M implies relations between the topological invariants of M, notably the characteristic classes. For example, it can be shown (Borel–Serre) that the only spheres that admit an almost-complex structure are $\mathbf{S}_2$ and $\mathbf{S}_6$. In the other direction, the same differential manifold may be subjacent to several nonisomorphic complex structures: for example, there are infinitely many nonisomorphic complex structures on $\mathbf{S}_2 \times \mathbf{S}_2$ (B 35; BAMS 72 (Chern)).

The general notion of a *connection* on a manifold endowed with a G-structure was also introduced in substance by E. Cartan. Essentially this is a structure that allows one to "compare" the tangent spaces at two infinitely near points. In order to define it we require at each point $r \in S_G(M)$ a "horizontal" supplement, in the tangent space to $S_G(M)$ at r, to the subspace tangent to the fiber at r; it is necessary that this horizontal subspace should vary differentiably with r, and that the set of horizontal subspaces should be stable under G (B 24, 101; [D, Chapters 17 and 20]; BAMS 72 (Chern); [100]). Given a connection, it is possible to define the *parallel transport* of a frame along a path γ in M: it is enough to lift γ to a path in $S_G(M)$ for which the tangent at each point is "horizontal." The *geodesics* of a connection are the curves for which a tangent vector remains tangent under parallel transport along the curve.

The presence of a connection also enables one to define the derivative of a tensor field in the direction of a tangent vector at a point (the *covariant derivative* relative to the connection). Furthermore, to each connection there are intrinsically attached two tensors, the *curvature* tensor and the *torsion* tensor. For a Riemannian structure, there is a distinguished connection, called the *Levi-Civita connection*, characterized by the fact that its torsion is zero [D, Chapters 17 and 20].

Riemannian manifolds. The assignment of a Riemannian structure on M is equivalent to the assignment of a ds^2, a tensor field that on each tangent space is a positive-definite quadratic form. If $\dim(M) = n$, this tensor field gives rise canonically to a "p-dimensional element of area" for $1 \leqslant p \leqslant n$, which is a positive measure on each p-dimensional submanifold. In particular, when $p = 1$, the length of a curve in M is defined, and the geodesics of the Levi-Civita connection are precisely the extremal curves with respect to this length. The global study of the geodesics of a Riemannian manifold has been pursued unremittingly since the time of Jacobi (see [D, Chapter 20]; LN 55), and has given rise to Morse theory [124]. A problem studied first by Poincaré is that of the existence and number of distinct closed geodesics on a compact manifold; this is related to the topology of the manifold, and is still not completely solved (B 364, 406; [144], [223]).

The problem of extremal submanifolds with respect to the p-dimensional area can be posed not only for $p = 1$, but also for $1 < p \leqslant n - 1$, and leads to a system of nonlinear partial differential equations of the second order. Up to now, this problem has been considered mainly in the case $p = n - 1$, in which the extremals are called "minimal hypersurfaces." When $n = 3$, it goes back to Lagrange, and the study of minimal surfaces in $\mathbf{R}^3$ was the subject of much work throughout the 19th century (Weierstrass, Schwarz, etc.), and today still presents many unanswered questions (BAMS 71

(Nitsche), 75 (Osserman)). When $n > 3$, the following problem, posed by S. Bernstein, has been solved only recently: whether a minimal hypersurface in $\mathbf{R}^{n+1}$ with equation $x_{n+1} = F(x_1, \ldots, x_n)$, where F is defined throughout $\mathbf{R}^n$, is necessarily a hyperplane: this is true for $n \leqslant 7$ and false for all $n \geqslant 8$ (B 353, 579, Nice I (Chern), Nice D 11 (Miranda)).

Riemannian manifolds whose curvature tensor (with respect to the Levi-Civita connection) has particular properties have been the subject of many investigations. Usually attention is restricted to *complete* manifolds. Completeness is a property that can be expressed in several equivalent forms (Hopf–Rinow): one of these uses the notion of *distance* on a Riemannian manifold, which is defined as the greatest lower bound of the lengths of curves joining two points, and a manifold is *complete* if every bounded subset (with respect to this distance function) is relatively compact. This property implies that any two points of the manifold can be joined by a geodesic arc of minimum length [D, Chapter 20]. Since Riemann, one associates with each 2-plane P_x contained in the tangent space $T_x(M)$ to a Riemannian manifold M at a point x its *sectional* (or *two-dimensional*) *curvature* $A(P_x)$, which is the Gaussian curvature at the point x of the surface generated by the geodesics passing through x with tangent contained in P_x. For complete manifolds, assumptions on the *sign* of $A(P_x)$ imply very particular properties of M. For example, if $A(P_x) \leqslant 0$ for all $x \in M$ and all 2-planes $P_x \subset T_x(M)$, the universal covering of M is diffeomorphic to $\mathbf{R}^n$ (Hadamard–E. Cartan). If there exists a constant $c > 0$ such that $A(P_x) \geqslant c$ for all $x \in M$ and all $P_x \subset T_x(M)$, then M must be compact (O. Bonnet–Myers) [D, Chapter 20]. The case in which it is assumed only that $A(P_x) > 0$, or $A(P_x) \geqslant 0$, has also been elucidated (Nice C 3 (Gromoll)). A remarkable result is that if $\beta \leqslant A(P_x) \leqslant 1$ for all $x \in M$ and all $P_x \subset T_x(M)$, with $\beta > 1/4$, then M must be homeomorphic to $\mathbf{S}_n$, and the constant 1/4 is the best possible (Rauch–Berger–Klingenberg); also there exists $\beta(n) > 1/4$ such that $\beta(n) \leqslant A(P_x) \leqslant 1$ implies that M is *diffeomorphic* to $\mathbf{S}_n$ (Gromoll–Calabi) (B 410, Nice I (Chern), LN 55).

Another problem that goes back to the beginnings of Riemannian geometry is the possibility of embedding a Riemannian manifold M of dimension n in a Euclidean space $\mathbf{R}^n$ of suitable dimension, in such a way that the Riemannian structure of M is induced by that of $\mathbf{R}^N$. The existence of such embeddings was proved by J. Nash, but the best value of N is unknown (B 147, 237; Nice C 4 (Gromov)). The geometry of Riemannian submanifolds of $\mathbf{R}^N$ goes back to the mathematicians of the 18th century (for $N = 3$), who introduced the classical invariants (radii of curvature, etc.). Recently it has been shown that certain restrictions of a global nature on these invariants have very restrictive consequences for compact manifolds (for example, that the manifold is homeomorphic to $\mathbf{S}_n$) (B 193; LN 66, 335).

3. The topology of differential manifolds

The fundamental fact of the theory of differential manifolds is the relationship between their topology and the *differential forms* on the manifold. This was foreseen by Poincaré and formulated as a precise conjecture by E. Cartan; it was established in 1929 by G. de Rham, and may be expressed by saying that the cohomology with real coefficients $H^{\cdot}(M; \mathbf{R})$ of a differential manifold M is canonically isomorphic to that of the cochain complex (**B** I) formed by the spaces $\Lambda^p(M)$ of differential p-forms on M, with respect to the exterior differential $d : \Lambda^p(M) \to \Lambda^{p+1}(M)$ $(0 \leqslant p \leqslant \dim(M))$.

Moreover, the duality between homology $H_p(M; \mathbf{R})$ and cohomology $H^p(M; \mathbf{R})$ arises here, on passing to the quotients, from the existence of the canonical bilinear form $\int_C \omega = \langle C, \omega \rangle$, the integral of a p-form ω over a p-chain C, and from Stokes's formula $\langle C, d\omega \rangle = \langle \partial C, \omega \rangle$, where ∂C is the boundary of C.

Another important relation between differential geometry and topological invariants consists in a canonical procedure which, for a manifold M endowed with a G-structure (where G is a compact connected Lie group) enables the characteristic classes of M relative to G (**A** I) to be expressed in terms of a connection on M (Chern–Weil theory) (B 38, 440; BAMS 72 (Chern); LN 67).

We refer to (**A** V) for the relations between the topology of a compact differential manifold and the differential operators on the manifold (theories of Hodge, Atiyah–Singer, Atiyah–Bott, etc.).

4. Infinite-dimensional differential manifolds

Nonlinear functional analysis leads naturally to the idea that, just as topological vector spaces are the natural substratum of linear functional analysis, so the proper framework for nonlinear problems should be "manifolds" that are to topological vector spaces what ordinary manifolds are to the spaces $\mathbf{R}^n$.

The typical example is the calculus of variations, and notably Morse theory, in which the "points" of the "manifold" are the geodesics of an (ordinary) Riemannian manifold [124].

Since there is no difficulty in defining the notion of a differentiable mapping between Banach spaces, we can define a "differential manifold modeled on a Banach space E" simply by replacing $\mathbf{R}^n$ by E in the usual definition by charts. When E is a Hilbert space, differentiable partitions of unity exist, and all the definitions of the theory of finite-dimensional differential or Riemannian manifolds can be extended to manifolds "modeled" on E. The remarkable fact is that the theory of these manifolds is much simpler than that of manifolds of finite dimension; all Hilbert manifolds are diffeomorphic to open subsets of E, and if two open subsets of E have the same homotopy type, then they are diffeomorphic (B 284, 378, 540; BAMS 72 (Eells); Nice C 1 (R. D. Anderson), C 2 (Kuiper), C 4 (Ebin–Marsden, Eells–Elworthy); LN 259, 282; SAMS XV).

5. Connections with the natural sciences

The fundamental postulate of the theory of Relativity is that space-time is a differential manifold endowed with a *pseudo-Riemannian* structure, i.e., a G-structure where G is the Lorentz group, which leaves invariant the quadratic form $x_0^2 - x_1^2 - x_2^2 - x_3^2$ on $\mathbf{R}^4$. The theory of geodesics for such a structure and the theory of singularities of differentiable mappings therefore play an important part in relativistic theories of cosmology, in particular in the study of singularities of space-time ("black holes") ([141]; BAMS 83 (R. Sacks-H. Wu); LN 209).

About ten years ago, R. Thom developed some extremely original ideas on the possibility of applying the theory of singularities of differentiable mappings to the qualitative study of physicochemical and biological phenomena, and even to linguistics: this is what he calls *catastrophe theory*, which has aroused considerable interest in many places, and some controversy [180].

6. The originators

The principal ideas in the theory of differential manifolds and G-structures are due to the following mathematicians:

The notion of a differential manifold. C. F. Gauss (1777–1855), B. Riemann (1826–1866), H. Weyl (1885–1955).

Singularities of differentiable mappings. H. Whitney, R. Thom, B. Malgrange, J. Mather, D. Sullivan.

Vector fields. A. Poincaré (1854–1912), H. Hopf (1894–1971), J. F. Adams, M. Atiyah.

G-structures, connections. E. Cartan (1869–1951), T. Levi-Civita (1873–1941), S. Chern.

Riemannian manifolds. B. Riemann (1826–1866), E. Cartan (1869–1951), J. Nash.

Topology of differential manifolds. E. Cartan (1869–1951), G. de Rham, S. Chern, A. Weil, W. Thurston.

Infinite-dimensional manifolds. M. Morse (1892–1977), S. Smale, V. Arnol'd.

The following have also made substantial contributions to these theories: C. Allendoerfer (1911–1974), W. Ambrose, R. Anderson, L. Auslander, A. Avez, F. Almgren, E. Beltrami (1835–1899), M. Berger, S. Bernstein (1880–1968), C. Bessaga, L. Bianchi (1856–1928), W. Blaschke (1885–1962), J. Boardman, S. Bochner, E. Bombieri, R. Bonič, O. Bonnet (1819–1892), D. Burghelea, E. Calabi, J. Cheeger, E. Christoffel (1829–1900), S. Cohn-Vossen (1902–1936), G. Darboux (1842–1917), E. De Giorgi, A. Douady, D. Ebin, B. Eckmann, J. Eells, C. Ehresmann (1905–1979), H. Eliasson, K. Elworthy, C. Fefferman, W. Fenchel, A. Fet, J. Frampton, E. Giusti, D. Gromoll, M. Gromov, J. Hadamard (1865–1963). A. Haefliger, P. Hartman, D. Henderson, D. Hilbert (1862–1943), W. Y. Hsiang, I. James, H. Karcher, W. Klingenberg, U. Koschorke, J. L. Koszul, N. Kuiper, S. Kobayashi, R. Lashof, H. Lawson, J. Levine, H. Lewy, A. Lichnerowicz, W. Liebmann (1874–1939), R. Lipschitz (1832–1903), P. Libermann, L. Lusternik, J. Marsden, W. Meyer, J. Milnor, G. Mostow, N. Moulis, K. Mukherjea, S. Myers (1910–1955), A. Nijenhuis, L. Nirenberg, J. Nitsche, K. Nomizu, R. Osserman, R. Palais, A. Pelczynski, R. Penrose, W. Pohl, I. Porteous, M. Rauch, A. Ribaucour (1845–1893), G. Ricci (1853–1925), W. Rinow, E. Ruh, L. Schnirelmann (1905–1938), F. Schur (1856–1932), H. A. Schwarz (1843–1921), G. Segal, J. Simons, I. Singer, N. Steenrod (1910–1971), E. Stiefel (1909–1978), E. Thomas, V. Topogonov, J. Tougeron, A. Tromba, K. Weierstrass (1815–1897), J. West, G. W. Whitehead, H. Yamabe (1923–1960), K. Yano, S. Yau, R. Böhme, J. Douglas, H. Federer, W. Fleming, W. Meeks, F. Morgan, F. Tomi.

References

B: 24, 35, 36, 38, 101, 134, 147, 166, 193, 233, 237, 284, 336, 353, 364, 378, 406, 410, 424, 440, 526, 527, 529, 540, 573, 579.

LN: 55, 66, 67, 192, 197, 209, 259, 282, 335, 371, 373, 484, 520, 525, 535, 552, 570, 588, 597, 610, 640, 678.

BAMS: 64 (Pitcher), 71 (Nitsche), 72 (Chern, Eells), 75 (Thom, Thomas, Osserman) 83 (K. Chen, R. Gardner, R. Sacks-H. Wu), 84 (Osserman).

SAMS: XV

Astérisque: 32–33, 45, 58.

[100], [124], [141], [144], [180], [204], [223].

A III

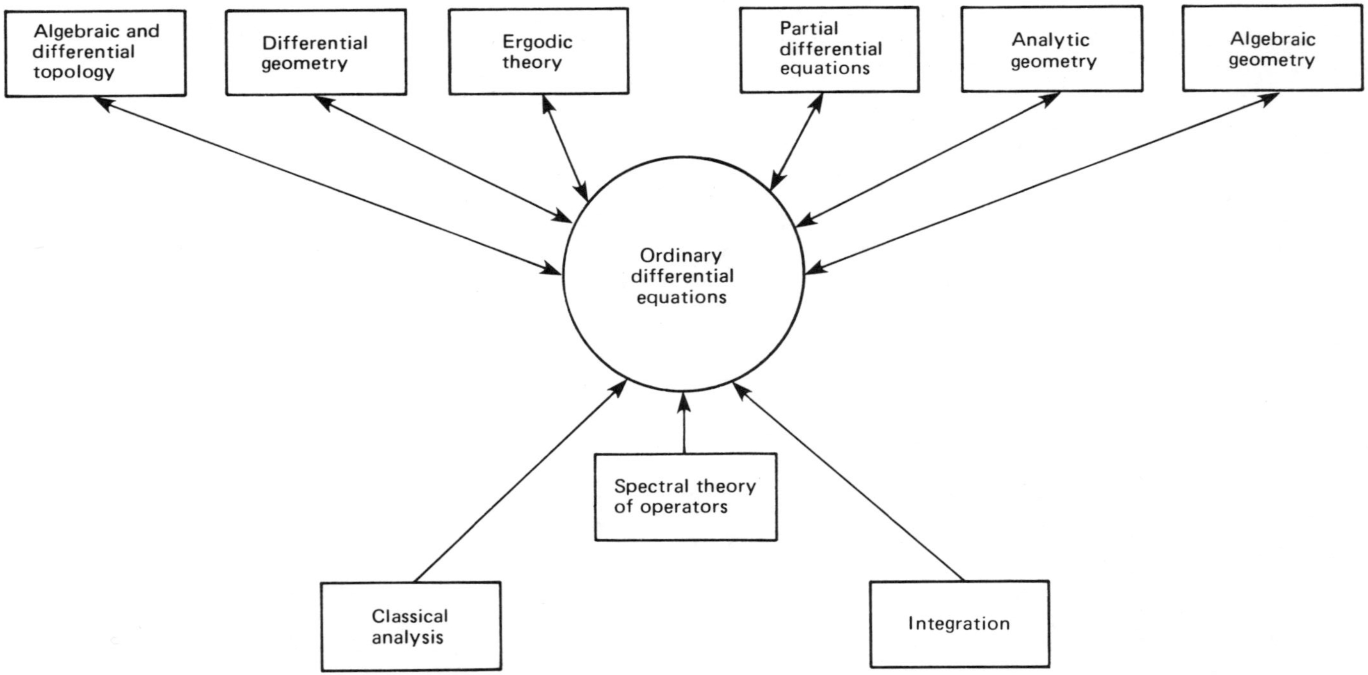

Algebraic and differential topology
Differential geometry
Ergodic theory
Partial differential equations
Analytic geometry
Algebraic geometry
Ordinary differential equations
Spectral theory of operators
Classical analysis
Integration

A III

Ordinary differential equations

For 300 years, the theory of ordinary differential equations has been one of the most intensively studied branches of mathematics, and a great variety of methods have been devised to attack the innumerable problems it has raised.

1. The algebraic theory

In the 18th century, the study of differential equations was directed primarily toward obtaining "general" solutions by operations considered as "simple," such as "quadratures" and series expansions. This period of empiricism generated a heterogeneous collection of results and was followed in the 19th century by an effort of reflection on the methods used, analogous to that which, between 1770 and 1830, led to the theory of Galois for algebraic equations. And indeed these investigations culminated in a "Galois theory," in an almost completely algebraised framework, first for linear differential equations (Picard–Vessiot theory), and then for algebraic differential equations, in ever closer liaison with the modern theory of algebraic groups (**A** IX) (B 17; [101]).

2. Ordinary differential equations in the complex domain

After the creation by Cauchy of the theory of holomorphic functions, the analysts of the 19th century embarked on the study of singular points, in the complex domain, of solutions of analytic differential equations. This study culminated in the spectacular results of Painlevé on second-order equations all of whose integrals are meromorphic [89]. Recently, this subject has again become an area of active research, in the current of ideas flowing from the general theory of singularities in analytic geometry (**A** VIII).

3. The qualitative study of ordinary differential equations

Around 1880, Liapunov and H. Poincaré gave a new direction to the theory by initiating a global geometrical study of the family of integral curves of a differential equation. Liapunov was primarily interested in problems of *stability* of an integral curve under small variations of the initial conditions; the methods he invented in order to determine the stability of an integral curve have been applied and developed in a great many investigations ([111]; LN 35), and even the notion of stability is capable of many variations. Poincaré started with a first-order differential equation, written in the form $\frac{dx}{X} = \frac{dy}{Y}$, where X and Y are polynomials in x and y with no common factor, and straightaway set himself the most general problem, namely, the "qualitative" description of all the integral curves of the equation. In order to be able to deal with infinite branches, he projected the plane Oxy onto a sphere (with center outside the plane) from the center of the sphere, and this led him to the study of integral curves of a field of tangent vectors to the sphere. A little later, in order to deal with first-order differential equations $F(x, y, y') = 0$ not solved for y', he considered the problem as being equivalent to the determination, on the surface $F(x, y, p) = 0$, of the integral curves of the equation $dy - p\,dx = 0$; again this is a particular case of integral curves of a vector field on a surface. Generally speaking, problems relative to differential equations of higher order, or to systems of differential equations, can be thought of in terms of the integral curves of a vector field on a differential manifold M of arbitrary dimension. The most frequently studied case is that in which M is a compact manifold and X is a C^∞-vector field: if we denote by $F_X(x, t)$ the value at $t \in \mathbf{R}$ of the integral v such that $v(0) = x$, then $F_X(x, t)$ is defined for *all* t, and the mapping $(t, x) \mapsto F_X(x, t)$ is a C^∞-action of the additive group $\mathbf{R}$ on the manifold M (**B** II). A whole chapter of the qualitative theory of differential equations is thus included as a particular case in the study of such actions by an arbitrary topological group G ([67], [133], [173]).

The fundamental notions in the study of a vector field X and its integral curves are those of critical point (**A** II) and closed integral curve. At a critical point a, the characteristic multipliers of X are by definition the eigenvalues of the Jacobian matrix of the components of the field X at the point a (relative to any system of local coordinates). A closed integral curve $\gamma : t \mapsto \gamma(t)$ by definition contains no critical point and is periodic; if $\tau > 0$ is the smallest period, then for each point $x \in \gamma$, the mapping $y \mapsto F_X(y, \tau)$ is a diffeomorphism of a neighborhood of x onto a neighborhood of x, and its tangent linear mapping at x is an automorphism of the tangent space $T_x(M)$. The characteristic multipliers of γ are the eigenvalues of this automorphism (one of them is always equal to 1).

One of the essential problems (which arose already in the 18th century, in connection with the three-body problem) is the existence and stability of closed integral curves. On manifolds of dimension 2, rather elementary geometrical considerations lead to criteria for existence and nonexistence (B 21; [133]); a famous example is the Van der Pol equation

$$u'' + \alpha(u^2 - 1)u' + \beta u = 0$$

(where α, β are positive constants) for which one can show the existence of exactly one periodic solution. In the case of manifolds of dimension >2, the main subject of investigation has been *Hamiltonian* differential systems (which are the most important for applications to mechanics): M is of even dimension $2n$, and carries a function H such that in a neighborhood of each point of M there is a system of local coordinates p_i, q_i $(1 \leqslant i \leqslant n)$ for which the system of differential equations takes the form

$$(1) \qquad \frac{dp_i}{dt} = -\frac{\partial \mathrm{H}}{\partial q_i}, \qquad \frac{dq_i}{dt} = \frac{\partial \mathrm{H}}{\partial p_i} \qquad (1 \leqslant i \leqslant n).$$

It follows immediately that the function H (the *Hamiltonian* of the system) is constant along each integral curve. Existence theorems for closed integral curves can then be obtained by the use of "perturbation" methods. For example, if γ is a closed integral curve for which the characteristic multiplier 1 occurs with multiplicity 1, Poincaré showed that in a neighborhood of γ there exists a family of closed integral curves depending on a parameter. Again, if x is a critical point of a Hamiltonian system, having two characteristic multipliers $e^{\pm i\beta}$ with multiplicity 1, then there exists a two-dimensional submanifold containing x, consisting of closed integral curves encircling x and tending toward x (Liapunov–Kelley) [1].

Other existence theorems are consequences of fixed-point theorems in topology ([74], [168]). Finally, in connection with the three-body problem, by considering the Hamiltonian H as a "perturbation" of a simpler Hamiltonian H_0 for which the closed integral curves are known, Poincaré was able to establish the existence of closed integral curves "close" to the circular orbits known since Euler. In 1963 Arenstorf succeeded in extending Poincaré's method to the case of orbits "close" to elliptic orbits of the two-body problem, of arbitrary eccentricity [1].

The most remarkable progress in this direction is due in the first place to Kolmogoroff, who inaugurated in 1954 a new method of treating "perturbations" of Hamiltonian systems, and succeeded in avoiding the difficulties of "small divisors" created in the classical series expansions by the presence of "resonances" between the periods of the bodies in motion in "nonperturbed" systems. Suppose in (1) that the Hamiltonian H is periodic with respect to the q_i, so that H may be thought of as a function on the product $\mathbf{T}^n \times \mathrm{B}$, where

$\mathbf{T}^n$ is the n-dimensional torus and B is a bounded open subset of $\mathbf{R}^n$, and the q_i may be thought of as n "angles" mod 2π, determining a point of $\mathbf{T}^n$. The "nonperturbed" case (also called "integrable") is that in which H is a function $H_0(p)$ not depending on the q_i, so that the system (1) admits n first integrals $p_i = \text{const.}$ $(1 \leqslant i \leqslant n)$. Geometrically, this means that the orbits lie on n-dimensional tori $p_i = C_i$ $(1 \leqslant i \leqslant n)$. It can also be shown that if the Hessian [D, Chapter 16] of H_0 does not vanish, then each orbit is dense in the corresponding torus $T_0(\omega)$ (where ω is the vector $(\partial H_0/\partial p_i)_{1 \leqslant i \leqslant n}$), except for a set of values of the vector ω of measure zero.

In general, we consider a Hamiltonian $H(p, q) = H_0(p) + H_1(p, q)$ where the "perturbation" H_1 is small compared to H_0. The work of Kolmogoroff, followed notably by J. Moser and V. Arnol'd, has shown that for almost all vectors ω there exists a torus $T(\omega)$ that is a union of integral curves of the system (1), each torus $T(\omega)$ being close to the corresponding torus $T_0(\omega)$ of the nonperturbed system; furthermore, the complement in $\mathbf{T}^n \times B$ of the union of the $T(\omega)$ has a measure that tends to 0 with the norm of H_1. But practically nothing is known about the behavior of the integral curves contained in this complement (B 217, 237, 264; [1], [4]).

4. The classification problem

Since about 1960 the classification of ordinary differential equations (or actions of $\mathbf{R}$) on a compact manifold M has been an extremely active area of research, led by S. Smale, M. Peixoto, and D. Anosov. Two actions of $\mathbf{R}$ on M are considered as isomorphic if there exists a homeomorphism of M onto itself that transforms the orbits of one action into the orbits of the other. At the same time, we shall consider the classification of actions of $\mathbf{Z}$ on M: this comes down to regarding two diffeomorphisms f, g of M onto itself as being in the same class if there exists a homeomorphism h of M onto itself such that $g = hfh^{-1}$ (in which case f and g are said to be conjugate). We shall begin with $\mathbf{Z}$-actions.

As in the case of singularities of differentiable mappings (**A** II), we cannot hope for significant results without eliminating the "pathological" cases, i.e., we must restrict attention to "generic" diffeomorphisms. For this purpose, we define C^r-topologies $(r \geqslant 1)$ on the set Diff(M) of diffeomorphisms of M: two diffeomorphisms are C^r-close if their jets of orders $\leqslant r$ are uniformly close in M. A property of a diffeomorphism is then said to be *C^r-generic* if the set of diffeomorphisms that have that property is a countable intersection of dense open sets in Diff(M) with respect to the C^r-topology. The principal generic property of a diffeomorphism f was discovered by Kupka and Smale: a *periodic* point of f is by definition a fixed point x of a power f^p, and is *hyperbolic* if the tangent linear mapping to f^p at the point x has no eigenvalues of modulus 1; the set $W^s(x)$ (resp. $W^u(x)$) of points y such that $f^{np}(y) \to x$ as $n \to \infty$ (resp. $n \to -\infty$) is then a submanifold of M, and the generic property of Kupka–Smale is that every periodic point of f is hyperbolic, and that if x, y are two periodic points (distinct or not), the submanifolds $W^s(x)$ and $W^u(y)$ intersect transversally.

An important notion is that of a *structurally stable* diffeomorphism, i.e., a diffeomorphism f that has a neighborhood in Diff(M) consisting of diffeomorphisms conjugate to f. The structurally stable diffeomorphisms form a nonempty open set in Diff(M), and in fact every diffeomorphism is isotopic to a structurally stable diffeomorphism. When $M = \mathbf{S}_1$, the set of structurally stable diffeomorphisms is dense in Diff(M), but this is no longer the case for manifolds of dimension >1.

Among the structurally stable diffeomorphisms are the *Morse–Smale* diffeomorphisms, which are those satisfying the Kupka–Smale property, having only finitely many periodic points and such that for each $x \in M$, the sequence $f^n(x)$ tends to a periodic point as n tends to $\pm\infty$. The set of these diffeomorphisms is always open and nonempty.

Another important class is the *Anosov diffeomorphisms*. To define these, assume that M carries a Riemannian structure, and hence a Euclidean norm on each tangent space $T_x(M)$. A diffeomorphism f is said to be an Anosov diffeomorphism if the tangent bundle T(M) decomposes into a direct sum $E^s \oplus E^u$ of vector bundles, each stable under the tangent mapping $T(f)$, and such that $T(f)$ (resp. $T(f^{-1})$) is a contraction on E^s (resp. E^u). The Anosov diffeomorphisms are structurally stable and form a (possibly empty) open set in Diff(M) [167].

There are analogous notions and results for differential equations on M (B 348, 374; BAMS 73 (Smale), 78 (J. Robbin), 80 (M. Shub); SAMS XIV; LN 206; [2], [48]).

5. Boundary-value problems

Many problems in analysis require solutions of a differential equation defined on an interval of **R** and satisfying various conditions at the endpoints (finite or not) of the interval. A typical example is to find solutions of a second-order equation that take given values at the (finite) endpoints of the interval. These problems have not been the subject of a general theory valid for equations of arbitrary order except in the case of *linear* equations, in the context of the spectral theory of operators (**C** III).

6. Connections with the natural sciences

Ever since the 17th century, almost all natural phenomena that involve certain quantities varying continuously as functions of a parameter (usually time) have led to problems about differential equations, and these problems have been a constant source of stimulation for the mathematical theory. We shall not attempt to list these innumerable applications. However, a special mention should be given to celestial mechanics, which historically was the first of these applications, and without doubt has instigated the largest quantity of important mathematical work ([168], [173]), the practical interest of which has been considerably augmented by its applications to the control of guided missiles and artificial satellites. As another example out of the common run, we may cite the research on the functioning of the heart and its representation by solutions of suitably chosen differential equations ([48] (Zeeman)).

7. The originators

We shall restrict ourselves to the *qualitative* theory, in which the most important ideas are due to the following mathematicians: H. Poincaré (1854–1912), A. Liapunov (1857–1918), G. D. Birkhoff (1884–1944), A. Denjoy (1884–1974), C. Siegel (1896–1981), A. Kolmogorov, S. Smale, A. Peixoto, V. Arnol'd, D. Anosov, J. Moser.

The following have also contributed substantially to the theory: R. Abraham, V. Alexyev, A. Andronov, R. Arenstorf, J. Auslander, A. Avez, J. Bendixson (1861–1936), N. Bhatia, R. Bowen (1947–1978), C. Camacho, L. Cesari, J. Chazy (1882–1955), R. Ellis, J. Franks, H. Furstenberg, W. Gottschalk, J. Guckenheimer, J. Hadamard (1865–1963), O. Hajek, J. Hale, P. Hartman, G. Hedlund, M. Herman, H. Hilmy, M. Hirsch, W. Kaplan, A. Kelley, H. Kneser (1898–1973), N. Kuiper, I. Kupka, J. La Salle, S. Lefschetz (1884–1972), A. Liénard, J. Littlewood (1885–1977), A. Manning, L. Markus, J. Massera, J. Mather, M. Morse (1892–1977), R. Moussu, V. Nemytskii (1900–1967), S. Newhouse, J. Palis, O. Perron (1880–1975), I. Petrowski (1901–1973), C. Pugh, L. Pontrjagin, G. Reeb, J. Robbin, R. Roussarie, A. Schwartz, H. Seifert, S. Shub, K. Sitnikov, J. Sotomayor, V. Stepanov (1889–1950), S. Sternberg, D. Sullivan, K. Sundman (1873–1949), G. P. Szegö, B. Van der Pol (1889–1959). T. Wazewski, H. Whitney, R. Williams, A. Wintner (1903–1958).

References

B: 17, 21, 217, 237, 264, 348, 374, 580.
LN: 35, 206, 468, 552, 583, 597, 668, 712, 738.
BAMS: 73 (Smale), 78 (Robbin), 80 (Shub).
SAMS: XIV.
Astérisque: 30, 31, 40, 49–51, 56.
[1], [2], [4], [48], [67], [74], [89], [101], [111], [133], [167], [168], [173], [220].

A IV

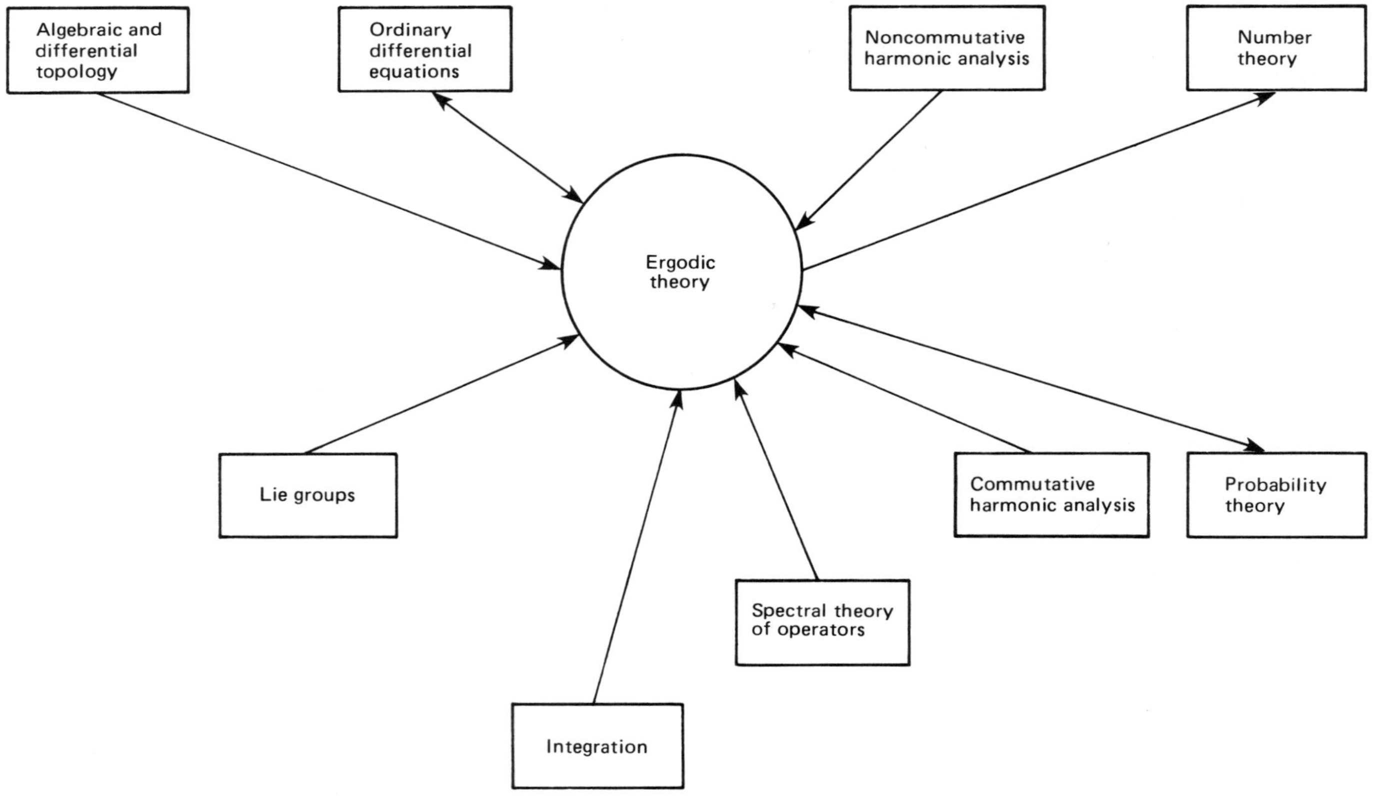

Algebraic and differential topology
Ordinary differential equations
Noncommutative harmonic analysis
Number theory
Ergodic theory
Lie groups
Integration
Spectral theory of operators
Commutative harmonic analysis
Probability theory

A IV

Ergodic theory

Ergodic theory originated in the development of statistical mechanics and the kinetic theory of gases, in which experimental evidence suggested a tendency to "uniformity": if we consider at a given instant a heterogeneous mixture of several gases, the evolution of the mixture in the course of time tends to make it homogeneous. This can be expressed in probabilistic terms, and a correct mathematical formulation of these physical concepts requires their axiomatization and reduction to probabilistic measure theory (**B** VII).

The classical problems concern the orbits of a vector field on a differential manifold M (or an action of **R** on M), with the supplementary hypothesis that there exists on M a nonzero positive measure invariant under this action. One may of course consider in the same way an action of **Z** on M, that is to say, a diffeomorphism of M leaving invariant a positive measure. However, in the majority of problems it appears that differentiability plays no part, but rather measurability does. We therefore consider a set M endowed with a positive measure μ and an action $(s, x) \mapsto s \cdot x$ of **Z** (or **R**) on M, subject only to the condition that $x \mapsto s \cdot x$ should be μ-measurable for all s. We shall consider mainly the case of **Z**-actions, so that we are dealing with a μ-measurable bijection T of M onto itself, and its iterates T^n, $n \in \mathbf{Z}$. The most frequent hypothesis is that T leaves the measure μ invariant, and it is enough to assume that T is a bijection of a subset M′ of M, with μ-negligible complement, onto a subset M″ with μ-negligible complement. If M_1 is another set equipped with a positive measure μ_1, a μ_1-measurable transformation T_1 of M_1 into itself that leaves μ_1 invariant is said to be *isomorphic* to T if there exists an isomorphism $F : M \to M_1$ of measure spaces such that $FT = T_1F$.

1. The ergodic theorem

A first fundamental result is the *ergodic theorem* of G. D. Birkhoff: for each μ-integrable function f on M, the "time average" $f^*(x) = \lim_{n\to\infty} \frac{1}{n} \sum_{j=0}^{n-1} f(T^j x)$ exists almost everywhere, and the function f^* is integrable and satisfies

$f^*(Tx) = f^*(x)$. If in addition the measure μ is bounded, we have $\int f^* \, d\mu = \int f \, d\mu$. It should be remarked that even if M is an analytic manifold, f an analytic function, and T a diffeomorphism, it can happen that $f^*(x)$ fails to exist at the points x of a dense subset of M. There are numerous generalizations of this theorem, notably by replacing the operator $f \mapsto f \circ T$ by an operator of norm $\leqslant 1$ on the space $L^1(\mu)$, subject to a variety of conditions (B 293; [60]).

If the measure μ is bounded and nonzero, the transformation T is said to be *ergodic* if f^* is constant almost everywhere for each integrable function f; an equivalent condition is that the only measurable subset A of M of measure >0 such that T(A) and A differ only by a set of measure 0, is M itself (up to a set of measure 0).

A simple example of an ergodic transformation is a rotation of the circle $\mathbf{S}_1$ through an angle $2\pi\alpha$, where α is irrational. Another example that has recently acquired great importance is the *Bernoulli scheme* (or *Bernoulli shift*), in which M is the infinite product $I_r^{\mathbf{Z}}$, where I_r is a finite set with r elements, to each of which is attached a mass $p_j > 0$ such that $\sum_{j=1}^{r} p_j = 1$; we take on M the product measure $\bigotimes_{n \in \mathbf{Z}} \mu_n$, where μ_n is the above measure on the nth factor $I_r^{(n)}$. The Bernoulli shift $B(p_1, \ldots, p_r)$ is the transformation that sends each point $(x_n)_{n \in \mathbf{Z}}$ to the point $(x'_n)_{n \in \mathbf{Z}}$ such that $x'_n = x_{n+1}$ for all n.

A recent deep result is that an Anosov diffeomorphism of a compact manifold (**A** III) is ergodic (Nice D 12 (Sinaï)).

There are corresponding notions for **R**-actions $(t, x) \mapsto \varphi_t(x)$. Birkhoff's theorem generalizes by taking as "time average" the expression $f^*(x) = \lim_{T \to \infty} \frac{1}{T} \int_0^T \varphi_t(x) \, dt$, and the definition of ergodicity is unaltered. Anosov's theorem generalizes and leads to the solution of a famous problem of Riemannian geometry: if V is a compact Riemannian manifold of sectional curvature (**A** II) everywhere <0, then the geodesic field on the manifold M of unit tangent vectors to V (which preserves the canonical measure on M) is ergodic (B 28; BAMS 77 (E. Hopf); [4], [139]).

2. Classification problems

A central problem is to classify up to isomorphism the transformations T that leave a measure invariant. We shall limit ourselves to the case in which the measure space M is isomorphic to the interval [0, 1] of **R**, endowed with Lebesgue measure.

A first principle of classification comes from associating with T the unitary operator U on the Hilbert space $L^2(\mu)$ defined by $U \cdot f = f \circ T$; if T_1 and T_2 are isomorphic, the corresponding operators U_1, U_2 are equivalent, and in particular have the same spectrum with the same multiplicity, and equivalent spectral measures (**C** III). The ergodic transformations T are characterized by the fact that 1 is an eigenvalue of U with multiplicity 1; all the eigenvalues are then simple, and form a subgroup of the group **U** of complex numbers of absolute value 1, and the corresponding eigenfunctions have a constant absolute value. For ergodic transformations with *discrete* spectrum, the isomorphism problem has been completely solved: if U_1 and U_2 have the same spectrum, then T_1 and T_2 are isomorphic. On the other hand, the spectral type of U is the same for all Bernoulli schemes, and hence cannot distinguish them (the spectrum is continuous and of infinite multiplicity away from the eigenvalue 1) ([4], [72], [93]; Nice D 12 (Stepin)).

Decisive progress was made by A. Kolmogoroff, who in 1958 introduced the notion of *entropy*, derived from C. Shannon's information theory. If M is a set carrying a probability measure μ (so that $\mu(M) = 1$) and A is a measurable subset of M, the probability that $x \in A$ is $\mu(A)$, and the information on x given by A is taken to be $-\log \mu(A)$ (so that if $\mu(A \cap B) = \mu(A)\mu(B)$, i.e., if A and B are measurable and "independent" in the sense of probability theory, the informations of A and B are added). If $\alpha = \{A_1, \ldots, A_m\}$ is a finite partition of M into measurable subsets, the *entropy* $H(\alpha)$ of the partition is the "mean value" of the information of the A_j, i.e., $-\sum_{k=1}^{m} \mu(A_k) \log \mu(A_k)$. If now T is a bijection of M onto itself that leaves μ invariant, let $T^{-j}(\alpha)$ denote the partition formed by the $T^{-j}(A_k)$ for all j, and $\bigvee_{j=0}^{n} T^{-j}(\alpha)$ the partition obtained by superposition of the partitions $T^{-j}(\alpha)$ for $0 \leqslant j \leqslant n$ (we take $T^0(\alpha) = \alpha$). Then it can be shown that the number $\frac{1}{n+1} H\left(\bigvee_{j=0}^{n} T^{-j}(\alpha)\right)$ tends to a limit $h(T, \alpha)$ as $n \to \infty$, and this limit $h(T, \alpha)$ is called the entropy of T with respect to α. Finally, we denote by $h(T)$ the least upper bound of the $h(T, \alpha)$ as α runs through all finite partitions of M into measurable sets; $h(T)$ is called the *entropy* of T. For a Bernoulli scheme $B(p_1, \ldots, p_r)$, the entropy is found to be $-\sum_{j=1}^{r} p_j \log p_j$, and this new invariant therefore distinguishes transformations of the same spectral type. But the study of entropy has led to a whole series of even more remarkable results, culminating in the recent theorem of Ornstein to the effect that two Bernoulli schemes with the same entropy are isomorphic. Furthermore, many ergodic transformations are isomorphic to Bernoulli schemes: for example, Anosov diffeomorphisms and ergodic automorphisms of a torus. However, ergodic transformations of positive entropy are known which are not isomorphic to Bernoulli schemes, in particular a class of transformations defined by A. Kolmogoroff, which can be characterized in various ways, one of which is that $h(\mathrm{T}, \alpha) > 0$ for all partitions α containing at least two subsets of positive measure (B 420; BAMS 77 (Ornstein), 78 (B. Weiss); Nice D 6 (Ornstein); LN 214; [4], [163]). Two transformations can therefore have the same entropy without being isomorphic.

There are analogous notions and results for **R**-actions. In particular, *Bernoulli fields* can be defined, and Ornstein and Weiss have proved that the geodesic field on a Riemannian manifold of negative sectional curvature is a Bernoulli field [163].

An important type of **R**-action arises from the theory of homogeneous spaces of Lie groups (**B** II): if X = G/H is such a homogeneous space, we obtain an action of **R** on X by composing the canonical action of G on X with a homomorphism of **R** into G. The theory of Lie groups and noncommutative harmonic analysis provide methods for analyzing these actions, and in particular for determining when they are ergodic. In this way we obtain in particular ergodic **R**-actions of zero entropy ([4], [8], [62]; LN 318 (L. Auslander)). Also the idea of ergodic action can be generalized by replacing **Z** or **R** by an arbitrary Lie group G, which leads inter alia to the idea of "virtual subgroups" of G. Mackey (B 559 Nice D 2 (Mackey); LN 318 (B. Weiss); [115]).

3. Connections with the natural sciences

Although its origin lies in questions of statistical mechanics, ergodic theory has remained up to now a purely mathematical theory. However, there are applications concerning information and coding theory ([16], [116]).

4. The originators

The most important ideas are due to the following mathematicians: G. D. Birkhoff (1884–1944), B. Koopman, A. Kolmogorov, Y. Sinaï, D. Anosov, D. Ornstein.

The following have also contributed substantially to the theory: R. Adler, H. Anzaï, V. Arnol'd, L. Auslander, A. Avez, R. Azencott, R. Bowen (1947–1978), A. Brunel, R. Chacon, N. Dunford, S. Fomin, N. Friedman, H. Furstenberg, I. Gelfand, B. Gourevich, L. Green, F. Hahn, P. Halmos, G. Hedlund, E. Hopf, S. Kakutani, A. Katok, Y. Katznelson, M. Keane, A. Kouchnirenko, W. Krieger, K. Jacobs, G. Margulis, G. Mackey, C. Moore, W. Parry, J. Pesin,

M. Pinsker, V. Rokhlin, P. Shields, M. Smorodinsky, A. Stepin, W. Veech, J. von Neumann (1903–1957), B. Weiss, R. Williams, R. Zimmer.

References

B: 28, 293, 420, 518, 559.
LN: 214, 318, 458, 470, 532, 729.
BAMS: 77 (E. Hopf, Ornstein), 78 (B. Weiss).
[4], [8], [16], [60], [62], [72], [93], [115], [116], [139], [163], [220].

A V

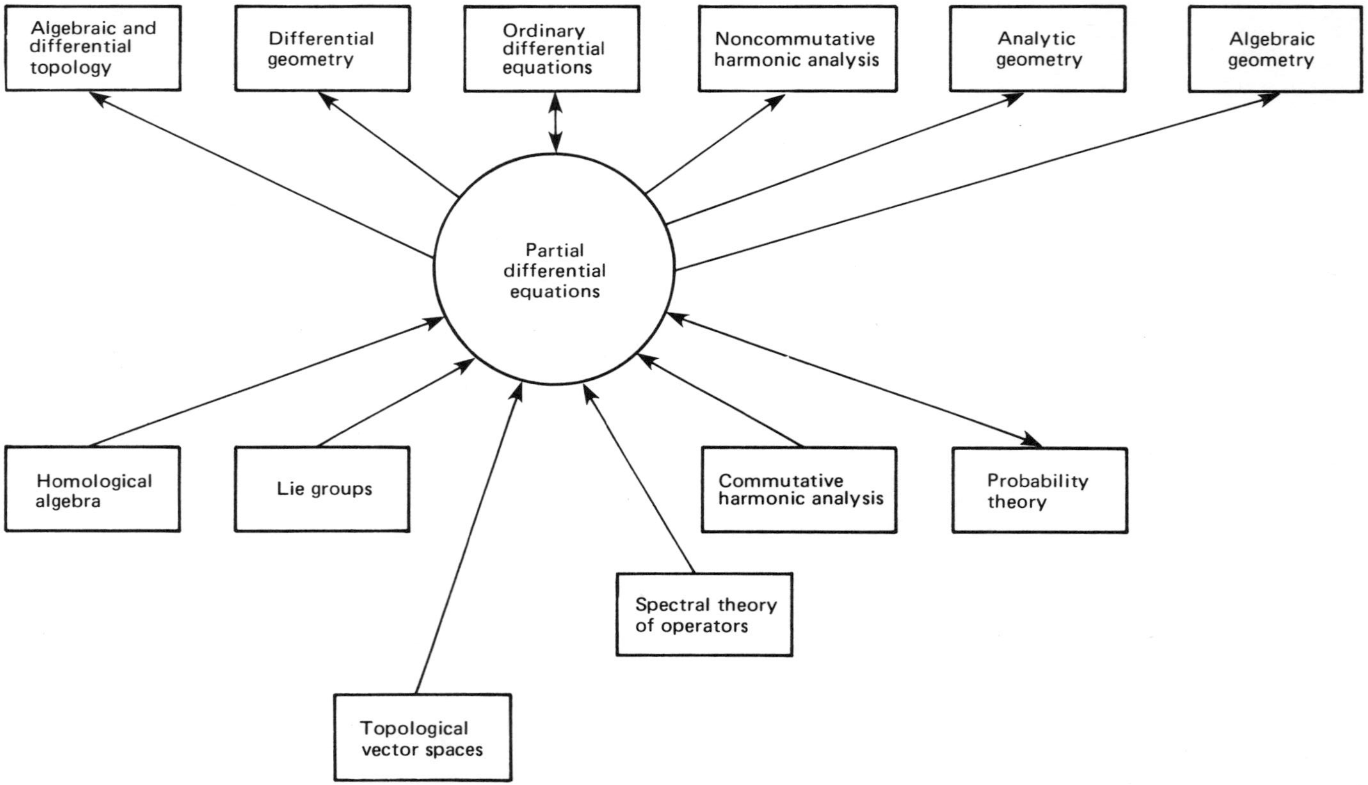
Algebraic and differential topology
Differential geometry
Ordinary differential equations
Noncommutative harmonic analysis
Analytic geometry
Algebraic geometry
Partial differential equations
Homological algebra
Lie groups
Commutative harmonic analysis
Probability theory
Spectral theory of operators
Topological vector spaces

A V

Partial differential equations

The theory of partial differential equations has been studied incessantly for more than two centuries. By reason of its permanent symbiosis with almost all parts of physics, as well as its ever closer connections with many other branches of mathematics, it is one of the largest and most diverse regions of present-day mathematics, and the vastness of its bibliography defies the imagination.

For a long time, the theory of ordinary differential equations served more or less consciously as a model for partial differential equations, and it is only rather recently that it has come to be realized that the differences between the two theories are much more numerous and more profound than the analogies.

1. The local study of differential systems

Here the paradigm was the Cauchy–Lipschitz theorem of existence and uniqueness of solutions of ordinary differential equations: if I is an open neighborhood of a point $t_0 \in \mathbf{R}$, consider a differential equation

$$\frac{dx}{dt} = \mathrm{A}(x, t), \tag{1}$$

where x takes its values in an open set H in $\mathbf{R}^n$, and A is a function with values in H which is continuously differentiable on $\mathrm{H} \times \mathrm{I}$ (or at least satisfies a Lipschitz condition in x on a neighborhood of each point of $\mathrm{H} \times \mathrm{I}$); then for each $x_0 \in \mathrm{H}$, there exists a suitably small neighborhood $\mathrm{J} \subset \mathrm{I}$ of t_0 such that the equation (1) admits a unique solution $t \mapsto x(t)$ in J such that $x(t_0) = x_0$. [D, Chapter 10].

The only analogous general theorem we possess for partial differential equations is the Cauchy–Kowalewska theorem. Consider a system of r equations in r unknown real-valued functions $v_1, \ldots, v_r$ of $p + 1$ real variables $x_1, \ldots, x_{p+1}$, of the form

$$\text{(2)} \qquad \frac{\partial v_j}{\partial x_{p+1}} = \mathrm{H}_j\left(x_1, \ldots, x_{p+1}, v_1, \ldots, v_r, \frac{\partial v_1}{\partial x_1}, \frac{\partial v_1}{\partial x_2}, \ldots, \frac{\partial v_r}{\partial x_{p-1}}, \frac{\partial v_r}{\partial x_p}\right) \qquad (1 \leqslant j \leqslant r)$$

in which the right-hand sides do not involve any derivatives with respect to x_{p+1}, and are assumed to be real *analytic* functions of the $p + 1 + r + rp$ variables that feature in them, in a neighborhood V_0 of the origin in the space $\mathbf{R}^{p+1+r+rp}$. Then there exists a suitably small neighborhood $\mathrm{V} \subset \mathrm{V}_0$ of 0 in $\mathbf{R}^{p+1}$ such that the system of equations (2) admits a unique solution $(v_1, \ldots, v_r)$ consisting of *analytic* functions on V, such that $v_j(x_1, \ldots, x_p, 0) = 0$ in $\mathrm{V} \cap \mathbf{R}^p$ for $1 \leqslant j \leqslant r$ [D, Chapter 18].

However, most systems of partial differential equations encountered are not of this type (2), and it is worth knowing whether they can be reduced to this type by changes of variables or introduction of new unknowns. This is not always possible, as is shown by the elementary example

$$\text{(3)} \qquad \frac{\partial z}{\partial x} = \mathrm{P}(x, y, z), \qquad \frac{\partial z}{\partial y} = \mathrm{Q}(x, y, z).$$

Many attempts at classification of partial differential equations were made in the 19th century, with varying degrees of success, until E. Cartan obtained a general principle of a geometrical nature with his theory of *Pfaffian systems*. The idea here is that a system $(v_1, \ldots, v_r)$ of functions of p real variables defines a submanifold X with equations $x_{p+j} = v_j(x_1, \ldots, x_p)$ $(1 \leqslant j \leqslant r)$ in $\mathbf{R}^{r+p}$ (or in a $\mathbf{R}^N$ with larger N), and to impose relations involving their first derivatives is equivalent to requiring the (p-dimensional) *tangent space* to X at each point to satisfy a certain number of conditions. In fact, these conditions can always be reduced to the vanishing of a certain number of differential forms, called a Pfaffian system. Consider for example a partial differential equation of the second order for an unknown function z of two variables x, y:

$$\mathrm{F}\left(x, y, z, \frac{\partial z}{\partial x}, \frac{\partial z}{\partial y}, \frac{\partial^2 z}{\partial x^2}, \frac{\partial^2 z}{\partial x\, \partial y}, \frac{\partial^2 z}{\partial y^2}\right) = 0.$$

We introduce five new unknown functions p, q, r, s, t of x and y, and the equation is then equivalent to the Pfaffian system

$$dz - p\, dx - q\, dy = 0, \qquad dp - r\, dx - s\, dy = 0, \qquad dq - s\, dx - t\, dy = 0$$

on the manifold with equation $\mathrm{F}(x, y, z, p, q, r, s, t) = 0$ in $\mathbf{R}^8$.

By geometric arguments (which do not depend on the choice of independent variables) Cartan was able to determine the maximum dimension of integral manifolds of a given Pfaffian system: this dimension can be strictly less than the number of independent variables in the original problem. For example, a system (3) in general possesses only integral curves [D, Chapter 18].

E. Cartan considerably developed this theory, especially in two directions, related to the general notion of *prolongation* of a differential system: this is the intrinsic formulation of the idea of obtaining new equations from a given system of partial differential equations, by differentiating the given equations $\left(\text{for example, from the system (3) we obtain a new equation } \frac{\partial P}{\partial y} + Q\frac{\partial P}{\partial z} = \frac{\partial Q}{\partial x} + P\frac{\partial Q}{\partial z}\right)$. When p independent variables are *fixed*, a natural problem is whether there exist integral manifolds (of dimension p) that are expressed locally by equations giving the remaining variables as functions of the p given ones (as in the system (2)). The fundamental result, conjectured by E. Cartan and subsequently proved by Kuranishi (for systems with *analytic* coefficients) is that the answer to this question can be decided by a *finite* number of prolongations, and that if the answer is affirmative, the system after suitable prolongation reduces to the form (2) (systems "in involution") (B 522). The other direction is related to the general notion of G-structures (**A** II) and to a generalization of the notion of a Lie group, already considered by Lie himself and nowadays called "Lie pseudogroups" (they are not groups in the usual sense) (B 118, 326; BAMS 70 (Guillemin–Sternberg)). The modern theory translates the notions and results of E. Cartan into the language of jets (**A** II), which permits the techniques of homological algebra to be applied (B 329; BAMS 75 (Spencer)).

2. Completely integrable systems and foliations

The Pfaffian systems that are direct generalizations of ordinary differential equations are those in which at each point the tangent space is *uniquely determined*; this means that if the system consists of $n - p$ linearly independent equations $\omega_j = 0$ $(1 \leqslant j \leqslant n - p)$ on an open set in $\mathbf{R}^n$ (or on an n-dimensional manifold), one seeks to find p-dimensional integral manifolds (example (3) is the simplest case). The condition that such an integral manifold should pass through each point was obtained by Jacobi, Clebsch, and Deahna: in the form given by Frobenius, it is that $\omega_1 \wedge \cdots \wedge \omega_{n-p} \wedge d\omega_j$ should be identically zero for $1 \leqslant j \leqslant n - p$. In this case the system is said to be *completely integrable*, and at each point there exists a chart with respect to which the integral manifolds have local expressions of the form $x_{p+j} = C_j$ $(1 \leqslant j \leqslant n - p)$, where the C_j are arbitrary constants. Moreover, it can be shown that, as in the case of ordinary differential equations, there exist *maximal* connected integral manifolds, which form what are called the "leaves" of a *foliation* of dimension p (or of codimension $n - p$) of the manifold on which the Pfaffian system is defined (they are not, in general, locally closed submanifolds) [D, Chapter 18].

The study of properties of foliations from the point of view of differential topology was inaugurated by Ehresmann and Reeb in 1948, but only recently has it begun to attract the attention of many mathematicians: it is now a very active field of research. The emphasis is on the topological properties of the leaves, in particular on the existence of compact leaves (which generalizes the periodic trajectories in the theory of ordinary differential equations (**A** III)). The example that has served as a model is the Reeb foliation of the sphere $\mathbf{S}_3$, which is of codimension 1 and has only one compact leaf; only recently have generalizations to other compact manifolds been obtained (B 499). On the other hand, a completely integrable Pfaffian system on a manifold M determines a sub-bundle E of the tangent bundle T(M), satisfying the Frobenius condition at each point; but it has recently been realized that such a sub-bundle must also satisfy *global* conditions of a topological nature. The first of these was obtained by Bott, and expresses that the Pontrjagin classes of order k of the quotient bundle $Q = T(M)/E$ must vanish for $k > 2q$, where q is the rank of Q (LN 279). The present study of these problems depends on techniques from homotopy theory (in which homological algebra also plays a large part) introduced by Haefliger; it is necessary to enlarge somewhat the notion of foliation, by admitting "singular" leaves whose dimension is smaller than that of the "generic" leaves. The theory is also related to the cohomology of vector fields (**B** I) of Gelfand and Fuks (B 192, 339, 390, 393, 412, 434, 523, 524, 551, 574; LN 197, 206, 279, 392, 484, 493, 652, 712, 725; Nice I (Bott); BAMS 80 (Lawson); [34]).

3. Linear partial differential equations: general theory

A linear partial differential equation of order m on an open subset X of $\mathbf{R}^n$ is an equation of the form $P \cdot u = f$ where $P = \sum_{|\nu| \leq m} A_\nu(x)D^\nu$ is a linear combination of derivatives of order $\leq m$, the coefficients being functions of $x \in X$, and f a given real-valued function on X. We shall limit our attention to the case in which the A_ν are real-valued functions of class C^∞; the notion of "solution" can then be extended to the case where f is a *distribution* [D, Chapter 17], and a solution is a distribution u satisfying $P \cdot u = f$.

In the same way we define systems of linear partial differential equations, or *vector* partial differential equations $P \cdot u = f$, where now $f = (f_1, \ldots, f_{N''})$ is a given vector-valued function of $x \in X$, $u = (u_1, \ldots, u_{N'})$ is an unknown vector-valued function of x, and the $A_\nu(x)$ are functions of x whose values are $N'' \times N'$ matrices. With the help of charts we pass from this situation to the case where f is a section of a vector bundle F over a differential manifold X, and u is a section of a vector bundle E over X (which may or may not be the same as F), and P is a differential operator from E to F. In this generalized situation we can still define "distributional solutions."

For a vector equation with $N' = N'' = N$ (a "determined" system), the aim is to find an integral manifold in $\mathbf{R}^{N+n}$ of the form $x_{n+j} = u_j(x_1, \ldots, x_n)$ $(1 \leqslant j \leqslant N)$, hence of dimension n; in order to be able to apply the Cauchy–Kowalewska theorem (when the A_ν and f are analytic), one needs the existence of an integral manifold of dimension $n - 1$ that projects onto a given hypersurface S in $\mathbf{R}^n$ (which can then locally be reduced to a hyperplane by a change of variables, so that the Cauchy–Kowalewska theorem can be applied). It is easy to see that such an integral manifold need not always exist, and the condition that it should depends only on the terms of highest degree m in P: if we put $\sigma_P(x, \xi) = \sum_{|\nu| = m} A_\nu(x)\xi^\nu$ for a nonzero vector $\xi = (\xi_1, \ldots, \xi_n)$ in $\mathbf{R}^n$ and a point $x \in X$, a normal vector ξ to the hypersurface S must satisfy

$$\Phi(x, \xi) = \det(\sigma_P(x, \xi)) \neq 0. \tag{4}$$

The hyperplanes whose normal vectors ξ make the left-hand side $\Phi(x, \xi)$ of (4) (a homogeneous polynomial in ξ) vanish are called *characteristic*, and they play a fundamental role in the whole theory (whether the A_ν and f are analytic or merely C^∞). The hypersurfaces S all of whose tangent hyperplanes are characteristic are called the *characteristic hypersurfaces* (or just "characteristics") of the operator P; they are the hypersurfaces that locally can be expressed in the form $z(x_1, \ldots, x_n) = \text{const.}$, where z is an integral of the first-order partial differential equation

$$\Phi(x_1, \ldots, x_n, p_1, \ldots, p_n) = 0 \tag{5}$$

(where $p_j = \partial z/\partial x_j$).

The decomposition of Φ (as a polynomial in ξ) into irreducible factors now intervenes in an essential way: if such a factor appears with multiplicity k, the operator P is said to have "multiple characteristics" (of multiplicity k); the factors that are $\neq 0$ whenever $\xi \neq 0$ correspond to what are (improperly) called "imaginary characteristics," and to each of the other factors there corresponds a family of "real" characteristics, which are solutions of the equation (5) with Φ replaced by the factor under consideration. The method of Lagrange and Cauchy [D, Chapter 18] reduces the integration of (5), when Φ is irreducible, to that of a system of $2n$ first-order ordinary differential equations

$$\frac{dx_k}{dt} = \frac{\partial \Phi}{\partial p_k}, \qquad \frac{dp_k}{dt} = -\frac{\partial \Phi}{\partial x_k} \qquad (1 \leqslant k \leqslant n). \tag{6}$$

To obtain (at any rate locally) the integral hypersurfaces of (5), we consider the n-dimensional submanifolds of the hypersurface (5) (of dimension

$2n - 1$) obtained by taking an $(n - 1)$-dimensional submanifold of (5) and forming the union of the integral curves of (6) that intersect this submanifold, and then we project these submanifolds into $\mathbf{R}^n$. The integral curves of (6) are called the *bicharacteristic bands* of the operator P, and their projections in $\mathbf{R}^n$ the *bicharacteristic curves* of P [D, Chapter 18].

Problems. As for ordinary differential equations, the essential problems of the theory of linear partial differential equations center on questions of *existence* and *uniqueness* of solutions of $P \cdot u = f$, but have many diverse aspects. They can be considered *globally*, where the domain X of the variables is fixed; but they can also (as for the Cauchy theorems) be studied from the *local* point of view, that is to say in an *unspecified* neighborhood of a point of X. In either case, the data for these problems will contain not only the given equation, but also various supplementary conditions on the given function f or the unknown function u; these may be either "boundary-value conditions" on the behavior of u and f in a neighborhood of the boundary of X (when X is embedded in a larger manifold), or they may be "regularity" conditions imposed on u or f. A general and suggestive way of presenting them is to envisage u and f as points of two topological vector spaces $\mathscr{A}$, $\mathscr{B}$ (distinct or not) defined by the given conditions; the problem then consists of studying the *image* and the *kernel* of P, regarded as a linear mapping of $\mathscr{A}$ into $\mathscr{B}$.

Once in possession of a theorem of existence and uniqueness, other problems present themselves: whether explicit formulas or, alternatively, methods of "approximation" (in various senses) can be given for the solution. Finally, it may be asked whether the solution varies "continuously" (in various senses) when the data (i.e., the function f, the coefficients of P, or the domain X) are subjected to variation. When this is the case, the problem is said, in Hadamard's phrase, to be "well posed" (cf. LN 316).

Techniques. A first point to consider is the judicious choice of the function spaces $\mathscr{A}$ and $\mathscr{B}$ in which to work. For maximum generality, one can use the general spaces of distributions such as $\mathscr{D}'(\mathrm{X})$, $\mathscr{E}'(\mathrm{X})$, or $\mathscr{S}'(\mathbf{R}^n)$ [D, Chapters 17 and 22] or, even more generally, spaces of "hyperfunctions" (B 214, LN 126, 287, 325, 449; Nice D 10 (Sato)). If on the other hand one seeks solutions that are as "regular" as possible (in view of applications to analysis or physics), it is natural to take spaces of C^∞ or analytic functions (or intermediates such as the "Gevrey classes"). A class of spaces that has turned out to be very useful is the *Sobolev spaces* and their many variants (LN 82). The simplest of these are the spaces $\mathrm{H}^m(\mathrm{X})$, where m is a positive integer: $\mathrm{H}^m(\mathrm{X})$ consists of the classes of functions in $\mathrm{L}^2(\mathrm{X})$ whose partial derivatives (in the sense of distributions) belong to $\mathrm{L}^2(\mathrm{X})$, up to and including order m, and is a Hilbert space with respect to the scalar product $(f \mid g) = \sum_{|\nu| \leq m} \int_X D^\nu f(x) \overline{D^\nu g(x)}\, dx$. The fact that they are Hilbert spaces makes them very amenable to the techniques of functional analysis, but their elements can be highly pathological as functions (for example, essentially unbounded in a neighborhood of each point). Their main use is therefore intermediary, for example, to establish the existence of solutions which are then proved by other methods to be more "regular."

The mathematical tools most frequently used, apart from the general theorems of the theory of topological vector spaces (the Hahn–Banach theorem, the Banach–Steinhaus theorem, the closed graph theorem, the Krein–Milman theorem) are what are called "a priori inequalities" and, most recently, the notion of a *pseudodifferential operator*.

A priori inequalities are relations between norms in different spaces, for example $\|u\|_{E_1} \leq a\|P \cdot u\|_{E_2} + b\|u\|_{E_3}$, where E_1, E_2, E_3 are suitably chosen normed spaces: the constants a, b may depend on parameters. Such inequalities are the consequences of particular hypotheses on the operator P and the type of functions (or distributions) u under consideration. They lead by duality to proofs of existence theorems; on the other hand if, by setting $P \cdot u = 0$ one is able to conclude from the inequality that $u = 0$ (for example by varying the parameters), one obtains a uniqueness theorem ([82], [184]).

Existence theorems obtained by these methods are not "effective," i.e., even if the solution is unique, they provide no explicit "construction" for it. In certain classical problems (such as the Dirichlet problem) it is possible to compute explicitly an "inverse" of the differential operator, in terms of which the solution is then expressed; generally this inverse is an integral operator. This leads to the idea of constructing an algebra of operators that contains both differential operators and integral operators, in which "inversion" is analogous to the mapping $x \mapsto x^{-1}$ in a ring. A first step in this direction was the introduction of the "singular integral operators" of Calderon–Zygmund (B 178, 242, 298, 528; LN 204; BAMS 72 (Calderon)). The modern presentation of this theory uses Fourier transforms (**B** IV). In $\mathbf{R}^n$ we may write, for $u \in \mathscr{D}(\mathbf{R}^n)$,

$$(7) \qquad \sum_\nu A_\nu(x) D^\nu u(x) = \int_{\mathbf{R}^n} \exp(2\pi i(x \mid \xi))(A(x, \xi)\mathscr{F}u(\xi))\, d\xi,$$

where $A(x, \xi) = \sum_\nu A_\nu(x)(2\pi i \xi)^\nu$ and $\mathscr{F}u$ is the Fourier transform of u. We obtain more general operators by replacing the polynomial $A(x, \xi)$ by more general functions, the "symbols of operators" $\sigma(x, \xi)$, subject to growth conditions in ξ (for $|\xi| \to \infty$) on themselves and their derivatives. These "pseudodifferential operators" can be added and composed, and it is to be expected that the algebra they form should be "comparable" in structure (in a certain sense) with the algebra formed by the "symbols" that define them. There are many variants of the definition of "symbols," adapted to the problems to be solved [11]; the most common are those that satisfy conditions of the form

$$|D_x^\alpha D_\xi^\beta \sigma(x, \xi)| \leqslant C(1 + |\xi|)^{m-|\beta|}$$

on their derivatives, when x varies in a compact subset of $\mathbf{R}^n$; the symbol σ is then said to be *of order m*, and the corresponding pseudodifferential operator is also said to be *of order m*.

The scalar product $(x|\xi)$ in the exponential on the right-hand side of (7) can be replaced by more general "phase functions" $\varphi(x, \xi)$, which are better adapted to certain problems (B 269, 308, 411; LN 287, 384 (Trèves), 416, 459; Nice I (Hörmander); SAMS X, XXII).

Results. For a long time, it was hoped that the Cauchy–Kowalewska theorem would remain valid under the weaker assumptions that in (2) the functions H_j were of class C^∞ in place of analytic. This is in fact true for a single equation [D, Chapter 18]. But in 1956, H. Lewy gave the first example of a system of two linear equations with C^∞ coefficients:

$$\text{(8)} \qquad \begin{cases} \dfrac{\partial v_1}{\partial x_1} = \dfrac{\partial v_2}{\partial x_2} - 2x_2 \dfrac{\partial v_1}{\partial x_3} - 2x_1 \dfrac{\partial v_2}{\partial x_3} - f(x_3), \\[2ex] \dfrac{\partial v_2}{\partial x_1} = -\dfrac{\partial v_1}{\partial x_2} + 2x_1 \dfrac{\partial v_1}{\partial x_3} - 2x_2 \dfrac{\partial v_2}{\partial x_3}, \end{cases}$$

which, for a suitable choice of C^∞-function f, admits *no* solution (even in the distribution sense). It is more convenient to write (8) as a single equation for the complex function $u = v_1 + iv_2$, with complex coefficients:

$$\text{(9)} \qquad \frac{\partial u}{\partial x_1} + i\frac{\partial u}{\partial x_2} - 2i(x_1 + ix_2)\frac{\partial u}{\partial x_3} = -f(x_3).$$

This unexpected result triggered off a whole series of investigations aiming to find necessary or sufficient conditions for an equation $P \cdot u = f$ of type (9) (in which the coefficients of P and the functions u and f are complex) to admit at least one solution. The relation $\Phi(x, \xi) = 0$ that defines the characteristic hyperplanes is equivalent to $\sigma_P(x, \xi) = 0$. The case mainly studied so far is that in which the real characteristics are simple and nonsingular, which means that if $\sigma_P(x, \xi_0) = 0$ for some vector $\xi_0 \neq 0$ in $\mathbf{R}^n$, the differential of σ_P at ξ_0 (x being considered as fixed and σ_P as a function of ξ alone) is nonzero. Also the *local* existence problem has been intensively studied, namely, whether for each $x_0 \in X$ there exists a solution in an unspecified neighborhood of x_0. By the use of pseudodifferential operators this problem has been almost completely solved (B 213, 391; LN 384 (Trèves); BAMS 76 (Trèves); SAMS XXIII (Trèves); Nice D 10 (Trèves, Egorov); [85]). This question is also related to the study of regularity of solutions (Stockholm (Hörmander); [184]). In particular two properties of the operator P have been studied, namely, *hypoellipticity* and *analytic hypoellipticity*. The former signifies that if a distribution u is such that $P \cdot u$ is a C^∞-function, then u itself is a C^∞-function; the latter, when the coefficients of P are analytic, is obtained by replacing "C^∞" by "analytic." Again from the local point of view, there are fairly complete results on these two problems (Nice D 10 (Trèves); [85]).

When the coefficients are analytic, it is possible to generalize the classical theorem on linear differential equations, to the effect that the only singularities of the solutions are those of the coefficients. This generalization involves the general theory of residues (**A** VIII) (B 202).

More generally, when u is a distribution, there are relations between the "singularities" of u (i.e., the points x such that u is not a C^∞-function in a neighborhood of x) and those of $P \cdot u$: the so-called "propagation of singularities." In this direction, general results of a global nature have been obtained (B 525; [82], [85]).

4. Equations with constant coefficients

If an operator $P = \sum_{\nu} A_\nu D^\nu$ on $\mathbf{R}^n$ has constant coefficients A_ν, we may express $P \cdot u$ (for any distribution u) in the form of a *convolution* $S * u$, where $S = P \cdot \varepsilon_0$ is a distribution with support consisting of the origin [D, Chapter 17]. The formalism of convolution of distributions then leads us to define distributions E that are "*elementary solutions*" of the operator P, i.e., which satisfy the equation $S * E = \varepsilon_0$, the Dirac measure at the origin. If such a solution is known, the equation $P \cdot u = T$ has a solution for any distribution T with compact support, namely, $u = E * T$. One of the first results of the theory was the proof of existence of elementary solutions for all operators P with constant coefficients, and these solutions can be required to satisfy restrictive conditions of growth at infinity (B 87; [184]). In general, if S and T are distributions with compact support, the equation $S * u = T$ for a tempered distribution u is equivalent, by Fourier transformation, to $(\mathscr{F}S)(\mathscr{F}u) = \mathscr{F}T$. The existence of tempered solutions therefore appears as a particular case of the problem of division of distributions, namely, to find a distribution U satisfying $f \cdot U = T$, where T is a given distribution on an open set in $\mathbf{R}^n$ and f is a C^∞-function. This problem can be solved when the function f is analytic; the methods used are based on a study of the manifold on which f vanishes (B 203).

Several authors have studied generally the problem of existence of solutions of equations $P \cdot u = f$ (where P is an operator with constant coefficients), or more generally $S * u = f$, where f is any distribution, or a function of class C^∞: these are problems that the existence of elementary solutions does not solve completely. These investigations make use of the Fourier transform, and also techniques from local algebra and homological algebra (B 246, 254); in certain cases there are explicit formulas for the solutions (B 48; LN 256).

We remark also that for operators with constant coefficients there are necessary and sufficient conditions for hypoellipticity (B 130, 135).

Invariant operators on homogeneous spaces. On $\mathbf{R}^n$, the differential operators with constant coefficients are precisely those that are *invariant under translations.* The natural context for the study of such operators is therefore the theory of differential operators on a homogeneous space G/H of a Lie group G that are *invariant* under the action of G (B 285, 498, 583; BAMS 70 (Helgason); [34]). Such operators also play a large role in the theory of Lie groups and their representations ([76], [190]). To this context belong properties that involve the action of the group: for example, in $\mathbf{R}^n$, properties of harmonic functions on a Euclidean ball are of this type, because Laplace's equation and Euclidean balls are invariant under displacements. Likewise, there is a theory of generalized harmonic functions on a symmetric space G/K (**B** II) (B 268; LN 17). On the other hand, problems that are invariant under diffeomorphisms, such as hypoellipticity conditions and general boundary-value problems (see below), have hardly any connection with equations with constant coefficients, because an arbitrary diffeomorphism will change such an equation into one with variable coefficients. The reason that equations with constant coefficients have been more intensively studied than other types is partly that the classical equations of mathematical physics are of this type (which is hardly surprising, because the phenomena they describe are invariant under displacements), and also that there exist particular techniques (such as the Fourier transform) that facilitate the theory.

5. Boundary-value problems for linear equations: I. General theory

As in the case of ordinary differential equations, problems that give rise to partial differential equations contain, in addition to the equation, supplementary conditions "at the boundary" that should completely determine the solution. The typical problem is based on the existence and uniqueness theorems of Cauchy: for a linear operator P of order m with complex coefficients, does there exist a solution of the equation $P \cdot u = f$ (where f is given) on an open set $X \subset \mathbf{R}^n$ that is such that u and its normal derivatives up to order $m - 1$ are prescribed functions on a hypersurface $\Sigma \subset X$? There is an analogous formulation of this "Cauchy problem" for differential systems.

The Cauchy–Kowalewska theorem for operators with analytic coefficients, and the notion of characteristics, lead one to expect that, locally at any rate, the problem should have a unique solution provided that Σ is not a characteristic. This is by no means the case, as various counterexamples show. Various conditions on the operator P and the hypersurface Σ are known, involving the real characteristics and the "imaginary characteristics," as well as their multiplicities, under which existence or uniqueness for the local Cauchy problem is guaranteed; for equations with constant coefficients, there are also general global results [82]. The two cases most studied, and for which the theory is best developed, are those of elliptic operators and operators of evolution.

6. Boundary-value problems for linear equations: II. Spectral theory of elliptic operators

The use of pseudodifferential operators and their generalizations is related to a class of integral operators, called *regularizing* or *smoothing* operators. On an open set $X \subset \mathbf{R}^n$, such an operator is of the form

$$(K.f)(x) = \int_X \mathrm{K}(x, y) f(y)\, dy,$$

where K is a C^∞-function on $X \times X$. This operator is defined on the space $\mathscr{D}(X)$, but extends by continuity to the space $\mathscr{E}'(X)$ of distributions with compact support, and has the remarkable (and characteristic) property that it transforms *every* distribution $T \in \mathscr{E}'(X)$ into a C^∞-*function.*

A differential operator P on X is said to be *elliptic* if it has no real characteristics, i.e., if $\sigma_P(x, \xi) \neq 0$ for all $\xi \neq 0$ and all $x \in X$. An equivalent property is the existence of a *parametrix* Q, i.e., a pseudodifferential operator such that $PQ = I + R_1$ and $QP = I + R_2$, where R_1 and R_2 are regularizing. This implies immediately that P is *hypoelliptic*, because if $P \cdot T = f$ for a distribution T and a C^∞-function f, then we have $T = Q \cdot f - R_2 \cdot T$, and the right-hand side is of class C^∞ because R_2 is regularizing. An analogous argument shows (it is a particular case of the general existence result mentioned above) that *locally* an elliptic equation $P \cdot u = f$ always has solutions; but there are examples known of elliptic operators on all of $\mathbf{R}^n$ for which an equation $P \cdot u = f$ with an $f \in \mathscr{D}(\mathbf{R}^n)$ has *no* solution defined in a ball $|x| < R$ containing the support of f [143].

It has been known for a long time that for elliptic partial differential equations (for example, Laplace's equation), the global Cauchy problem has in general no solution. The underlying reasons are revealed by the theory of pseudodifferential operators. The typical case is that in which X is a bounded open set in $\mathbf{R}^n$, whose boundary ∂X is a C^∞-hypersurface, and P (defined on $\mathbf{R}^n$) is elliptic of order m and admits a parametrix Q such that $Q \cdot (P \cdot T) = T$ for each distribution T of compact support. For each function $u \in \mathscr{E}(X)$ that, together with all its derivatives, extends by continuity to $\overline{X} = X \cup \partial X$, let $\mathrm{Dch}_m(u)$ denote the vector function $(g_0, g_1, \ldots, g_{m-1})$, where g_j is the jth normal derivative $\partial^j u/\partial n^j$ at a point of ∂X. Also let u^0 denote the function u extended by 0 outside X, considered as a distribution on $\mathbf{R}^n$ with support contained in $\overline{X}$. Then it can be shown that $P \cdot u^0 = (P \cdot u)^0 + N \cdot \mathrm{Dch}_m(u)$, where N is a linear operator on $(\mathscr{E}(\partial X))^m$ with values in the space of distributions supported by ∂X, called "multiple layers." By applying the operator Q to both sides, we obtain $u^0 = Q \cdot ((P \cdot u)^0) + Q \cdot (N \cdot \mathrm{Dch}_m(u))$. For a function $v \in \mathscr{E}(X)$ that, together with all its derivatives, extends by continuity to $\overline{X}$, $Q \cdot v^0$ is called the *Q-potential* of the mass-density v on X. For each $g \in (\mathscr{E}(\partial X))^m$, $Q \cdot (N \cdot g)$ is called the *Q-potential* of the multiple layer $N \cdot g$. Hence if $P \cdot u = f$ and $\mathrm{Dch}_m(u) = g$ are given, u is well determined and is the sum of a mass Q-potential and a multiple layer Q-potential. It can be shown that $Q \cdot f^0$, restricted to X, is a C^∞-function that, together with all its derivatives, has a continuous extension to $\overline{X}$, and that the same is true of $Q \cdot (N \cdot g)$, and we must therefore have

$$g = \mathrm{Dch}_m(Q \cdot f^0) + \mathrm{Dch}_m(Q \cdot (N \cdot g)).$$

One shows that $C : g \mapsto \mathrm{Dch}_m(Q \cdot (N \cdot g))$ is a pseudodifferential operator of $(\mathscr{E}(\partial X))^m$ into itself, called a *Calderon operator*; we must have therefore

$$g - C \cdot g = \mathrm{Dch}_m(Q \cdot f^0). \tag{10}$$

A deeper study shows that, if $n \geqslant 3$, m must be even and that the relation (10) is equivalent to $m/2$ linear relations between the m components $g_0, \ldots, g_{m-1}$ of g and its derivatives, so that not more than *half* of the usual Cauchy data can be arbitrarily prescribed on the boundary. This idea can be made precise by considering a differential operator B of $(\mathscr{E}(\partial X))^m$ onto $(\mathscr{E}(\partial X))^{m/2}$ and replacing the Cauchy problem by the boundary-value problem of finding $u \in \mathscr{E}(X)$ that, together with all its derivatives, has a continuous extension to $\overline{X}$ and is such that $P \cdot u = f$ and $B \cdot (\mathrm{Dch}_m(u)) = g$, where $f \in \mathscr{E}(X)$ and $g \in (\mathscr{E}(\partial X))^{m/2}$ are given. One can then give sufficient conditions on B for the problem to reduce to the solution of Fredholm equations on ∂X, and the problem is then said to be *elliptic* (B 308; Nice D 10 (Boutet de Monvel); [83]). A typical example of an elliptic problem is the *Dirichlet problem* for an elliptic operator of order $2p$, where the boundary conditions are the assignment of the first p normal derivatives on ∂X.

In an elliptic boundary-value problem, the complex numbers ζ such that the problem $P \cdot u - \zeta u = f$, $B \cdot (\mathrm{Dch}_m(u)) = g$ has a unique solution for all choices of f and g are called *regular values* with respect to P and B. The *spectrum* of P (for the boundary operator B) is the complement in $\mathbf{C}$ of the set of regular values. The example of the classical Dirichlet problem (for the Laplacian) may lead one to expect that the spectrum is always a discrete set in $\mathbf{C}$. This is far from being the case, and examples are known of Dirichlet problems for certain elliptic operators where the spectrum is the whole of $\mathbf{C}$. To guarantee behavior analogous to the classical case, it is necessary to assume, for example, that P is in addition *hermitian*, considered as an unbounded operator on $L^2(X)$, with domain $\mathscr{D}(X)$, so as to be able to apply the spectral theory of operators (**C** III). Under conditions somewhat stricter than ellipticity, there exist self-adjoint extensions A_P of P whose domains are contained in the Sobolev space $H^p(X)$ and are such that, for a value ζ not contained in the spectrum of A_P, the unique solution of $A_P \cdot u - \zeta u = f$ in $\mathrm{dom}(A_P)$ is a solution of the corresponding boundary-value problem $P \cdot u + \zeta u = f$, $B \cdot (\mathrm{Dch}_m(u)) = 0$ (B 67, 110, 123, 262; LN 8, 102, 268; SAMS IV (Nirenberg); Nice D 10 (Agmon, Grisvard, Seeley); [3]). For hermitian operators, it is also possible to handle certain cases in which X is unbounded; the case $X = \mathbf{R}^n$ is important in atomic physics (LN 313, 433; [146]).

Second-order elliptic operators and potential theory. The second-order elliptic operators (of which the prototype is the Laplacian) occupy a separate place in the theory, by reason of a phenomenon that is peculiar to them, namely, the *maximum principle*. If $P = \sum_{j \leqslant k} a_{jk} D_j D_k + \sum_j a_j D_j$ is such that $\sum_{j \leqslant k} a_{jk}(x)\xi_j\xi_k \leqslant -C|\xi|^2$ for some constant $C > 0$, we cannot have $P \cdot u \geqslant 0$ for a function u bounded above on an open set $X \subset \mathbf{R}^n$ and $u(x_0) = \sup_{y \in X} u(y) \geqslant 0$ at some point $x_0 \in X$, unless u is constant. This phenomenon has innumerable consequences. It permits a much deeper study of the solutions of an equation $P \cdot u = f$ in X, notably as to their behavior at the boundary, which is no longer necessarily assumed to be differentiable; the classical Dirichlet problem no longer necessarily has a solution, and must be replaced by weaker conditions (B 117). Also the conditions on the coefficients of P can be considerably weakened (B 258, 302; Stockholm (Stampacchia)).

In fact, this theory is so far detached from the general theory of partial differential equations that it has an autonomous aspect. The fact that the solution of a boundary-value problem is expressed in terms of "Q-potentials" where Q is a parametrix of P (here an integral operator) has led to an independent study of *potentials* $(K \cdot \mu)(x) = \int K(x, y)\, d\mu(y)$ of a measure μ on $\mathbf{R}^n$ (or even of a distribution) relative to a "kernel" $K(x, y)$ subject to various conditions, but not necessarily related to a differential operator (the classical

Newtonian potential corresponds, for $n \geqslant 3$, to the kernel $|x - y|^{2-n}$). This subject has developed an enormous literature, containing a deep analysis of the maximum principle and its many variants, the idea of "balayage" introduced by H. Poincaré, and notions derived from physics, such as capacity or energy (B 52, 120, 139, 148, 187; LN 295, 297, 408; Stockholm (Choquet)). The methods used are mainly those of measure theory and Hilbert spaces; more recently the theory has taken an axiomatic direction, no longer restricted to $\mathbf{R}^n$ (B 377, 501; LN 22, 58, 68, 69, 175, 222, 226, 289, 494). The classical connections between the theory of Newtonian potential and holomorphic functions (B 23) have been augmented by other connections, with the theory of semigroups (B 187, 302, 403), homogeneous spaces (B 268; BAMS 71 (Furstenberg)), harmonic analysis (B 225; LN 404), and above all with probability theory, where most remarkable results have been obtained ([33], [121]).

7. Boundary-value problems for linear equations: III. Equations of evolution

In these equations, the unknown is a function of $n + 1$ variables, one of which plays a separate role; the two classical examples are the wave equation $\partial^2 u/\partial t^2 - \Delta u = 0$ and the heat equation $\partial u/\partial t - \Delta u = 0$ (where Δ is the Laplacian with respect to the n variables other than t). Since in these two equations t represents the time, it is often so called in general equations of evolution, and the other variables are referred to as "space variables." The operators in question are therefore of the form

$$P = \left(\frac{\partial}{\partial t}\right)^m + \sum_{j=1}^{m} A_j(t, x, \mathrm{D})\left(\frac{\partial}{\partial t}\right)^{m-j}, \tag{11}$$

where the A_j are differential operators that are linear combinations of derivatives with respect to $x_1, \ldots, x_n$, with coefficients depending on t and $x = (x_1, \ldots, x_n)$, of class C^∞ on $\mathrm{I} \times \mathrm{X}$, where I is an interval in $\mathbf{R}$ and X an open set in $\mathbf{R}^n$. The fundamental problem is the *Cauchy problem*, which is to solve the equation $P \cdot u = f$ with the conditions $\left(\frac{\partial}{\partial t}\right)^j u(t_0, x) = g_j(x)$ for $0 \leqslant j \leqslant m - 1$, the functions g_j and f being given. If $\mathrm{X} \neq \mathbf{R}^n$, supplementary conditions may be imposed on the behavior of the solution in a neighborhood of $\mathrm{I} \times \partial\mathrm{X}$ (the "mixed" problem).

When $\mathrm{X} = \mathbf{R}^n$ and the coefficients A_j in (11) *are independent of* x, a classical method (B 11) consists of applying to $P \cdot u$ a Fourier transformation with respect to the variables $x_1, \ldots, x_n$ *alone*; the transform w of u satisfies a linear differential equation of order m, and w and its first $m - 1$ derivatives are given at $t = t_0$. Supposing the function w known, u is obtained by applying the inverse Fourier transformation (with respect to the x_j) to w, provided that this makes sense. This immediately introduces an essential difference between the wave equation and the heat equation: for the former, the inverse Fourier transform is applicable without restriction on t (provided that the g_j have compact supports), whereas for the latter, it is necessary to restrict to values $t > 0$. The wave equation is the prototype of *hyperbolic* equations, and the heat equation is the prototype of *parabolic* equations.

Strictly hyperbolic equations. A differential operator P given by (11) is said to be *hyperbolic* if all its characteristics are real, that is to say, if the equation $\sigma_P(t, x, \tau, \xi') = 0$ in τ (where $\xi = (\tau, \xi')$ and $\xi' = (\xi_1, \ldots, \xi_n)$) has only real solutions for all $\xi' \in \mathbf{R}^n$; and P is *strictly hyperbolic* if in addition the characteristics are all simple, i.e., if for all $\xi' \neq 0$ all the roots of this equation are simple. There is an analogous definition for systems of linear equations: for a matrix operator P, σ_P is replaced by $\det(\sigma_P)$ in the above definition. The theory is most highly developed for strictly hyperbolic operators and systems.

For the wave equation, which is strictly hyperbolic, the method sketched above gives an explicit formula for the solution, already known to Cauchy: $u(t, x) = u_+(t, x) + u_-(t, x)$, where

(12)

$$u_{\pm}(t, x) = \frac{1}{2} \iint \exp 2\pi i((x - y \mid \xi) \pm \mid \xi \mid t)\left(g_0(y) \pm \frac{1}{2\pi i \mid \xi \mid} g_1(y)\right) dy\, d\xi,$$

from which the usual properties of wave propagation can be read off. In the general case, one establishes for a strictly hyperbolic operator a *local* (in a neighborhood of a point (s, x_0)) existence and uniqueness theorem. On the model of (12), we first introduce operators $E_{jh}(s)$ $(0 \leqslant j, h \leqslant m - 1)$ of the form

$$(E_{jh}(s) \cdot u)(t, x) = \iint \exp(i\varphi_j(t, x, s, y, \xi))a_{jh}(t, x, s, y, \xi)u(y)\, dy\, d\xi$$

(the integral is "improper" and has to be given a meaning); φ_j is a real "phase function" subjected to conditions that allow the integral to be defined, and is positively homogeneous in ξ, while a_{jh} is an "operator symbol." If we put $E_h(s) = \sum_{j=0}^{m-1} E_{jh}(s)$ for $0 \leqslant h \leqslant m - 1$, it can be shown that the φ_j and the a_{jh} can be determined in such a way that locally we have

$$PE_h(s) = R_h(s), \qquad \left(\frac{\partial}{\partial t}\right)^k E_h(s) = \delta_{hk} I$$

for $t = s$ and $0 \leqslant k \leqslant m - 1$, where $R_h(s)$ is a *regularizing* operator. If we then put

$$(G \cdot u)(t, x) = \int_{t_0}^{t} (E_{m-1}(s) \cdot u(s, \cdot))(t, x)\, ds,$$

we have $\left(\frac{\partial}{\partial t}\right)^k (G, u)(t_0, x) = 0$ and $P \cdot (G \cdot u) = u - V \cdot u$, where V is a Volterra integral operator; hence the Cauchy problem $P \cdot v = f$, $\left(\frac{\partial}{\partial t}\right)^k v(t_0, x) = 0$ for $0 \leqslant k \leqslant m - 1$ is solved by taking v to be of the form $G \cdot u$. Local uniqueness is then established by using the existence of solutions for the Cauchy problem relative to the transposed operator ${}^tP$. The method can be extended to the case in which P is hyperbolic with multiple characteristics, under certain supplementary conditions on these characteristics [35]. It also gives a meaning to the generalized Cauchy problem, where the required solutions are *distributions* that in a certain sense reduce to given distributions at $t = t_0$.

In this method the functions $\varphi_j(t, x, s, y, \xi)$ are taken in the form $\psi_j(t, s, x, \xi) - 2\pi(y \mid \xi)$, where y and ξ (vectors in $\mathbf{R}^n$) are considered as parameters; if we decompose $\sigma_P(t, x, \tau, \xi') = \prod_{j=1}^{m} (\tau - q_j(t, x, \xi'))$ into factors of the first degree, the function $(t, x) \mapsto \psi_j(t, s, x, \xi)$ is a solution of the equation

$$\frac{\partial z}{\partial t} = q_j(t, x, \operatorname{grad}_x z)$$

of one of the m families of characteristic hypersurfaces of P, with the initial condition $\psi_j(s, s, x, \xi) = 2\pi(x \mid \xi)$.

The corresponding bicharacteristic curves, in the case of the wave equation, coincide with the "rays" of geometrical optics. In the general case of strictly hyperbolic equations, the bicharacteristic curves have analogous properties. Among other things, they serve to define "domains of influence" in which there may be *global* existence and uniqueness of solutions; when the initial conditions are distributions, the "singularities" of the corresponding distribution solution are carried by the union of the bicharacteristic curves passing through the "singularities" of the "initial-value" distributions.

The study of "mixed problems" is much less developed, even for the wave equation (B 432; LN 442; BAMS 63 (F. John), 65 (H. Lewy), 76 (C. Morawetz); Nice D 10 (Phillips); [134], [224]). There are also other methods for attacking the Cauchy problem and mixed problems, with the use of a priori inequalities (B 178; SAMS XVI (Nirenberg); [82]).

One of the problems that goes back to the beginning of the theory of the wave equation is "Huyghens's principle," which in its modern form is whether an elementary distributional solution of the equation can have its support concentrated on a hypersurface. This question has been generalized by Petrowsky to hyperbolic equations with constant coefficients: this is the theory of "lacunae," whose modern presentation involves the cohomology of the characteristic hypersurfaces (B 319; Nice D 10 (Gårding)).

Parabolic equations. For parabolic operators (11), the hypersurfaces $t = \text{const.}$ are characteristic, and hence there cannot be local uniqueness; on the other hand, there are existence theorems for the Cauchy problem under quite general conditions. The type most studied is that of operators of the form

$$P = \frac{\partial}{\partial t} + A(x, \mathrm{D}), \tag{13}$$

where A is a matrix differential operator acting only on the space variables, whose coefficients depend only on t; suppose in addition that the operator A is elliptic and that its symbol $\sigma_A(x, \xi)$ is a matrix that satisfies an inequality of the form

$$|\exp(-\sigma_A(x, \xi + i\eta))| \leqslant \exp(-a|\xi|^{2p} + b|\eta|^{2p}), \tag{14}$$

where $a > 0$. A local existence theorem is then proved as in the case of strictly hyperbolic operators, by using a matrix operator

(15)

$$(E(s) \cdot u)(t, x) = \iint \exp(-(t - s)\sigma_A(y, \xi) + 2\pi i(x - y|\xi)I) \cdot u(y)\, dy\, d\xi,$$

which in the case of the heat equation reduces to the classical operator giving a solution of the global Cauchy problem

$$(E(s) \cdot u)(t, x) = \iint \exp(-4\pi^2(t - s)\xi^2 + 2\pi i(x - y)\xi)u(y)\, dy\, d\xi. \tag{16}$$

Here the integrals are of the usual type for $t > s$ by reason of (14), and the operators so defined are *regularizing*, which simplifies the theory [56].

A more general point of view is that of operational equations

$$\frac{\partial u}{\partial t} + A \cdot u = f, \tag{17}$$

where A is a (possibly unbounded) operator independent of t on a Banach space X and f is a given function on X: a solution is a function $t \mapsto u(t)$ defined for $t > 0$, with values in X. One seeks conditions under which the solution can be written $u = P_t \cdot f$, where P_t is an operator on X depending on t, such that $P_{t+s} = P_t P_s$ for $s, t > 0$. The family $t \mapsto P_t$ is a *semigroup* of operators, with *generator* $-A$. The case most studied (in connection with potential theory) is that in which A is a second-order elliptic operator, but X is not necessarily a Hilbert space (B 81, 289; LN 60 (Kato), 144 (Kato); Stockholm (Agmon); [77]).

8. Pseudodifferential operators on compact manifolds

By developing Riemann's ideas on the application of the "Dirichlet principle" to the theory of compact Riemann surfaces and the algebraic geometry of curves, Hodge from 1930 onward, showed how to apply fruitfully the theory of elliptic operators to the topology of compact manifolds and algebraic varieties of arbitrary dimension (B 26, 63). Since 1953 the theory has expanded and has obtained remarkable results, grouped around very wide generalizations of the Riemann–Roch theorem.

Let E and F be two complex vector bundles over a *compact* differential manifold X, and let $\Gamma(E)$, $\Gamma(F)$ denote the spaces of their global C^∞-sections. A *pseudodifferential operator from* E to F is then defined to be a linear mapping $P : \Gamma(E) \to \Gamma(F)$ that, when expressed in local coordinates, is a matrix of pseudodifferential operators in the usual sense. The symbol σ_P of such an operator can be defined intrinsically. For each $x \in X$ and $\xi \in T_x(X)^*$ (tangent covector at x), $\sigma_P(x, \xi)$ is a homomorphism $E_x \to F_x$ of vector spaces. If Q is a pseudodifferential operator from F to a third bundle G, we have $\sigma_{QP} = \sigma_Q \circ \sigma_P$. In local coordinates, $\sigma_P(x, \xi)$ is the matrix of symbols of the pseudodifferential operators that are the elements of the matrix representing P. The vector spaces $\Gamma(E)$ and $\Gamma(F)$ can be given pre-Hilbert structures, so that the adjoint $P^* : \Gamma(F) \to \Gamma(E)$ of a pseudodifferential operator P can be defined by the relation $(P \cdot u | v) = (u | P^* \cdot v)$; P^* is again a pseudodifferential operator, and $\sigma_{P^*}(x, \xi) = (\sigma_P(x, \xi))^*$.

A pseudodifferential operator P from E to itself is *elliptic* if its symbol $\sigma_P(x, \xi)$ is a bijection of the fiber E_x onto itself for each $x \in X$ and each $\xi \neq 0$ in $T_x(X)^*$. The theory of elliptic operators of order >0 which are *hermitian*, i.e., such that $P^* = P$ (**C** III) is particularly simple: there exists an orthonormal basis (u_k) of $\Gamma(E)$ such that $P \cdot u_k = \mu_k u_k$, where μ_k is real and $|\mu_k| \to \infty$ as $k \to \infty$. For each section $f \in \Gamma(E)$, we have $f = \sum_k (f | u_k) u_k$, the series being convergent in the Fréchet space $\Gamma(E)$, and $P \cdot f = \sum_k \mu_k (f | u_k) u_k$ with the same convergence. In particular, Ker(P) is the finite-dimensional subspace having as basis the u_k such that $\mu_k = 0$, and Im(P) is a closed topological supplement of Ker(P), spanned by the remaining u_k.

The objects of study in the generalized theory are *elliptic complexes* of complex vector bundles over X (**B** I):

$$\mathscr{E} : 0 \to E_1 \xrightarrow{d_1} E_2 \to \cdots \xrightarrow{d_{r-1}} E_r \to 0,$$

where the d_j are pseudodifferential operators of order >0, such that $d_j d_{j-1} = 0$ and the sequence of symbols

$$0 \to E_{1x} \xrightarrow{\sigma_1(x,\xi)} E_{2x} \to \cdots \xrightarrow{\sigma_{r-1}(x,\xi)} E_{rx} \to 0$$

is *exact* for each $x \in X$ and each $\xi \neq 0$ in $T_x(X)^*$. Then each operator $D_j = d_j^* d_j + d_{j-1} d_{j-1}^*$ (*Hodge's Laplacian*) is a hermitian elliptic operator of E_j into itself, to which the preceding results may be applied; hence $\Gamma(E_j)$ decomposes as an orthogonal direct sum

$$\mathrm{Ker}(D_j) \oplus \mathrm{Im}(d_{j-1}) \oplus \mathrm{Im}(d_j^*),$$

and we have

$$\mathrm{Ker}(d_j) = \mathrm{Ker}(D_j) \oplus \mathrm{Im}(d_{j-1}),$$

so that $H^j(\mathscr{E}) = \mathrm{Ker}(d_j)/\mathrm{Im}(d_{j-1})$ is isomorphic to $\mathrm{Ker}(D_j)$, and in particular is finite dimensional. This result applies in particular to the *de Rham complex*, in which E_j is the complexified bundle $\bigwedge^k T(X)^*$ of tangent j-covectors (whose sections are therefore the differential j-forms) and d_j is the exterior differential; $H^j(\mathscr{E})$ is therefore canonically isomorphic to the jth cohomology space $H^j(X, \mathbf{C})$ of X (**A** I). When X is a Riemannian manifold and the pre-Hilbert structures on the $\Gamma(E_j)$ are those induced by the Riemannian structure, the elements of $\mathrm{Ker}(D_j)$ are called the *harmonic j-forms* on the Riemannian manifold X, and the isomorphism of $\mathrm{Ker}(D_j)$ and $H^j(X, \mathbf{C})$ is known as the Hodge-de Rham theorem.

In general terms, the *Atiyah–Singer formula* enables the "Euler–Poincaré characteristic"

$$\chi(\mathscr{E}) = \sum_j (-1)^j \dim H^j(\mathscr{E})$$

to be expressed in terms of an element of the cohomology ring of X that depends only on the differential structure of X and the symbols of the d_j. It unifies and generalizes numerous previous results, notably the Riemann–Roch theorem for nonsingular complex projective varieties (**A** IX) (B 253; C 1963–4; LN 103 (Atiyah), 401; SAMS XVI (Atiyah), XXIII (I. Singer); [140]).

The theory of strictly hyperbolic or parabolic equations on a space of the form $I \times X$, where I is an interval in $\mathbf{R}$ and X a *compact* manifold (the variable $t \in I$ being the "time" variable) is also notably simplified, and contains global existence and uniqueness theorems. In particular, the theory of parabolic equations leads to a method of proof of the Atiyah–Singer formula. If $P : \Gamma(E) \to \Gamma(E)$ is an elliptic differential operator of order p on X, then P^*P and PP^* are self-adjoint elliptic operators. If we denote respectively by $t \mapsto \exp(-tP^*P)$ and $t \mapsto \exp(-tPP^*)$ the semigroups having these operators as generators, the operators $\exp(-tP^*P)$ and $\exp(-tPP^*)$ are (for $t > 0$) integral operators on $\Gamma(E)$ that admit *traces* (**C** III) given by the formulas

$$(18) \quad \mathrm{Tr}(\exp(-tP^*P)) = \sum_n \exp(-t\lambda_n), \quad \mathrm{Tr}(\exp(-tPP^*)) = \sum_n \exp(-t\mu_n),$$

where the λ_n (resp. μ_n) are the eigenvalues of P^*P (resp. PP^*). The problem which is solved by the Atiyah–Singer formula, for the elliptic complex $0 \to E \xrightarrow{P} E \to 0$, is here the calculation of the *index* of P, $\mathrm{ind}(P) = \dim \mathrm{Ker}(P) - \dim \mathrm{Coker}(P)$, and it is easily shown that for all $t > 0$ we have

$$(19) \qquad \mathrm{ind}(P) = \mathrm{Tr}(\exp(-tP^*P)) - \mathrm{Tr}(\exp(-tPP^*)).$$

Now the theory of parabolic equations shows that if A is a positive self-adjoint elliptic operator of order m on X, $\mathrm{Tr}(\exp(-tA))$ has as $t \to 0$ an asymptotic expansion of the form

$$(20) \qquad \mathrm{Tr}(\exp(-tA)) \sim \sum_{j=-\dim X}^{\infty} a_j t^{j/m}$$

in which the a_j can be calculated directly from the coefficients of the operator A and their covariant derivatives. By applying this formula to the right-hand side of (19) it is possible, for certain particular choices of the operator P on X, to calculate explicitly the difference between the constant terms in the asymptotic expansions involved, and thence to deduce the general formula of Atiyah–Singer (B 436, 439; LN 638; [34]).

The same method leads to a proof and a generalization of the Lefschetz trace formula giving the number of fixed points of a diffeomorphism of X (**A** I). If $g : X \to X$ is a diffeomorphism, and if $f : \Gamma(g^*(E)) \to \Gamma(E)$ is an operator induced by a bundle homomorphism $g^*(E) \to E$, then f composed with the canonical morphism $\Gamma(E) \to \Gamma(g^*(E))$ gives a linear operator $\gamma : \Gamma(E) \to \Gamma(E)$. If we assume that γ commutes with P and P^*, it induces linear mappings on the (finite-dimensional) vector spaces $\mathrm{Ker}(P)$ and $\mathrm{Ker}(P^*)$, and the generalized Lefschetz number is

$$L(P, \gamma) = \mathrm{Tr}(\gamma | \mathrm{Ker}(P)) - \mathrm{Tr}(\gamma | \mathrm{Ker}(P^*)).$$

It can be shown (much more easily than in the case of $\mathrm{ind}(P)$) to be equal to

$$\mathrm{Tr}(\exp(-t\gamma P^*P)) - \mathrm{Tr}(\exp(-t\gamma PP^*)),$$

which is independent of $t > 0$.

The method is easily extended to an elliptic complex, and when applied to the de Rham complex it gives, as a particular case, the classical Lefschetz formula for the number of fixed points of a diffeomorphism of g of X when these fixed points are isolated (B 295; [81]).

9. Nonlinear partial differential equations

Here it cannot be said that a general theory exists (for a survey, see Stockholm (Nirenberg)). There are far-reaching studies of certain very special types of equations, such as the Korteweg–de Vries equation $\frac{\partial q}{\partial t} = 3q\frac{\partial q}{\partial x} - \frac{1}{2}\frac{\partial^3 q}{\partial x^3}$ (B 474, 557; Nice D 11 (Lax)), and of equations arising from problems in the calculus of variations, such as the equation of minimal surfaces and its generalizations, which have generated an enormous literature (B 353, 579; BAMS 75 (Almgren); Nice D 11 (Almgren)). Part of the theory of linear equations generalizes to *quasi-linear equations*, which are linear in the derivatives of the unknown function, but not with respect to the function itself (B 184; Nice D 11 (Serrin, Uraltseva)). The notion of elliptic equation generalizes to nonlinear equations, and for such equations there are regularity theorems (BAMS 75 (Morrey)). A general idea is to consider a nonlinear equation as a "perturbation" of a "nearby" linear equation. In certain cases this leads, with the help of topological notions applied to the appropriate function spaces, to existence theorems (Leray–Schauder method; LN 346). The study of certain types of operators on Banach spaces can also be applied to certain nonlinear problems (SAMS XVI (Browder); Nice D 11 (Browder)).

10. Connections with the natural sciences

Almost all scientific theories that take account of phenomena involving at least two independent variables make use of partial differential equations or more general functional equations, from mechanics and physics through to biology (LN 322); mathematicians are therefore continually being presented with new problems about such equations. But the influence of the natural sciences is felt even in the mathematical treatment of these problems, in which notions derived from the physical world, such as energy, potential, and "extremal principles," are applied with profit.

11. The originators

The principal ideas in the theory of partial differential equations are due to the following mathematicians:

Local study of differential systems. J. Lagrange (1736–1813), A. Cauchy (1789–1857), C. Jacobi (1804–1851), R. Clebsch (1833–1872), S. Lie (1842–1899), E. Cartan (1869–1951), D. Spencer.

Foliations. C. Ehresmann (1905–1979), G. Reeb, S. Novikov, A. Haefliger, R. Bott, W. Thurston, A. Connes.

Linear equations (general theory). P. Laplace (1749–1827), J. Fourier (1768–1830), T. Carleman (1892–1949), L. Schwartz, L. Ehrenpreis, B. Malgrange, L. Hörmander, H. Lewy, A. Calderon, A. Zygmund, J. Kohn, L. Nirenberg, F. Trèves, J. Leray, R. Beals, C. Fefferman.

Elliptic linear equations. H. A. Schwarz (1843–1921), H. Poincaré (1854–1912), D. Hilbert (1862–1943), E. E. Levi (1883–1917), L. Gårding, M. Višik.

Potential theory and semigroups. D. Poisson (1781–1840), G. Green (1793–1841), C. F. Gauss (1777–1855), C. Neumann (1832–1925), H. A. Schwarz (1843–1921), H. Poincaré (1854–1912), H. Lebesgue (1875–1941), N. Wiener (1894–1964), O. Perron (1880–1975), M. Brelot, H. Cartan, J. Deny, E. Hille (1894–1980), K. Yosida, A. Beurling, J. Doob, G. Hunt, G. Choquet.

Equations of evolution. B. Riemann (1826–1866), J. Hadamard (1865–1963), E. E. Levi (1883–1917), S. Sobolev, I. Petrowsky (1901–1973), L. Gårding, J. Leray, P. Lax, V. Maslov.

Operators on compact manifolds. W. Hodge (1903–1975), M. Atiyah, I. Singer, R. Bott.

Nonlinear equations. S. Bernstein (1880–1968), J. Leray, J. Schauder (1896–1943), E. de Giorgi, J. Nash, P. Lax.

The following have also made substantial contributions to these theories: S. Agmon, M. Agranovič, V. Arnol'd N. Aronszajn (1908–1980), R. Bader, H. Bauer, P. Baum, A. Bensoussan, G. Bergandål, M. Berger, L. Bers, A. Bitsadze, R. Blumenthal, N. Boboc, S. Bochner, J. Bokobza, J. Bony, G. Bouligand (1890–1980), L. Boutet de Monvel, H. Brézis, F. Browder, F. Bureau, R. Carroll, A. Cerezo, J. Chazarain, S. Chern, Colin de Verdière, P. Cohen, R. Coifman, Y. Choquet-Bruhat, C. Constantinescu, H. Cordes, A. Cornea, M. Cotlar, R. Courant (1888–1972), P. Courrège, G. Darboux (1842–1917), A. Douglis, J. Duistermaat, G. Duvaut, A. Dynin, Ju. Egorov, S. Eidelman, G. Eskin, G. Evans (1887–1973), J. Faraut, W. Feller (1907–1970), G. Fichera, R. Finn, F. Frankl, I. Fredholm (1866–1927). A. Friedman, K. Friedrichs, G. Frobenius (1849–1917), O. Frostman, H. Furstenberg, M. Gaffney, E. Gagliardo, P. Garabedian, C. Gardner, R. Gardner, I. Gelfand, P. Germain, R. Getoor, M. Gevrey (1884–1957), D. Gilbarg, P. Gilkey, G. Giraud (1889–1943), E. Giusti, C. Godbillon, H. Goldschmidt, E. Goursat (1858–1936), P. Grisvard, M. Gromov, G. Grubb, V. Grušin, V. Guillemin, E. Heinz, S. Helgason, G. Herglotz (1881–1953), R. Hermann, R. M. Hervé, F. Hirsch, E. Holmgren (1871–1961). E. Hopf, T. Ikebe, K. Ito, H. Jenkins,

F. John, M. Kac, M. Kashiwara, T. Kato, T. Kawai, O. Kellogg (1878–1932), A. Kiselev, C. Kiselman, K. Kodaira, A. Koranyi, T. Kotake, S. Kowalewska (1850–1891), P. Krée, H. Kreiss, I. Kričever, H. Kumano-go, S. Kuroda, O. Ladyzenskaya, E. Landis, C. La Vallée Poussin (1866–1962), H. Lawson, A. Lax, P. Lejeune-Dirichlet (1805–1859), B. Levitan, L. Lichtenstein (1878–1933), G. Lion, J. L. Lions, W. Litman, S. Łojasiewicz, Y. Lopatinski, D. Ludwig, G. Lumer, E. Magenes, H. McKean, P. Malliavin, J. Marsden, R. S. Martin, J. Mather, A. Melin, R. Melrose, P. A. Meyer, Y. Meyer, S. Mihlin, S. Minakshisundaram, G. Minty, M. Miranda, S. Mizohata, G. Mokobodzki, G. Monge (1746–1818), C. Moore, C. Morawetz, C. Mórrey, J. Moser, L. Naïm, M. Narasimhan, J. Neveu, A. Newlander, N. Ninomiya, Y. Ohya, O. Oleinik, V. Palamodov, V. Patodi, J. Peetre, A. Phillips, R. Phillips, E. Picard (1856–1941), A. Pleijel, A. Pliš, G. Prodi, M. Protter, T. Priouret, D. Quillen, E. Radkevič, D. Ray, F. Rellich (1906–1955), M. Riesz (1886–1969), G. Robin (1855–1897), P. Rosenbloom, R. Roussarie, F. Rouvière, D. Ruelle, M. Sato, M. Schechter, J. Schwartz, R. Seeley, G. Segal, I. Segal, J. Serrin, P. Shapira, D. Sibony, B. Simon, J. Sjöstrand, L. Slobodetsky, K. Smith, G. Stampacchia, E. Stein, S. Sternberg, D. Sullivan, W. Sweeney, G. Tautz, M. Taylor, R. Temam, E. Titchmarsh (1899–1963), F. Tricomi (1897–1978), A. Unterberger, N. Uraltseva, R. Vaillancourt, P. van Moerbeke, F. Vasilesco (1897–1958), I. Vekua, J. Vey (1944–1980), V. Volterra (1860–1940), H. Weinberger, Alan Weinstein, Alex. Weinstein (1897–1979), A. Wentzel, H. Weyl (1885–1955), J. Wood, E. Zachmanoglou, S. Zaremba (1863–1942), N. Zeilon (1886–1958), M. Zerner, C. Bardos, R. Bowen (1947–1978), L. Corwin, R. Deift, L. Faddeer, B. Helffer, S. Klainerman, I. Kupka, F. Laudenbach, J. Nowerigat, M. Raïs, H. Rosenberg, L. Rothschild, R. Sacksteder, W. Strauss, E. Trubowitz.

References

B: 23, 26, 48, 52, 63, 67, 81, 87, 110, 117, 118, 120, 123, 130, 135, 139, 148, 178, 184, 187, 192, 202, 203, 213, 214, 225, 242, 246, 253, 254, 258, 262, 268, 269, 285, 289, 295, 298, 302, 308, 319, 326, 329, 339, 353, 377, 390, 391, 393, 403, 411, 412, 432, 434, 436, 439, 474, 490, 495, 496, 498, 499, 501, 512, 522, 524, 525, 528, 532, 551, 557, 560, 574, 583.

LN: 8, 17, 22, 58, 60, 68, 69, 82, 102, 103, 126, 144, 175, 197, 204, 206, 222, 226, 256, 268, 279, 287, 289, 295, 297, 313, 316, 322, 325, 346, 384, 392, 401, 404, 408, 415, 416, 433, 442, 449, 459, 484, 493, 494, 563, 565, 581, 597, 638, 652, 681, 684, 712, 713, 725, 727, 755, 756, 782, 787, 791, 814, 840, 841.

BAMS: 63 (F. John), 65 (H. Lewy), 70 (Guillemin-Sternberg, Helgason), 71 (Furstenberg), 72 (Calderon), 75 (Morrey, Spencer), 76 (Morawetz, Trèves), 80 (Lawson), 81 (F. John), 83 (Helgason, Folland) 84 (M. F. Taylor).

SAMS: IV, X, XVI, XXIII.

Astérisque: 2–3, 19, 34–35, 57.

[11], [33], [34], [56], [76], [77], [81], [82], [83], [85], [121], [134], [140], [143], [146], [184], [190], [224].

A VI

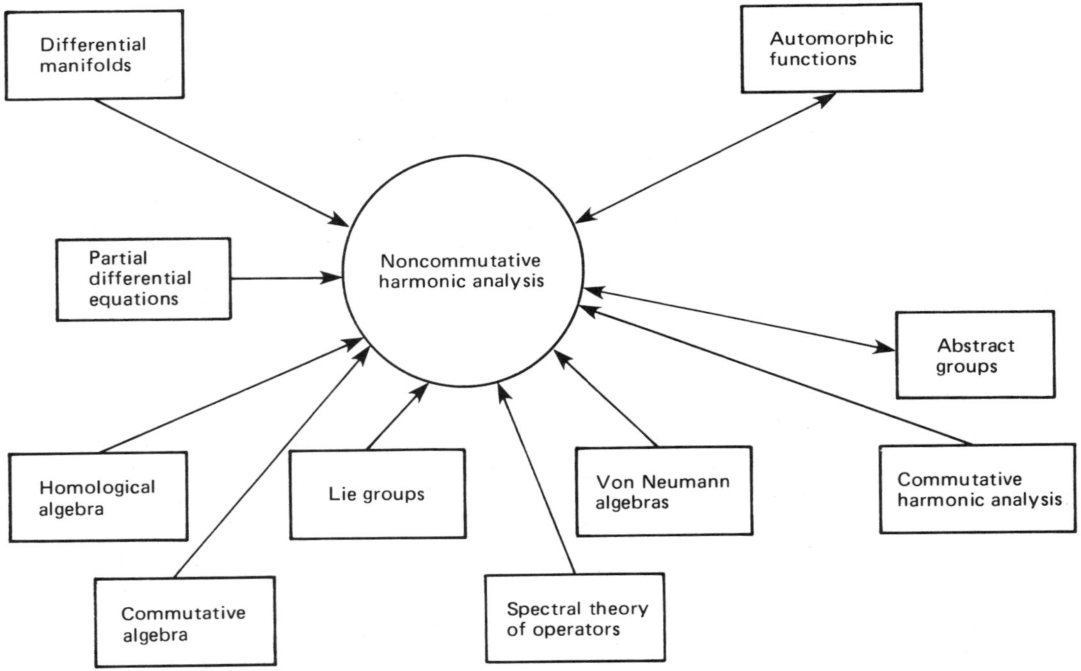

Differential manifolds
Automorphic functions
Partial differential equations
Noncommutative harmonic analysis
Abstract groups
Homological algebra
Lie groups
Von Neumann algebras
Commutative harmonic analysis
Commutative algebra
Spectral theory of operators

A VI

Noncommutative harmonic analysis

Numerous problems, coming from many parts of mathematics, have naturally led to the generalization to topological groups of the elementary theory of linear representations of finite groups (**B** III). The fundamental notions of this latter theory generalize as follows [D, Chapter 21].

(a) A *linear representation* of a topological group G in a Hausdorff topological vector space $\mathscr{H}$ is a homomorphism $\pi : G \to \mathrm{Aut}(\mathscr{H})$, where $\mathrm{Aut}(\mathscr{H})$ is the group of (bicontinuous) automorphisms of $\mathscr{H}$. The representation π is required to satisfy the following *continuity* condition: the mapping $s \mapsto \pi(s) \cdot x$ is continuous on G, for each $x \in \mathscr{H}$.

(b) A linear representation $\pi : G \to \mathrm{Aut}(\mathscr{H})$ is said to be (topologically) *irreducible* if $\mathscr{H}$ has no *closed* vector subspace (other than $\{0\}$ and $\mathscr{H}$) that is stable under all the automorphisms $\pi(s)$.

(c) The theory exists only for *locally compact* groups G. If we can define a notion of integration of functions on G with values in $\mathscr{H}$, then for each bounded measure μ on G we can define a continuous endomorphism $\pi(\mu)$ of $\mathscr{H}$ by the formula

$$\pi(\mu) \cdot x = \int_G (\pi(s) \cdot x)\, d\mu(s). \tag{1}$$

The most important case is that in which $\mathscr{H}$ is a *Hilbert* space and π a continuous *unitary* representation, i.e., such that $(\pi(s) \cdot x \,|\, \pi(s) \cdot y) = (x \,|\, y)$ for all $x, y \in \mathscr{H}$ and all $s \in G$. Then $\mu \mapsto \pi(\mu)$ is a representation of the Banach algebra $M_{\mathbf{C}}^1(G)$ of bounded complex measures on G, in the Hilbert space $\mathscr{H}$, in the sense of (**C** III). The algebra $M_{\mathbf{C}}^1(G)$ and certain of its subalgebras (such as the algebra $L_{\mathbf{C}}^1(G)$ when G is unimodular) play the role of the group algebra $\mathbf{C}[G]$ of a finite group.

Two unitary representations $\pi_1 : G \to \mathrm{Aut}(\mathscr{H}_1)$, $\pi_2 : G \to \mathrm{Aut}(\mathscr{H}_2)$ are said to be *equivalent* if there exists an *isometry* σ of $\mathscr{H}_1$ onto $\mathscr{H}_2$ such that $\pi_2(s) = \sigma\pi_1(s)\sigma^{-1}$ for all $s \in G$. If a unitary representation $\pi : G \to \mathrm{Aut}(\mathscr{H})$ is such that $\mathscr{H}$ is the Hilbert sum of a family $(\mathscr{H}_\alpha)$ of subspaces stable under all the $\pi(s)$, the representation π is said to be the *Hilbert sum* of the subrepresentations $\pi_\alpha : G \to \mathrm{Aut}(\mathscr{H}_\alpha)$, where $\pi_\alpha(s)$ is the restriction of $\pi(s)$ to $\mathscr{H}_\alpha$.

The *regular representation* $R : G \to \mathrm{Aut}(L^2_{\mathbf{C}}(G))$ is defined by the condition that $R(s)$ maps the class of a square-integrable function f on G to the class of the translated function $x \mapsto f(s^{-1}x)$.

(d) Suppose that G is unimodular and π unitary. It may happen that for certain subalgebras A of $L^1_{\mathbf{C}}(G)$ the *trace* $\mathrm{Tr}(\pi(f))$ of the operator $\pi(f)$ is defined for all $f \in A$ (**C** III), in which case $f \mapsto \mathrm{Tr}(\pi(f))$ is called the *character* of the representation π (on A) (B 41).

1. Elementary cases: compact groups and abelian groups

For a *compact* group G, the irreducible unitary representations are *finite-dimensional*. For any unitary representation $\pi : G \to \mathrm{Aut}(\mathscr{H})$, the Hilbert space $\mathscr{H}$ is the Hilbert sum of finite-dimensional subspaces $\mathscr{H}_\rho$ stable under all the $\pi(s)$, such that the restrictions $\pi(s)|\mathscr{H}_\rho$ define for each ρ an irreducible representation of G. Let $\hat{G}$ be a set of representatives of the equivalence classes of irreducible representations of G. For each $\rho \in \hat{G}$, $\chi_\rho(s) = \mathrm{Tr}(\rho(s))$ is a continuous function on G, called the *character* of the representation ρ, and the χ_ρ form an orthonormal basis of the center of the algebra $L^2_{\mathbf{C}}(G)$. For each function $f \in L^1_{\mathbf{C}}(G)$, the character $\mathrm{Tr}(\rho(f))$ is equal to $\int_G \chi_\rho(s) f(s)\, ds$, where ds is the Haar measure on G with total mass 1. If n_ρ is the dimension of the representation $\rho \in \hat{G}$ in the decomposition of the space $L^2_{\mathbf{C}}(G)$ with respect to the regular representation, there occur in the Hilbert sum n_ρ subspaces on which the corresponding irreducible representation is equivalent to ρ, and for each function $f \in L^2_{\mathbf{C}}(G)$, we have

$$(2) \qquad \int_G |f(s)|^2\, ds = \sum_{\rho \in \hat{G}} n_\rho \,\mathrm{Tr}(\rho(f)\rho(f)^*)$$

[D, Chapter 21].

If now G is a locally compact *abelian* group, the results of harmonic analysis on G (**B** IV) can be interpreted as describing the unitary representations of G. The irreducible representations are all of degree 1; each of them is equivalent to a *character* $s \mapsto \chi(s)$, and distinct characters define inequivalent representations. The set of equivalence classes of irreducible representations of G is therefore identified with the *dual* $\hat{G}$ of the group G, and here $\hat{G}$ is naturally endowed with a structure of a locally compact commutative group (**B** IV). An arbitrary unitary representation $\pi : G \to \mathrm{Aut}(\mathscr{H})$ decomposes into the Hilbert sum of monogenic representations, each of which is equivalent to a representation $s \mapsto M_\mu(s)$; the space of this representation is the Hilbert space $L^2_{\mathbf{C}}(\hat{G}, \mu)$, where μ is a positive bounded measure on $\hat{G}$, and $M_\mu(s)$ is multiplication by the class of the function $\chi \mapsto \chi(s)$ on $\hat{G}$. As in spectral theory (**C** III), the "direct sum" is replaced by a more general process of "direct integration" in order to pass from irreducible representations to arbitrary unitary representations. The decomposition (2) of the regular representation is here replaced by the Plancherel formula (**B** IV)

$$\int_G |f(s)|^2\, ds = \int_{\hat{G}} d\chi \left| \int_G f(s)\overline{\chi(s)}\, ds \right|^2 \tag{3}$$

[D, Chapter 22].

2. The fundamental problems

On the model of these two elementary cases, the two fundamental problems of noncommutative harmonic analysis on a locally compact group G are the following: (1) to determine, up to equivalence, all the irreducible representations of G; (2) to "decompose" any linear representation of G into irreducible representations, in a sense that generalizes the "direct integration" of spectral theory. These two questions are closely connected, since the irreducible representations are often obtained by "decomposition" of well-chosen representations. The method most used is that of *induced representations*, generalizing the definition of Frobenius for finite groups (**B** III). In the simplest case, one starts with a closed subgroup H of G and a unitary representation σ of H in a Hilbert space E. The classes of functions $g : G \to E$ belonging to $L^2_E(G)$ and such that $g(su) = \sigma(u^{-1}) \cdot g(s)$ for all $s \in G$ and $u \in H$ form a closed subspace F of $L^2_E(G)$, and for each $g \in F$ the function $g_t : s \mapsto g(ts)$ also belongs to F for all $t \in G$; if we put $\gamma(t)g = g_t$, then $t \mapsto \gamma(t)$ is the linear representation of G in F induced by σ (BAMS 69 (Mackey); LN 388; [46], [D, Chapter 22]).

The theory of von Neumann algebras (**B** V) provides a preliminary shaping-up of these problems. If $\pi : G \to \mathrm{Aut}(\mathscr{H})$ is a unitary representation, $\pi(G)$ generates a von Neumann subalgebra of $\mathscr{L}(\mathscr{H})$, and π is said to be *of type* I, II, or III according as this algebra is of type I, II, or III. Examples of each type are known. The representations of types II and III present pathological characteristics: for example, there are representations of type II that admit two "decompositions" into irreducible representations, in which all the representations in the same decomposition are equivalent, but the irreducible representations that feature in one of these decompositions are not equivalent to those in the other. On the other hand, this phenomenon cannot occur with representations of type I [46]. The groups most studied are the *groups of type* I, which are defined to be those whose unitary representations are all of type I. Compact groups and commutative locally compact groups are of type I; so are reductive Lie groups over **R** or a p-adic field $\mathbf{Q}_p$, linear algebraic groups (**A** IX) over **Q** and nilpotent Lie groups; on the other hand there are solvable Lie groups which are not of type I.

The set $\hat{G}$ of equivalence classes of irreducible unitary representations of G can be canonically topologized, and is discrete when G is compact, and locally compact when G is commutative, but in general (even for semisimple Lie groups) $\hat{G}$ is not necessarily Hausdorff [46]. However, if G is of type I, separable, and unimodular, a canonical measure μ on $\hat{G}$ can be defined, called the "Plancherel measure," with respect to which there is a formula of decomposition of the regular representation which generalizes (2) and (3): for any $f \in L^1 \cap L^2$ we have

$$\int_G |f(s)|^2 \, ds = \int_{\hat{G}} \mathrm{Tr}(\rho(f)\rho(f)^*) \, d\mu(\rho) \tag{4}$$

(BAMS 69 (Mackey); [46]). It should be remarked that the measure μ is in general carried by a proper subset of $\hat{G}$—in other words, certain irreducible unitary representations do not occur in the decomposition of the regular representation; on the other hand, they can occur in the representations induced by discrete subgroups of G.

The irreducible unitary representations of a (separable, unimodular) group of type I that are equivalent to subrepresentations of the regular representation correspond to closed points of $\hat{G}$ whose Plancherel measure is >0, and they constitute the *discrete series*. If π is such a representation, $\pi(f)$ is a Hilbert–Schmidt operator for $f \in L^1 \cap L^2$.

3. Harmonic analysis on real reductive Lie groups

The first examples of infinite-dimensional irreducible unitary representations were constructed in 1939 by Wigner, for the Lorentz group. In 1947 Bargmann determined all the irreducible unitary representations of **SL**(2, **R**) and **SL**(2, **C**) (B 13, 179), and then Gelfand and Naimark described several series of such representations for the classical groups (B 4; [63]); but even for the groups **SL**(n, **C**) when $n > 3$, not all the irreducible unitary representations are as yet known [172]. It should be said that the methods of these authors often produce representations on function spaces which are not Hilbert spaces, or nonunitary representations on Hilbert spaces (Nice D 2 (Naimark)).

These results find their place in the general study of the linear representations of connected reductive real Lie groups, which has been developed mainly by Harish-Chandra in a long series of memoirs. For such a group G, apart from the representations of the discrete series (when it exists), the method that has led to irreducible representations consists in considering the representations induced by certain representations of *parabolic* subgroups of G. These are subgroups Q whose Lie algebra $\mathfrak{q}$ is such that the complexification $\mathfrak{q}_{(\mathbf{C})}$ of $\mathfrak{q}$, in the complexification $\mathfrak{g}_{(\mathbf{C})}$ of the Lie algebra $\mathfrak{g}$ of G, contains a maximal solvable subalgebra of $\mathfrak{g}_{(\mathbf{C})}$ (the Lie algebra of a Borel subgroup (**A** IX)). The subalgebra $\mathfrak{q}$ is then its own normalizer, and the group Q is required to be its own normalizer in G. A parabolic subgroup Q admits a canonical decomposition Q = MAN, called the *Langlands decomposition*, in which M is reductive (but not necessarily connected), A is isomorphic to some $\mathbf{R}^n$, N is a connected nilpotent normal subgroup of Q, MA is the direct product of M and A, and MAN the semidirect product of MA and N. We start then with an irreducible unitary representation σ of M and a representation τ of degree 1 of A, which define a representation $\sigma \times \tau$ of Q by the formula $(\sigma \times \tau)(man) = \sigma(m)\tau(a)$, and then consider the representation of G induced by $\sigma \times \tau$. Depending on the choices of σ and τ, we obtain, by decomposing this induced representation, irreducible representations of G that constitute the *principal*, *complementary*, and *degenerate* series (LN 388). For "most" choices of $\sigma \times \tau$, the induced representation is irreducible (B 126, 131, 369; BAMS 75 (Kostant); SAMS XXVI (Blattner); LN 170 (Kostant)).

The main aim of the work of Harish-Chandra is to obtain explicitly the Plancherel measure for G (BAMS 76 (Harish-Chandra); LN 388). In this, the *Cartan subgroups* of G play an essential role. A Cartan subalgebra $\mathfrak{h}$ of $\mathfrak{g}$ is by definition such that its complexification $\mathfrak{h}_{(\mathbf{C})}$ is a maximal commutative subalgebra of $\mathfrak{g}_{(\mathbf{C})}$, and the corresponding Cartan subgroup is the centralizer of $\mathfrak{h}$ in G. The Cartan subgroups form a finite number of families $\mathscr{C}_i$ of conjugate subgroups ($1 \leqslant i \leqslant r$), where in general $r > 1$. The discrete series of G exists only when G has a *compact* Cartan subgroup. To each family $\mathscr{C}_i$ other than the family of compact Cartan subgroups, there corresponds a family of proper parabolic subgroups, called *cuspidal* subgroups; they are "associated" in the sense that in their Langlands decompositions the abelian groups A are conjugate. If Q = MAN is a Langlands decomposition of such a group, M has a compact Cartan subgroup, which is the largest compact subgroup contained in a Cartan subgroup of G of the family $\mathscr{C}_i$. There corresponds to $\mathscr{C}_i$ a "cuspidal principal series" of irreducible unitary representations of G, obtained by decomposing the representations induced by representations $\sigma \times \tau$ of Q, where τ is a character of A and σ a representation of the *discrete* series of M. The irreducible unitary representations that occur in the Plancherel measure are those of the discrete series (when it exists) and those of the cuspidal principal series: in particular, the representations of the complementary or degenerate series do not feature in the decomposition of the regular representation. A simple case is that of the *complex* reductive groups: here there is only one family of Cartan subgroups (which are not compact) and the determination of the Plancherel measure is relatively simple (B 143).

In the general case the theory is much more difficult, and depends on a deep study of the discrete series of G (assumed to exist) and in particular on the construction of the corresponding characters. In general, for each irreducible unitary representation $\pi : G \to \mathrm{Aut}(\mathscr{H})$, and each C^∞-function f on G with compact support, the operator $\pi(f)$ has a trace $\Theta_\pi(f)$, and Θ_π is a distribution on G, invariant under inner automorphisms. Furthermore, for each left- and right-invariant differential operator Z on G (i.e., belonging to the center $\mathfrak{Z}$ of the infinitesimal algebra $\mathfrak{G}$ of G [D, Chapter 19]), we have $Z \cdot \Theta_\pi = \chi_\pi(Z)\Theta_\pi$, where χ_π is a homomorphism of $\mathfrak{Z}$ into $\mathbf{C}^*$. The first fundamental result is that in fact the distribution Θ_π can be identified with a locally integrable function that is analytic on a dense open subset of G. This result is reached by a long and difficult study of the invariant distributions on G which are $\mathfrak{Z}$-finite, that is to say, are such that their images under the operators $Z \in \mathfrak{Z}$ form a finite-dimensional vector space; this study is reduced to that of distributions defined on the Lie algebra $\mathfrak{g}$ of G and having analogous properties, to which the Fourier transformation in $\mathfrak{g}$ and the properties of elliptic operators can be applied. To obtain the local properties of Θ_π, it is also necessary to use induction on the dimension of $\mathfrak{g}$, by considering invariant distributions on the centralizer of an element of $\mathfrak{g}$ in G.

As to the discrete series, let C be a compact Cartan subgroup of G: to certain weights ξ of the Lie algebra of C there corresponds canonically a character Θ_ξ of the discrete series. A method reminiscent of that of Weyl for compact groups [D, Chapter 21] shows that in this way we obtain *all* the characters of the discrete series, but it requires a profound and extremely difficult study of the properties of Θ_ξ at infinity (B 323; SAMS XXVI (Trombi, Varadarajan, J. Wolf); LN 140, 266, 276, 388, 429; [190]). It should be remarked that the characters Θ_ξ determine the corresponding representations up to equivalence, but these representations are not all explicitly known; for some of them, the representation space can be identified with certain spaces defined cohomologically (B 398; LN 266 (Okamoto)).

An important point to emphasize is the occurrence, in this theory, of *spherical functions* on G [D, Chapter 22]. These are analytic functions on G, invariant under left and right translations by the elements of a maximal compact subgroup K of G, which are in addition eigenfunctions of the differential operators $Z \in \mathfrak{Z}$. The spherical functions that are of positive type [D, Chapter 22] define canonically irreducible linear representations of G, which may be characterized as those containing the trivial representation of K (representations "of class 1," or "spherical" representations). These are the representations that occur in the "direct integral" decomposition of the canonical representation of G on $L^2_{\mathbf{C}}(G/K)$. Spherical functions can be defined for more general pairs (G, K), where G is a locally compact group and K is a compact subgroup of G satisfying certain conditions ("Gelfand pairs"); in particular, if G is commutative and $K = \{e\}$, the spherical functions are just the characters of G; and if $G = \mathbf{SO}(3)$, $K = \mathbf{SO}(2)$, they are the "zonal spherical harmonics" of Legendre and Laplace (whence the terminology). When G is reductive and K is a maximal compact subgroup, all the spherical functions have been explicitly determined by Harish-Chandra (B 79, 144; [D, Chapter 22], [177], [190]).

Finally we remark that recently a purely algebraic study of the linear representations of semisimple groups has been initiated, which considers the universal enveloping algebra $U(\mathfrak{g})$ (**B** I) of a complex semisimple Lie algebra $\mathfrak{g}$, and the simple modules for this algebra. At the present time there is a substantial number of results on the two-sided ideals of $U(\mathfrak{g})$ which are the annihilators of these modules (B 425, 489; LN 497 (Duflo); [202]).

4. Harmonic analysis on reductive p-adic groups

Algebraic groups over a local field (**A** IX) and their infinite-dimensional linear representations have recently acquired great importance, by reason of their applications to automorphic functions (**A** VII) and number theory (**A** X). A problem still not completely solved is whether the theory developed for real Lie groups can be generalized to apply to these groups. The main obstacle is that the analytic methods based on differential operators are no longer applicable; if the local field is of characteristic $p > 0$, it is not even possible to "climb up" from the Lie algebra to the group. Also the theory has a much more algebraic aspect, right from the initial definitions, than the theory of linear representations of real reductive groups. Let G be a reductive algebraic group, defined over a local field F, and connected in the Zariski topology (**A** IX). If G_F is the group of F-rational points, we consider linear representations $G_F \to \mathrm{Aut}(V)$, where now V is a complex vector space, in general of infinite dimension, but is not equipped with a topology (so that Aut(V) is the group of automorphisms of V in the algebraic sense). Topology enters via G_F, which is a totally disconnected, locally compact group; the C^∞-functions from G to V of the classical theory are replaced by *locally constant* functions. The continuity conditions imposed on a linear representation $\pi : G_F \to \mathrm{Aut}(V)$ are now: (1) for each $v \in V$, the function $s \mapsto \pi(s) \cdot v$ is locally constant and compactly supported; (2) for each open subgroup H of G_F, the space of vectors $v \in V$ such that $\pi(t) \cdot v = v$ for all $t \in H$ is finite dimensional. Representations π satisfying these conditions are called *admissible*.

Likewise, the notions of irreducibility and equivalence are here purely algebraic: π is irreducible if *no* subspace of V, other than $\{0\}$ and V, is stable under all the $\pi(s)$. Two representations $\pi_1 : G_F \to \mathrm{Aut}(V_1)$, $\pi_2 : G_F \to \mathrm{Aut}(V_2)$ are equivalent if there exists a linear bijection σ of V_1 onto V_2 such that $\pi_2(s) = \sigma\pi_1(s)\sigma^{-1}$ for all $s \in G_F$. Finally, to define the representation induced by an admissible representation $\sigma : H_F \to \mathrm{Aut}(V)$, where H is a closed subgroup of G, consider the space of functions $g : G_F \to V$ that are locally constant and whose support is of the form ΩH_F for some compact $\Omega \subset G_F$, and which satisfy $g(su) = \sigma(u^{-1}) \cdot g(s)$ for all $s \in G_F$ and $u \in H_F$; the representation induced by σ is that obtained by making G_F act in the natural way on this space. It can be shown that this representation is again admissible.

The connection with irreducible unitary representations is provided by the fundamental fact, established first by Jacquet–Langlands for the group **GL**(2) and then by Harish-Chandra in general, that each (topologically) irreducible unitary representation comes from an (algebraically) irreducible admissible representation $\pi : G_F \to \mathrm{Aut}(V)$ by completing V with respect to a π-invariant scalar product (B 471). Knowledge of the irreducible admissible representations would therefore a fortiori provide the irreducible unitary representations. In fact, the irreducible admissible representations are completely known only for the group **GL**(2) (B 332, 415; LN 114); for this group the Plancherel measure is also known (B 332; [64]).

To study irreducible admissible representations, we try to proceed as in the classical case of reductive groups over **R** (see above), and hence give prominence to the notions of parabolic subgroup and maximal compact subgroup. The notion of parabolic subgroup here is that which comes from the theory of algebraic groups (**A** IX), so that a parabolic subgroup of G_F is the group P_F of F-rational points of a parabolic subgroup P of G defined over F. From here onward it is necessary to assume that F is of characteristic 0, because it is only in this case that an algebraic group has a Levi decomposition (**A** IX), which plays an essential role in the study of parabolic subgroups.

Since the group G_F is totally disconnected, the compact subgroups to be considered are the open compact subgroups. There exist maximal open compact subgroups, but (unlike the case of Lie groups over **R**) two such maximal compact subgroups need not be conjugate in G_F. Progress here is due to the results of Bruhat–Tits (Nice C 5 (Bruhat), Vancouver (Tits)), who have discovered that for certain "good" maximal open compact subgroups there are analogs for G_F of the Iwasawa and Cartan decompositions.

By considering a representation induced by a representation of a maximal open compact subgroup, Mautner first encountered the notion of a *supercuspidal* representation. These are clearly in evidence in the work of Jacquet–Langlands in **GL**(2), and the notion has been extended to the case of an arbitrary reductive group G by Harish-Chandra (B 387, 415, 471; SAMS XXVI (Harish-Chandra); LN 162); it is closely related to the classical notion of a cusp form in the theory of modular forms (**A** VII). The importance of these supercuspidal representations arises from a fundamental result of Jacquet and Harish-Chandra: every irreducible admissible representation of G can be obtained by "decomposing" the representation induced by a representation $\sigma : P_F \rightarrow \mathrm{Aut}(W)$ of a parabolic subgroup P_F, obtained by considering a Levi decomposition $P = MN$ of P (where M is reductive and N the radical of P) and taking σ to be equal to an irreducible supercuspidal representation on M_F and trivial on N_F (B 471).

For every irreducible admissible representation π, the character $\Theta_\pi(f)$ is defined for all locally constant functions f of compact support. Using the notions and results above, Harish-Chandra has recently been able to extend to characters of G_F some of his results on the characters of reductive groups over **R**: in particular, Θ_π can be identified with a locally integrable function, which is locally constant on a dense open subset of G (B 387, 471; SAMS XXVI (Harish-Chandra); LN 162, 166, 260, 462, 466).

We remark finally that a theory of spherical functions on reductive groups over a local field can be developed, using the results of Bruhat–Tits (Nice C 5 (Macdonald)).

5. Harmonic analysis on nilpotent and solvable Lie groups

The fundamental ideas that lead to a description of the irreducible unitary representations of a simply-connected nilpotent Lie group G over **R** are due to Kirillov. To each linear form $f \in \mathfrak{g}^*$ on the Lie algebra $\mathfrak{g}$ of G, there is associated an alternating bilinear form $B_f(x, y) = f([x, y])$; a subalgebra $\mathfrak{h}$ of $\mathfrak{g}$ is called a *real polarization* of $\mathfrak{g}$ with respect to f if the vector subspace $\mathfrak{h}$ of $\mathfrak{g}$ is a maximal totally isotropic subspace of $\mathfrak{g}$ with respect to B_f (i.e., if $f([x, y]) = 0$ for all $y \in \mathfrak{h}$ is equivalent to $x \in \mathfrak{h}$; this definition is valid for any Lie group). If now G is nilpotent and simply connected, for each $f \in \mathfrak{g}^*$ there exists a real polarization $\mathfrak{h}$ of $\mathfrak{g}$ with respect to f. If $H = \exp(\mathfrak{h})$ is the connected subgroup of G corresponding to $\mathfrak{h}$, we define a character χ_f of H by the formula $\chi_f(\exp x) = e^{if(x)}$ for $x \in \mathfrak{h}$, and the unitary representation of G induced by this character is irreducible. Moreover, *every* irreducible unitary representation of G is obtained in this way: for a given $f \in \mathfrak{g}^*$, two real polarizations give rise to equivalent representations, so that the class $\rho(f)$ of these representations depends only on f; and for $f_1, f_2 \in \mathfrak{g}^*$, we have $\rho(f_1) = \rho(f_2)$ if and only if there exists $s \in G$ such that $f_2 = {}^t\mathrm{Ad}(s)^{-1} \cdot f_1$. In other words, the set $\hat{G}$ is in canonical one–one correspondence with the set of *orbits* in $\mathfrak{g}^*$ of the coadjoint representation $s \mapsto {}^t\mathrm{Ad}(s)^{-1}$ of G. Further, the characters of the representations and the Plancherel measure can be determined explicitly as functions of these orbits (B 249; SAMS XXVI (C. Moore); LN 266, 388).

The theory of unitary representations of solvable nonnilpotent groups is much more complicated and is not yet complete. A solvable group is not necessarily of type I; there may exist no real polarizations of $\mathfrak{g}$ for a given $f \in \mathfrak{g}^*$, and even when they exist, the corresponding unitary representation, constructed as above, may fail to be irreducible. The most important results are those of L. Auslander and Kostant, related to the general methods of Kostant (Nice D 2 (Kostant); LN 170) for constructing irreducible representations. The new idea is to consider the complexification $\mathfrak{g}_{(\mathbf{C})}$ of the Lie algebra $\mathfrak{g}$; for each $f \in \mathfrak{g}^*$, the form B_f extends canonically to an alternating form on $\mathfrak{g}_{(\mathbf{C})}$, and a *polarization* with respect to f is now a subalgebra $\mathfrak{h}$ of $\mathfrak{g}_{(\mathbf{C})}$ such that $\mathfrak{h}$ is a maximal totally isotropic subspace for B_f and such that $\mathfrak{h} + \bar{\mathfrak{h}}$ is a subalgebra of $\mathfrak{g}_{(\mathbf{C})}$ (where $\bar{\mathfrak{h}}$ is the complex conjugate of $\mathfrak{h}$). For certain forms $f \in \mathfrak{g}^*$ (called *integrable*), the existence of polarizations can be proved and irreducible unitary representations of G obtained (by taking subrepresentations of induced representations). The classes of these representations no longer depend only on the orbit of f under the coadjoint representation: if O is an orbit, they are indexed by the dual of the fundamental group $\pi_1(\mathrm{O})$. Finally, for G to be of type I, it is necessary and sufficient that each orbit should be locally closed in $\mathfrak{g}^*$ and should contain an integrable form (B 447; SAMS XXVI (C. Moore); Nice D 2 (Kostant); LN 388; [13], [145]). There remain still to be answered many questions about the characters and the Plancherel measure for groups of type I. The investigation of solvable Lie groups that are not of type I has been begun by Pukanszky; here the decomposition into irreducible representations has to be replaced by a coarser decomposition, into so-called factor representations $\pi : \mathrm{G} \to \mathrm{Aut}(\mathscr{H})$ (for which the von Neumann algebra generated by $\pi(\mathrm{G})$ is a factor (**B** V)) (B 558; Nice D 2 (Pukanszky); SAMS XXVI (C. Moore)).

We mention finally that the study of linear representations of nilpotent and solvable groups over a local field has also begun (LN 388).

6. Representations of group extensions

Let G be a locally compact group and N a closed normal subgroup of G. The problem is to find the irreducible unitary representations of G from a knowledge of those of N and G/N. This problem has been investigated in general by Mackey, and the methods he has created (notably those of "little groups") have played an important part in the theory of unitary representations of solvable groups (B 447; SAMS XXVI (C. Moore, J. Brezin, Kleppner–Lipsman); LN 388).

Finally, it should be noted that many of the irreducible unitary representations of "classical" Lie groups (the group of displacements, the Poincaré group, etc.) are realized in Hilbert spaces that are *function spaces*, the elements of which are combinations of "special functions" such as Bessel functions and hypergeometric functions and their degenerations; an important part of the properties of these functions, which used to appear fortuitous, is now much better understood and is derived in a natural way from the properties of the groups from which they arise ([123], [187]).

7. Connections with the natural sciences

The unitary representations of the Lorentz group and the Poincaré group (historically the first to be considered) continue to play a fundamental role in quantum mechanics, and it seems that representations of other noncompact Lie groups may also play a role in the physics of "elementary particles."

8. The originators

The principal ideas in the theory of unitary representations of Lie groups are due to the following mathematicians:

General theory of linear representations of locally compact groups. J. von Neumann (1903–1957), G. Mackey.

Representations of classical groups. V. Bargmann, I. Gelfand.

Representations of real reductive groups, spherical functions. Harish-Chandra, R. Langlands, I. Gelfand, A. Selberg.

Representations of reductive p-adic groups. F. Mautner, Harish-Chandra, H. Jacquet, R. Langlands.

Representations of nilpotent or solvable groups. A. Kirillov, B. Kostant.

The following have also made substantial contributions to these theories: M. Atiyah, L. Auslander, P. Bernat, I. Bernshtein, R. Blattner, W. Borho, J. Brezin, I. Brown, F. Bruhat, J. Carmona, W. Casselman, N. Conze, J. Dixmier, M. Duflo, E. Effros, L. Ehrenpreis, T. Enright, J. Ernest, J. Fell, R. Gangolli, S. Gelbart, P. Gérardin, S. Gindikin, R. Godement, M. Graev, H. Hecht, S. Helgason, T. Hirai, R. Howe, N. Iwahori, K. Johnson, A. Joseph, I. Kaplansky, F. Karpelevic, A. Kleppner, A. Knapp, R. Kunze, J. Lepowsky, R. Lipsman, H. Matsumoto, C. Moore, M. Naimark, M. Narasimhan, E. Nelson, K. Okamoto, K. Parthasaraty, I. Piatetskii-Shapiro, L. Pukanszky, S. Quint, M. Raïs, R. Ranga Rao, W. Roelcke, H. Rossi, H. Saito, P. Sally, G. Schiffmann, W. Schmid, I. Segal, J. Shalika, T. Shintani, A.

Silberger, E. Stein, W. Stinespring, R. Takahashi, O. Takenouchi, S. Tanaka, J. Tits, T. tom Dieck, P. Trombi, G. van Dijk, V. Varadarajan, M. Vergne, D. Verma, N. Vilenkin, N. Wallach, A. Weil, J. Wolf, D. Zhelobenko, G. Zuckerman.

References

B: 4, 13, 41, 79, 126, 131, 143, 144, 179, 249, 323, 332, 369, 387, 398, 415, 425, 447, 471, 489, 508, 558.

LN: 114, 140, 162, 166, 260, 266, 276, 388, 429, 436, 462, 466, 497, 562, 570, 576, 587, 602, 728, 739, 766.

BAMS: 69 (Mackey), 75 (Kostant), 76 (Harish-Chandra).

SAMS: XXVI.

[13], [46], [63], [64], [123], [145], [172], [177], [187], [190], [202].

A VII

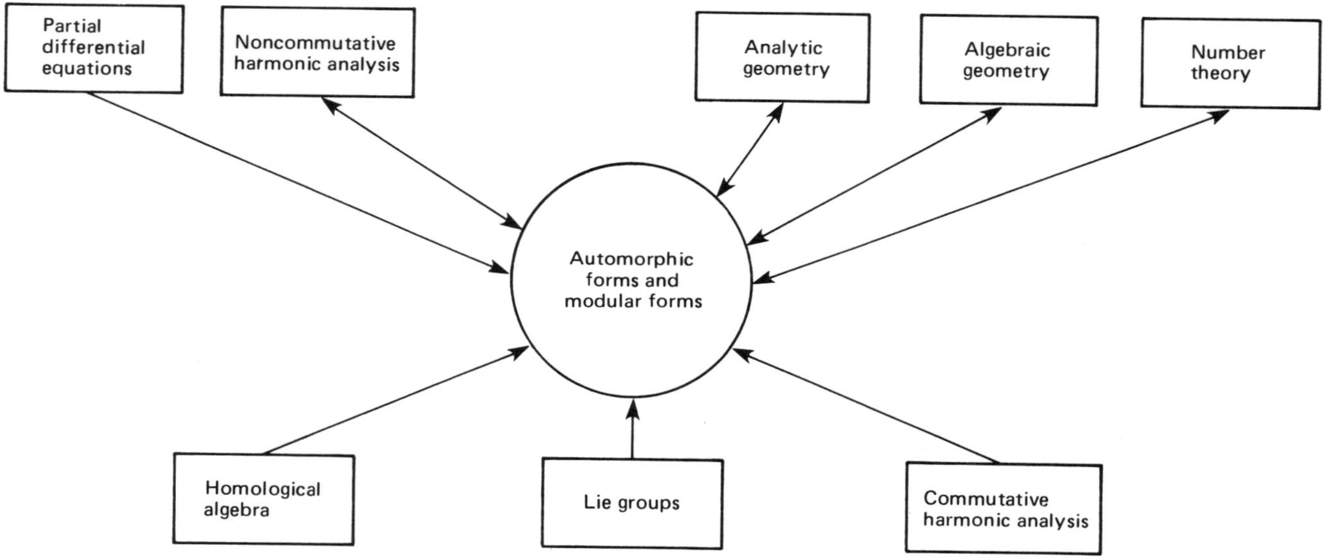

Partial differential equations
Noncommutative harmonic analysis
Analytic geometry
Algebraic geometry
Number theory
Automorphic forms and modular forms
Homological algebra
Lie groups
Commutative harmonic analysis

A VII

Automorphic forms and modular forms

The notion of a modular function was known to Gauss (who published nothing on this subject); it was not rediscovered and studied until the 1860s, and then became part of the general theory of automorphic functions of a complex variable, created by Poincaré in the 1880s. The generalizations to several variables of this theory were developed only after the work of Siegel on quadratic forms with integer coefficients (**A** X), which elucidated the place of Lie groups in the theory; during the same period, Hecke opened up new paths in the arithmetic theory of modular forms, which previously had been thought to be complete. Since then, the theory of automorphic forms and modular forms has become an extraordinary crossroads of mathematics, at which a great variety of theories have reacted on one another: analytic geometry, algebraic geometry, homological algebra, noncommutative harmonic analysis, and number theory.

1. The analytic aspect

Let X be a bounded connected open set in $\mathbf{C}^n$, or the image of such under a biholomorphic bijection, and let G be the group of automorphisms (i.e., biholomorphic bijections) of X, endowed with the compact-open topology (**A** I). Let Γ be a discrete subgroup of G. A holomorphic function f on X is said to be an *automorphic form* (with respect to Γ) if there exists a function $\alpha(\gamma, z)$ defined on $\Gamma \times X$, holomorphic in z on X and everywhere nonzero, such that for each $\gamma \in \Gamma$ we have

$$f(\gamma \cdot z) = \alpha(\gamma, z) f(z) \tag{1}$$

for all $z \in X$.

The function α is called a *factor of automorphy* and satisfies the relation

$$\alpha(\gamma\gamma', z) = \alpha(\gamma, \gamma' \cdot z)\alpha(\gamma', z). \tag{2}$$

An *automorphic function* on X is a meromorphic function invariant under Γ. For example, the quotient of two nonproportional automorphic forms having the same factor of automorphy is a nonconstant automorphic function.

The classical case (Poincaré) is that in which X is the upper half-plane $H : \mathscr{I} z > 0$, and G is the group (isomorphic to **PSL**(2, **R**)) of transformations $\gamma : z \mapsto (az + b)/(cz + d)$ of H, where a, b, c, d are real and $ad - bc = 1$; we take $\alpha(\gamma, z) = (cz + d)^k$, where k is an integer, and the corresponding automorphic forms are said to be of *weight k*. *Modular forms* correspond to the group Γ (isomorphic to **PSL**(2, **Z**)) consisting of the $\gamma \in G$ such that a, b, c, d are integers.

Poincaré and his successors also studied the discrete subgroups of **SL**(2, **C**) (called *Kleinian* groups) and the corresponding automorphic functions (B 491; LN 400; [14]).

In Siegel's generalization, the space X is the Siegel space $\mathfrak{S}_n$ of complex $n \times n$ symmetric matrices Z with positive definite imaginary part, and G is the symplectic group **Sp**(2n, **R**). If we write the matrices in this group in block form $\begin{pmatrix} A & B \\ C & D \end{pmatrix}$, where A, B, C, D are $n \times n$ matrices, G acts on $\mathfrak{S}_n$ by the rule

$$\begin{pmatrix} A & B \\ C & D \end{pmatrix} \cdot Z = (AZ + B)(CZ + D)^{-1}.$$

Siegel's modular group is the subgroup Γ of G consisting of matrices with integer entries, and $\alpha(\gamma, Z) = (\det(CZ + D))^k$.

Let X now be a bounded domain in $\mathbf{C}^n$, and take $\alpha(\gamma, z) = J_\gamma(z)^{-k}$, where $J_\gamma(z)$ is the Jacobian of γ at the point z, and k is an integer $\geqslant 0$; then for each bounded holomorphic function on X, the *Poincaré series* $\sum_{\gamma \in \Gamma} f(\gamma \cdot z) J_\gamma(z)^k$ converges uniformly on each compact subset of X if $k \geqslant 2$, and is an automorphic form with α as factor of automorphy. If k is sufficiently large, it can be shown that there exist $n + 1$ Poincaré series Q_j $(0 \leqslant j \leqslant n)$ such that the quotients Q_j/Q_0 $(1 \leqslant j \leqslant n)$ are n analytically independent automorphic functions.

The orbit space X/Γ carries a canonical structure of analytic space. If X/Γ is *compact*, it is isomorphic to an (in general singular) projective algebraic variety (C 1953–4; [9], [17]).

2. The intervention of Lie groups

The group G of automorphisms of a bounded domain $X \subset \mathbf{C}^n$ is a Lie group (H. Cartan), which may consist only of the identity element. The (opposite) case in which G is *transitive* has been studied most; the stabilizer

H of a point of X is then a compact subgroup of G, and X may be identified with the homogeneous space G/H. The most interesting case is that in which X is *symmetric* (**B** II), that is to say, each point of X is an isolated fixed point of an involutory automorphism of X. All such spaces are explicitly known (E. Cartan) and include in particular the Siegel space; the irreducible ones are of the form G/K, where G is simple, noncompact, with center consisting only of the identity element, and K is a maximal compact subgroup with non-discrete center (B 62; [76]). Moreover, the groups G considered are algebraic, defined over **Q**, so that arithmetic discrete subgroups (**A** X) can be defined. For such a subgroup Γ, X/Γ is not in general compact, but has a canonical compactification that is a complex projective algebraic variety in which X/Γ is a Zariski open set (C 1957–8; SAMS IX (Baily)).

The notion of automorphic form can now be generalized to an arbitrary symmetric space G/K, where the only assumptions made are that G is semi-simple (or even reductive) and K is a maximal compact subgroup of G (with no assumptions on the center of K). It is convenient also to consider functions f with values in a finite-dimensional complex vector space V, the factor of automorphy $\alpha(\gamma, z)$ in (1) being now an automorphism of V. We assume that α is the restriction to $\Gamma \times X$ of a function (also denoted by α) that is continuous and invertible on all of $G \times X$ and satisfies the relation $\alpha(ss', x) = \alpha(s, s' \cdot x)\alpha(s', x)$. Let x_0 be the point of X that is the image of K, and put $f^\alpha(s) = \alpha(s, x_0)^{-1} f(s \cdot x_0)$ for $s \in G$; then the restriction σ to K of the function $s \mapsto \alpha(s, x_0)$ is a homomorphism $K \to \mathrm{Aut}(V)$, and the functions f^α corresponding to automorphic forms with factor of automorphy α are exactly those which satisfy the relations

$$(3) \qquad f^\alpha(su) = \sigma(u^{-1}) f^\alpha(s) \qquad (s \in G, u \in K),$$

$$(4) \qquad f^\alpha(\gamma s) = f^\alpha(s) \qquad (s \in G, \gamma \in \Gamma).$$

We are therefore led to change our terminology and to call *automorphic forms* (of type σ) the functions $g = f^\alpha$ *on* G which satisfy (3) and (4). In fact we consider only such functions that are of class C^∞ and slowly increasing (when G is embedded in $\mathbf{GL}(n, \mathbf{C})$), and that satisfy a condition that is a substitute for holomorphy: for each left- and right-invariant differential operator P on G, the function g is to be an eigenvalue of P, i.e. $P \cdot g = \chi(P)g$ for some scalar $\chi(P)$. When $\Gamma\backslash G$ is compact, for given σ and χ, it can be shown that the vector space of automorphic forms of type (σ, χ) is *finite*-dimensional.

The condition (4) signifies that $g = f^\alpha$ may be considered as a function on the homogeneous space $\Gamma\backslash G$ of right cosets of Γ in G. We are interested in particular in such functions that belong to $L^2_{\mathbf{C}}(\Gamma\backslash G)$ (with respect to an invariant measure on $\Gamma\backslash G$), and the relationship of this theory with non-commutative harmonic analysis (**A** VI) is now clear: we have to "decompose" the canonical representation of G on $L_c^2(\Gamma\backslash G)$ into irreducible representations, and then (at any rate for the irreducible subrepresentations) decompose each of these with respect to the action of K, in order to obtain automorphic forms corresponding to the various representations σ of K, as in (3).

The "philosophy of cusp forms" (**A** VI), developed by Langlands from ideas of I. Gelfand and A. Selberg, dominates this theory as it dominates the theory of unitary representations of G itself (which may be considered as corresponding to the case $\Gamma = \{e\}$) (**A** VI). A function $f \in L_c^2(\Gamma\backslash G)$ is said to be a *cusp form* if, for each proper parabolic subgroup P of G, with unipotent radical U (the largest unipotent normal subgroup of P), we have $\int_{U/(U\cap\Gamma)} f(su)\,du = 0$ for all $s \in G$, where du is an invariant measure on $U/(U \cap \Gamma)$. In the case of modular forms, this reduces to the classical definition. The subspace $L_0^2(\Gamma\backslash G)$ of cusp forms is closed in $L^2(\Gamma\backslash G)$ and invariant under the action of G; it can be shown to decompose as a Hilbert sum of G-stable subspaces, on each of which the action of G defines an irreducible unitary representation. When G is semisimple and Γ is such that $\Gamma\backslash G$ is compact (but Γ is not necessarily an arithmetic subgroup), the same result is true for $L^2(\Gamma\backslash G)$ itself; but even in this case little is known about the irreducible representations which appear in the decomposition of $\Gamma\backslash G$ (B 244, 261, 278; SAMS IX (Godement, Langlands), XXVI (Gangolli); LN 62; [61]).

Returning to arithmetic groups Γ, we have next to consider the remaining part of $L^2(\Gamma\backslash G)$, i.e., the subspace of $L^2(\Gamma\backslash G)$ orthogonal to the sum of $L_0^2(\Gamma\backslash G)$ and the space of constant functions. This subspace has to be decomposed as a "direct integral" of spaces of irreducible representations (**C** III), and this task requires all the resources of the theory of Lie groups. The general idea is to consider a first decomposition into a Hilbert sum of subspaces, indexed by the classes of "associated" parabolic subgroups of G; for a group P in one of these classes, the reductive subgroup M in the Langlands decomposition of P (**A** VI) contains an arithmetic subgroup Θ defined naturally by Γ. A second decomposition of the subspace corresponding to the class of P involves the decomposition of $L_0^2(\Theta\backslash M)$ of which we have spoken above, with the help of functions that generalize the Eisenstein series of the classical theory of modular forms. It seems to be difficult to obtain more precise results except in particular cases (B 321; SAMS IX (Langlands); LN 62; [102]).

3. The intervention of adèle groups

The classical theory of modular forms involves not only the modular group **SL**(2, **Z**) but also its congruence subgroups (**A** X). In order to deal simultaneously with all these groups in a general framework, the theory of adèle groups (**A** X) is appropriate. Let G be a reductive linear algebraic group defined over a global field F (**A** X); if A is the ring of adèles of F, there is a theory of the decomposition of the canonical representation of G_A on the space $L^2(G_F \backslash G_A)$, which develops like the theory sketched above for G and $L^2(\Gamma \backslash G)$, and brings new results (B 278, 321, 466; LN 349 (Deligne); [61]). In particular, the subspace $L_0^2(G_F \backslash G_A)$ of "cusp forms" is defined, and the corresponding representations are the subject of the "program of Langlands," which consists of a vast generalization of the results of Hecke on modular forms and their relations with Dirichlet series (B 51, 59, 74, 80; [157]; LN 320 (Ogg)).

The advantage of working with the adèle group G_A is that every irreducible unitary representation of G_A is obtained as a "tensor product" (in a certain sense) of irreducible representations of the *local* groups G_v at the places v of the field F. In order to generalize Hecke's theory it is necessary to define, for each place v of F, an "Euler factor" $L(\rho_v, s)$ attached to an irreducible representation ρ_v of G_v. For a finite place v, this Euler factor should be of the form $P((Nv)^{-s})^{-1}$, where P is a polynomial such that $P(0) = 1$, and Nv is the norm of the place v; for an infinite place, it should be a product of factors $\pi^{-s/2}\Gamma((s + m)/2)$, $\pi^{-s}\Gamma(s + m)$, and e^{as+b}. If now ρ is an irreducible unitary representation of G_A that appears in $L_0^2(G_F \backslash G_A)$ and decomposes as a "tensor product" of representations ρ_v of G_v, one expects that the product $L(\rho, s) = \prod_v L(\rho_v, s)$ (defined for $\mathcal{R}s$ sufficiently large) should have an analytic continuation to a meromorphic function defined on all of **C**, and that it should satisfy a functional equation of the form

$$L(\rho, s) = \varepsilon(\rho, s)L(\check{\rho}, 1 - s), \tag{5}$$

where $\check{\rho}$ is the contragredient of ρ, and ε is an exponential.

In fact, there is a general method of construction of the $L(\rho_v, s)$, but it is not known in general whether $L(\rho, s)$ can be analytically continued to a meromorphic function or satisfies an equation (5) (B 349). However, by means of a systematic study of the representations of the local groups G_v (**A** VI), Jacquet and Langlands have been able to show that, for $G = \mathbf{GL}(2)$, these properties are true for every irreducible representation ρ of G_A which appears in $L_0^2(G_F \backslash G_A)$, and that the functions $L(\rho, s)$ are entire and bounded in every vertical strip $\alpha \leqslant \mathcal{R}s \leqslant \beta$. Conversely (still for $G = \mathbf{GL}(2)$), if this is the case for ρ and for every representation $\rho \otimes \chi$, where χ is a character of the idèle group $A^\times$ which is trivial on $F^\times$, then ρ appears as a component of $L_0^2(G_F \backslash G_A)$ (B 415; LN 114). This generalizes results of Hecke for the group $\mathbf{SL}(2, \mathbf{Z})$, and of A. Weil for the subgroups $\Gamma_0(N)$ of $\mathbf{SL}(2, \mathbf{Z})$ consisting of the matrices $\begin{pmatrix} a & b \\ c & d \end{pmatrix}$ with $c \equiv 0 \pmod{N}$ (B 346; LN 189).

4. Applications to number theory

The theory of numbers and Diophantine geometry contain many examples of Dirichlet series satisfying equations like (5), and it is natural to ask whether certain of the series arise from the preceding theory.

(a) *Extensions of abelian class-field theory.* Let $\mathfrak{G}$ be the (compact) Galois group of the separable closure $\bar{F}$ of F. The abelian characters of $\mathfrak{G}$ are precisely the irreducible unitary representations of $\mathfrak{G}$ of degree 1, and Artin's reciprocity law (**A** X) defines a canonical bijection of the set of these characters onto the torsion group of the dual of the locally compact commutative group $A^{\times}/F^{\times}$; but the latter is a subset of $L^2(G_F \backslash G_A)$, where $G = \mathbf{GL}(1)$. We may therefore expect that there should be an analogous relation between the set of irreducible unitary representations of $\mathfrak{G}$ of degree $d > 1$ and the set of irreducible representations appearing in $L_0^2(G_F \backslash G_A)$, where $G = \mathbf{GL}(d)$. The theory of Jacquet–Langlands is a step in this direction, and provides a canonical injection of the former set into the latter when $d = 2$ (B 550; SAMS XX (Shalika); LN 114).

(b) *Elliptic curves and modular forms.* If E is an elliptic curve defined over F, the Hasse–Weil zeta function $\zeta_E(s)$ of E (**A** X) is holomorphic for $\mathscr{R}s$ sufficiently large. Deligne has shown that when F is a global field of characteristic $p > 0$ (i.e., a finitely generated extension of transcendence degree 1 of a finite field), $\zeta_E(s + \frac{1}{2})$ is equal to a Jacquet–Langlands L-function $L(\rho, s)$ for a suitably chosen representation ρ acting on $L_0^2(G_F \backslash G_A)$ (LN 349). When F is a number field, this result has been established only in certain particular cases. It would follow if one knew that every elliptic curve E defined over $\mathbf{Q}$ admitted a parametrization $X_0(N) \to E$ (a surjective morphism defined over $\mathbf{Q}$), where $X_0(N)$ is the algebraic curve (in general of genus > 1) obtained by compactifying the orbit space $H/\Gamma_0(N)$. These curves $X_0(N)$, by reason of their origin, have a very rich structure which amongst other things makes possible an analysis of the structure of the set of rational points on the curve or on its Jacobian (B 469). When an elliptic curve E is parametrized by $X_0(N)$, one has likewise precise information on the arithmetical properties of E (B 414, 575; LN 476).

(c) *The Ramanujan–Petersson conjecture.* Among the most important classical modular forms there is the form of weight 12

$$\Delta(z) = q \prod_{n=1}^{\infty} (1 - q^n)^{24} = \sum_{n=1}^{\infty} \tau(n) q^n, \tag{6}$$

where $q = e^{2\pi iz}$ and $\mathscr{I}z > 0$. Ramanujan conjectured that $|\tau(p)| \leqslant 2p^{11/2}$ for all prime numbers p, and Petersson generalized this conjecture to one for all modular cusp forms. The analogy between the conjectured inequalities and those which arise from the Weil conjectures (**A** X) leads one to suspect that there should exist a relation between the "Euler factors" of the Dirichlet series associated with modular cusp forms and the zeta functions of certain algebraic varieties over finite fields. By exploiting the relations between automorphic forms and certain cohomology groups of Fuchsian groups, studied by Eichler and Shimura (B 216; BAMS 80 (Knopp); SAMS IX (Murakami); LN 210; [164]), Deligne was able to obtain the desired expression for these Euler factors, and his general proof of the Weil conjectures establishes the truth of the Ramanujan–Petersson conjectures (B 307, 355).

(d) *Congruences and modular forms.* Ramanujan discovered a remarkable congruence satisfied by the integers $\tau(n)$:

(7) $$\tau(n) \equiv \sigma_{11}(n) \pmod{691},$$

where $\sigma_k(n)$ is the sum of the kth powers of the divisors of n. Other authors subsequently discovered many analogous congruences for the coefficients of the series expansions of modular forms. Recently it has been possible to attach these scattered results to a general theory: consider modular forms whose (rational) coefficients are p-adic integers (for some prime number p); by reduction mod p we obtain (formal) series over $\mathbf{F}_p$, and the congruences referred to above are deduced by studying the ring generated by these series. Deligne's result on the Euler factors of the Dirichlet series associated with modular forms plays a decisive role. These properties lead to a definition of modular forms with p-adic coefficients, which turn out to be related to an analogous generalization of Dirichlet series, the p-adic zeta and L-functions defined earlier by Leopoldt, Kubota, and Iwasawa (B 325, 575; LN 350; [91]).

5. Automorphic forms, abelian varieties, and class fields

The origin of modular forms lies in the theory of elliptic functions: the quotient space H/**SL**(2, **Z**) is in one–one correspondence with the set of isomorphism classes of elliptic curves (LN 326). Moreover, the points $z \in \mathrm{H}$ such that the field $\mathbf{Q}(z)$ is a quadratic extension of $\mathbf{Q}$ correspond to elliptic curves E such that End(E) is bigger than **Z** (curves having "complex multiplication"), and the field $\mathbf{Q}(j(z))$ generated by the value at z of the modular function j is an abelian extension of $\mathbf{Q}(z)$ that depends on the conductor of End(E) in its integral closure (Kronecker's "Jugendtraum," the first example of class field theory (LN 21, 320 (Shimura)). These classical results (**A** X) have recently undergone considerable generalization, mainly by the work of

Shimura; the quotients X/Γ, where X is a symmetric space and Γ an arithmetic group, can often be interpreted as sets of isomorphism classes of abelian varieties defined over certain types of number fields, and endowed with certain additional structures (B 389; Nice C 5 (Shimura); BAMS 69 (Baily); LN 54; [164], [165]).

6. Relations with the arithmetic theory of quadratic forms

One of the central problems of the arithmetic theory of quadratic forms is the determination of numbers of "representations of one form by another" (**A** X). This problem is related to modular functions in the following way. Let S (resp. T) be a positive definite symmetric $m \times m$ (resp. $n \times n$) matrix of integers, and let $\mathrm{A}(S,T)$ denote the number of $m \times n$ integer matrices U such that ${}^tUSU = T$. Consider the function

$$\theta_S(Z) = \sum_{T \geqslant 0} \mathrm{A}(S, T) e^{\pi i \operatorname{Tr}(TZ)},$$

where T runs through the set of all positive definite symmetric $n \times n$ matrices of integers, and Z belongs to the Siegel space $\mathfrak{S}_n$. Then it can be shown that

$$\theta_S(Z) = i^{mn/2}(\det S)^{-n/2}(\det Z)^{-m/2}\theta_{S^{-1}}(-Z^{-1}). \tag{8}$$

When m is a multiple of 8 and S has even diagonal elements and determinant 1, this shows that θ_S is an *automorphic form* for Siegel's modular group $\mathbf{Sp}(2n, \mathbf{Z})$ (B 309; [9]).

With the same assumptions on m and S, in the case $n = 1$ the function $\theta_S(iz)$ is an ordinary theta function, which can be written $\sum_l r(l)q^l$ with $q = e^{2\pi i z}$, where $r(l)$ is the number of solutions $x \in \mathbf{Z}^m$ of the equation ${}^tx \cdot S \cdot x = 2l$. The usual theory of modular forms then shows that if $k = \frac{1}{4}m$, we have $\theta_S = \mathrm{E}_k + f$, where E_k is the Eisenstein series of weight $2k$, and f is a cusp form. Hence we obtain the asymptotic evaluation

$$r(l) = \frac{4k}{\mathrm{B}_k}\sigma_{2k-1}(l) + O(l^k),$$

where B_k is the kth Bernoulli number and $\sigma_{2k-1}(l)$ is the sum of the $(2k - 1)$th powers of the divisors of l [157].

7. Connections with the natural sciences

None at present.

8. The originators

The principal ideas in the theory of automorphic forms and modular forms are due to the following mathematicians:

Automorphic functions. H. Poincaré (1854–1912), C. Siegel (1896–1981), H. Maass.

Modular forms and relations with Dirichlet series. C. F. Gauss (1777–1855), B. Riemann (1826–1866), E. Hecke (1887–1947), H. Petersson, A. Weil.

Relations with noncommutative harmonic analysis. I. Gelfand, A. Selberg, R. Langlands.

Relations with cohomology. M. Eichler, G. Shimura, P. Deligne.

Relations with complex multiplication and class-field theory. L. Kronecker (1823–1891), A. Weil, G. Shimura, Y. Taniyama (1927–1958).

The following have also made substantial contributions to these theories: L. Ahlfors, A. Atkin, W. Baily, L. Bers, B. Birch, O. Blumenthal (1876–1944), A. Borel, H. Cartan, P. Cartier, W. Casselman, R. Dedekind (1831–1916), B. Dwork, G. Eisenstein (1823–1852), K. Fricke (1861–1930), G. Fubini (1879–1943), L. Fuchs (1833–1902), S. Gelbart, R. Godement, M. Graev, L. Greenberg, Harish-Chandra, K. Heegner, C. Hermite (1822–1901), H. Hijikata, D. Hilbert (1862–1943), F. Hirzebruch, R. Howe, L. K. Hua, A. Hurwitz (1859–1919), J. Igusa, Y. Ihara, H. Jacquet, N. Katz, F. Klein (1849–1925), H. Klingen, H. Kloosterman, M. Knopp, M. Koecher, M. Kuga, J. Lehner, A. Marden, B. Maskit, Y. Matsushima, T. Miyake, S. Murakami, M. Newman, A. Ogg, E. Picard (1856–1941), I. Pyatetskii-Shapiro, S. Ramanujan (1887–1920), R. Rankin, M. Rapoport, H. Saito, I. Satake, B. Schoeneberg, F. Schottky (1851–1935), H. Schwarz (1843–1921), J.-P. Serre, J. Shalika, H. Shimizu, T. Shintani, H. J. S. Smith (1827–1883), H. Stark, P. Swinnerton-Dyer, T. Tamagawa, S. Tanaka, J. Vélu, H. Weber (1842–1913), K. Weierstrass (1815–1897), K. Wohlfahrt, D. Zagier, V. Kac, D. Kubert, P. Kutzko, S. Lang, J. Lepowsky, I. G. Macdonald, B. Mazur.

References

B: 51, 59, 62, 74, 80, 216, 244, 261, 278, 307, 309, 321, 325, 346, 349, 355, 389, 414, 415, 466, 469, 483, 491, 510, 550, 575, 577.

LN: 21, 54, 62, 114, 189, 210, 260, 278, 320, 349, 350, 400, 476, 530, 544, 548, 601, 627, 654, 817, 825.

BAMS: 69 (Bailey), 80 (Knopp), 82 (Wallach), 3 (N.S.) (Kac–Peterson).

SAMS: IX, XX, XXVI, XXXIII.

[9], [14], [17], [61], [76], [91], [102], [157], [164], [165], [211].

A VIII

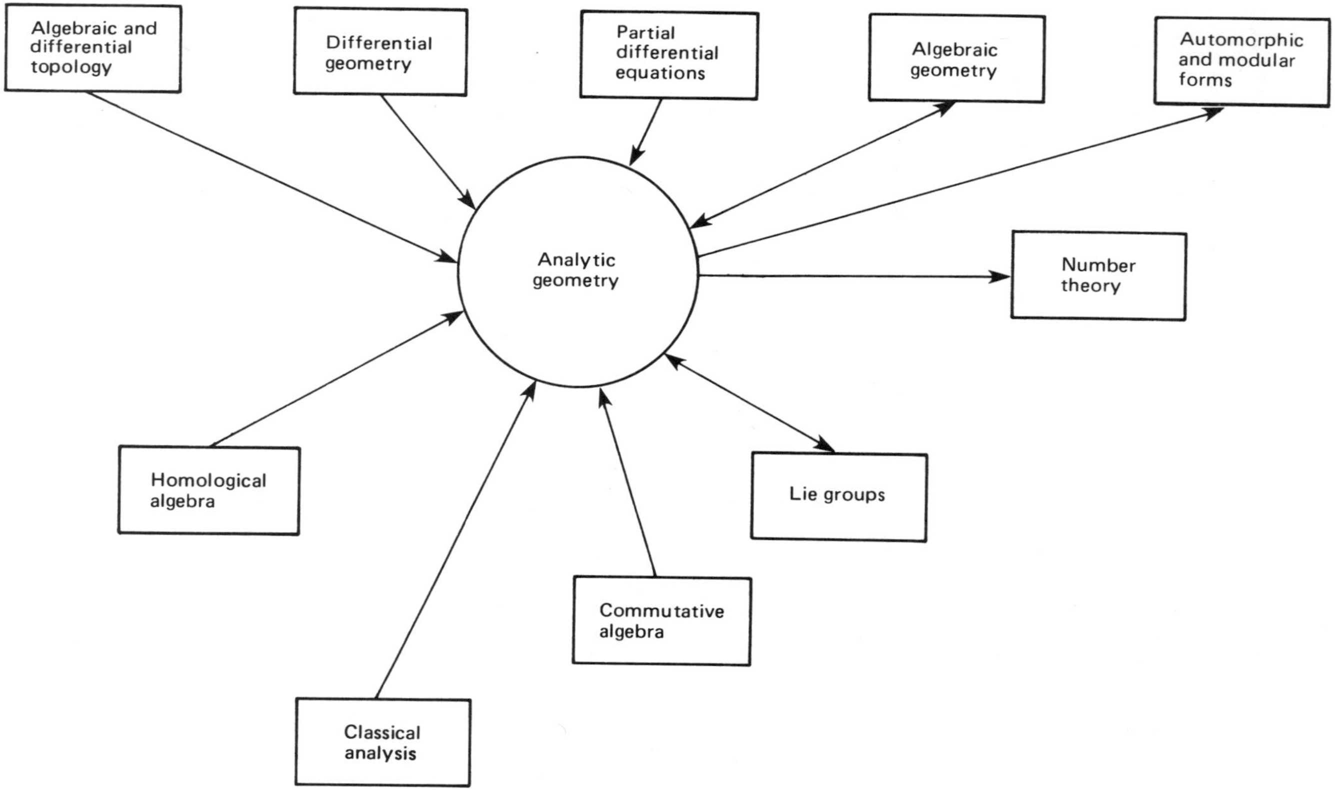

Algebraic and differential topology
Differential geometry
Partial differential equations
Algebraic geometry
Automorphic and modular forms
Analytic geometry
Number theory
Homological algebra
Lie groups
Commutative algebra
Classical analysis

A VIII

Analytic geometry

1. Functions of several complex variables and analytic spaces

The branch of mathematics now known as "analytic geometry" is the modern form of the theory of *analytic functions of several complex variables.*† The mathematicians of the 19th century built up the theory of analytic functions of one complex variable (Cauchy, Riemann, Weierstrass); from the beginning of the 20th century, functions of several complex variables came to be studied, and it became immediately clear that this subject contained a whole series of phenomena without analogs for functions of one variable. These investigations led naturally to ever closer and more fruitful contacts with differential geometry and differential topology on the one hand, and with algebraic geometry on the other. In the course of this evolution, the very conception of the subject underwent considerable modification and generalization, leading to the notion of an *analytic space.* The principal stages in this evolution were the following:

(a) It was soon realized that the theory could not be limited to the study of functions defined on open subsets of $\mathbf{C}^n$, nor even on "ramified domains" over such open sets (generalizing Riemann surfaces in the case $n = 1$). For example, the set of zeros of a function of n variables cannot in general be put in biholomorphic correspondence with such an open set.

(b) A first generalization consisted in defining "complex-analytic manifolds" in which each point has a neighborhood isomorphic to an open subset of $\mathbf{C}^n$ (**A** I). However, the example of algebraic geometry shows that this generalization is inadequate: an algebraic curve or surface may have *singularities,* that is to say, points that have no neighborhood isomorphic to an open subset of $\mathbf{C}^n$. A better generalization is to adapt the definition of a manifold by taking as "models" not only open subsets of $\mathbf{C}^n$ but also subsets

† The old sense of the "analytic geometry" (i.e., the method of cartesian coordinates) is no longer used outside the schoolroom.

of such open sets defined by a finite number of equations $f_j = 0$, where the f_j are holomorphic functions on the open set considered.

(c) This first definition of "analytic spaces" complicates the definition of "morphisms" (**C** I) between such spaces. This difficulty can be avoided by using the language of sheaves (**C** I). First of all, if X is a complex-analytic manifold, consider for each open subset U of X the **C**-algebra $\mathcal{O}(U)$ of holomorphic complex functions on U; as U varies, the elements of $\mathcal{O}(U)$ are the sections over U of a *sheaf* $\mathcal{O}_X$ of **C**-algebras, called the sheaf of germs of holomorphic functions on X; furthermore, for each point $x \in X$, there is an open neighborhood V of x and a homeomorphism u of V onto an open set $u(V)$ in $\mathbf{C}^n$, such that by transporting by u the induced sheaf $\mathcal{O}_V$, we obtain the sheaf $\mathcal{O}_{u(V)}$ of germs of holomorphic functions on $u(V)$. The important remark is that if conversely we have a Hausdorff topological space X and a sheaf $\mathcal{O}_X$ of **C**-algebras having this property, then there exists on X a unique structure of complex-analytic manifold for which $\mathcal{O}_X$ is the sheaf of germs of holomorphic functions.

For an analogous definition of analytic spaces as "ringed spaces" (**C** I) it is necessary to change the "models": in place of $u(V)$ open in $\mathbf{C}^n$, we now take $u(V)$ to be a subset of an open set W in $\mathbf{C}^n$, defined by a finite number of equations $f_j = 0$, where the f_j are holomorphic on W; the sheaf obtained by transporting $\mathcal{O}_V$ by means of u now has to be the quotient $\mathcal{O}_W/\mathcal{J}$, where $\mathcal{J}$ is the sheaf of ideals generated by the f_j in $\mathcal{O}_W$ (the stalks of $\mathcal{O}_W/\mathcal{J}$ are zero outside $u(V)$, so that $\mathcal{O}_W/\mathcal{J}$ is to be considered as a sheaf on $u(V)$). It should be remarked that the stalks of $\mathcal{O}_W/\mathcal{J}$ (and hence of $\mathcal{O}_X$) may well contain nilpotent elements $\neq 0$; the analytic space X is said to be *reduced* if this is not the case (B 115; C 1960–61; [12]). A morphism $X \to Y$ of analytic spaces consists of a continuous mapping $f : X \to Y$ and a homomorphism of sheaves of $\mathcal{O}_Y$-algebras, $\varphi : \mathcal{O}_Y \to f_*(\mathcal{O}_X)$ (**C** I).

This mode of definition of analytic spaces enables many problems of a geometrical nature to be reduced to the theory of *coherent sheaves* of modules (**C** I), especially through the use of *cohomology* with values in a sheaf (**B** I), as we shall see below ([27], [158]).

Domains of holomorphy and Stein spaces. One of the first results of the theory, obtained at the beginning of the century by Hartogs, and in strong contrast with the theory of functions of one variable, is the fact that if, for example, a function of two complex variables is holomorphic in a "shell" $r^2 < |z_1|^2 + |z_2|^2 < R^2$ contained between two spheres, then it necessarily has an analytic continuation to a holomorphic function defined *throughout* the ball $|z_1|^2 + |z_2|^2 < R^2$. This result leads to the consideration of open sets U in $\mathbf{C}^n$ in which this phenomenon does not arise, i.e., such that for each

$z_0 \notin U$, there exists a holomorphic function on U that cannot be extended to a function holomorphic at z_0. Such open sets are called *domains of holomorphy.* A characteristic property of bounded domains of holomorphy in $\mathbf{C}^n$, discovered by H. Cartan and P. Thullen, is that they are *holomorphically convex*: this means that for each compact subset K of the open set U considered, the set $\hat{K}_U$ of points $z \in U$ such that $|f(z)| \leqslant \sup_{x \in K} |f(x)|$ for *all* holomorphic functions f on U is also compact (Hartogs's theorem shows that this property is not satisfied by the "shell"). An equivalent condition is that for each infinite discrete subset D of V, there exists a holomorphic function f on U such that $f(D)$ is unbounded in $\mathbf{C}$.

In 1910 E. E. Levi observed that a domain of holomorphy $G \subset \mathbf{C}^n$ has particular properties in a neighborhood of a boundary point. A real function p of class C^2 is said to be *plurisubharmonic* (resp. strongly plurisubharmonic) in G if the hermitian form $L(p) = \sum_{j,k} \frac{\partial^2 p}{\partial z_j \partial \bar{z}_k} t_j \bar{t}_k$ (called the Levi form) is positive semidefinite (resp. positive definite) at each point of G. If now G is a bounded domain of holomorphy and x_0 a boundary point of G, there exists an open neighborhood U of x_0 and a plurisubharmonic function p on U such that $U \cap G$ is the set of points $x \in U$ at which $p(x) < p(x_0)$. Levi's problem is whether an open subset G of $\mathbf{C}^n$ having this property (in which case G is said to be *pseudoconvex*) is necessarily a domain of holomorphy. This problem was solved affirmatively, first by Oka for bounded open subsets of $\mathbf{C}^2$, then for bounded open subsets of $\mathbf{C}^n$ and bounded domains unramified over $\mathbf{C}^n$; on the other hand there exist domains of holomorphy ramified over $\mathbf{C}^n$ that are not holomorphically convex.

The notions of holomorphically convex domain and plurisubharmonic function may be extended to analytic spaces, but it is then no longer sufficient that a relatively compact open set be pseudoconvex for it to be holomorphically convex; it is, however, sufficient that it be *strongly* pseudoconvex (defined as above by replacing plurisubharmonic functions by strongly plurisubharmonic functions) (B 173; C 1951–152; LN 103; Stockholm (Grauert); [12], [84]).

The notion of domain of holomorphy generalizes to that of a *Stein space*, which is a holomorphically convex analytic space X such that, for each $x \in X$, there exists a finite number of holomorphic functions f_j on X such that x is isolated in the set of common zeros of the f_j (roughly speaking, there are "enough" holomorphic functions on X; the opposite extreme is provided by compact analytic manifolds, on which the only global holomorphic functions are the constants). Every closed analytic submanifold of a Stein manifold is a Stein manifold. Every covering manifold of a Stein manifold is a Stein manifold. More generally, if $f: X \to Y$ is a proper morphism of analytic spaces such that $f^{-1}(y)$ is finite for all $y \in Y$, and if Y is a Stein manifold, then X is a Stein space. On the other hand, a holomorphic fiber bundle (**A** I) in which the base and the fiber are Stein manifolds is not necessarily a Stein manifold [169 *bis*]. If X is a Stein space, there exists a proper injective (holomorphic) immersion of X into $\mathbf{C}^N$, for N sufficiently large (B 115, 173; Stockholm (Grauert); [12]). The importance of Stein spaces lies in the properties of coherent sheaves on such spaces, and the consequences of these properties for globalization problems (see below).

Analytic subspaces and coherent sheaves. The definition of an analytic subspace of an analytic space X is inspired by the classical definition of an algebraic subvariety of an affine or projective algebraic variety in terms of a finite number of polynomial equations, but it was clear from the beginning that such a definition for an analytic subspace could only be *local*: A is an analytic subspace of a reduced analytic space X if for each $x \in A$ there exists a neighborhood V of x such that $V \cap A$ is defined by the vanishing of a finite number of holomorphic functions on V. To pass from this to a definition valid for any analytic space X, we use the language of sheaves: an analytic subspace A is defined by an open subset U of X and a sheaf of ideals $\mathscr{I}$ of finite type of $\mathscr{O}_U$: it is the set of $x \in U$ at which $\mathscr{I}_x \neq \mathscr{O}_x$, and is endowed with the quotient sheaf $\mathscr{O}_U/\mathscr{I}$, which makes it an analytic space.

Questions about analytic subspaces (the possibility of defining them *globally* by equations, the study of the relations between these equations, etc.) have led to the definition of coherent sheaves and their cohomology. A fundamental fact is that for any analytic space X the sheaf $\mathscr{O}_X$ is always *coherent* (**C** I), and so is every $\mathscr{O}_X$-Module of finite type. On the other hand, it is important to possess criteria that will guarantee that the cohomology spaces $H^p(X, \mathscr{F})$ of a coherent sheaf $\mathscr{F}$ on an analytic space X are *finite* dimensional. For example, this is so for all $p \geqslant 0$ when X is a compact complex manifold (B 95). If $G \subset X$ is a strongly pseudoconvex open set, $H^p(G, \mathscr{O}_G)$ is finite dimensional for all $p \geqslant 1$, and is zero for p sufficiently large; this is an essential ingredient in the solution of Levi's problem (B 173; Stockholm (Grauert)). There are also results concerning only the H^p from a certain integer onward if we assume only the existence on G of functions whose Levi form has a given signature (instead of being positive definite); some of these results can be established and refined by methods taken from the theory of partial differential equations (B 234, 275; BAMS 70 (J. Kohn); [84]).

Globalization problems. In 1895, P. Cousin considered the problem of generalizing to functions of n complex variables the classical theorem of Mittag–Leffler on meromorphic functions of one variable. Given a covering

(U_α) of an open set X in $\mathbf{C}^n$, and on each U_α a meromorphic function f_α (the quotient of two holomorphic functions on U_α), such that $f_\alpha - f_\beta$ is holomorphic on $U_\alpha \cap U_\beta$, the problem is whether there exists a function f on X, meromorphic around each point, such that $f - f_\alpha$ is holomorphic on U_α for each α (additive Cousin problem). In the language of sheaves, this problem takes the following form and generalizes to any reduced analytic space X: consider the sheaf $\mathscr{M}_X$ of germs of meromorphic functions on X, which contains $\mathscr{O}_X$ as a subsheaf: the problem is whether a given element of the space $H^0(X, \mathscr{M}_X/\mathscr{O}_X)$ of global sections of $\mathscr{M}_X/\mathscr{O}_X$ is the image of an element of $H^0(X, \mathscr{M}_X)$ under the canonical mapping. The cohomology exact sequence applied to the short exact sequence

$$0 \to \mathscr{O}_X \to \mathscr{M}_X \to \mathscr{M}_X/\mathscr{O}_X \to 0$$

gives an exact sequence

$$0 \to H^0(X, \mathscr{O}_X) \to H^0(X, \mathscr{M}_X) \to H^0(X, \mathscr{M}_X/\mathscr{O}_X) \to H^1(X, \mathscr{O}_X) \to \cdots,$$

and the condition above signifies that the image in $H^1(X, \mathscr{O}_X)$ of the element of $H^0(X, \mathscr{M}_X/\mathscr{O}_X)$ in question should be zero. In particular, the additive Cousin problem always has a solution if $H^1(X, \mathscr{O}_X) = 0$.

Cousin also considered the generalization of the theorem of Weierstrass on the decomposition of an entire function as a product of elementary factors. Here we are given on each U_α (assumed to be connected) a meromorphic function f_α, not identically zero, such that $f_\alpha f_\beta^{-1}$ is a holomorphic function that does not vanish at any point of $U_\alpha \cap U_\beta$, and the problem now is whether there exists a function f on X, meromorphic around each point, such that $f f_\alpha^{-1}$ is a nonvanishing holomorphic function on U_α for each α (multiplicative Cousin problem). Here we must replace $\mathscr{M}_X$ by $\mathscr{M}_X^*$, the sheaf of germs of nonzero meromorphic functions, considered as a sheaf of *multiplicative groups*, and $\mathscr{O}_X$ must be replaced by $\mathscr{O}_X^*$, the subsheaf of germs of nonvanishing holomorphic functions. A sufficient condition for the multiplicative Cousin problem always to have a solution is that $H^1(X, \mathscr{O}_X^*) = 0$. Since there is a homomorphism of sheaves of groups $e: \mathscr{O}_X^* \to \mathscr{O}_X^*$ defined by $e(f) = \exp(2\pi i f)$, and since the kernel of this homomorphism is the locally constant sheaf $\mathbf{Z}$, we obtain from the short exact sequence.

$$0 \to \mathbf{Z} \to \mathscr{O}_X \to \mathscr{O}_X^* \to 0$$

an exact sequence of cohomology

$$(1) \quad H^1(X, \mathbf{Z}) \to H^1(X, \mathscr{O}_X) \to H^1(X, \mathscr{O}_X^*) \to H^2(X, \mathbf{Z}) \to H^2(X, \mathscr{O}_X) \to \cdots$$

from which it follows in particular that if $H^1(X, \mathscr{O}_X) = 0$, the (purely topological) condition $H^2(X, \mathbf{Z}) = 0$ will ensure that the multiplicative Cousin problem is always solvable.

The importance of Stein manifolds in these questions follows from their two fundamental properties (Theorems A and B of H. Cartan): every coherent $\mathcal{O}_X$-Module $\mathcal{F}$ on a Stein manifold X is such that (A) each stalk $\mathcal{F}_x$ is an $\mathcal{O}_x$-module generated by the image of $H^0(X, \mathcal{F})$ in $\mathcal{F}_x$; (B) $H^p(X, \mathcal{F}) = 0$ for all $p \geqslant 1$.

These properties have many other consequences. For example, on a Stein manifold, every meromorphic function is a quotient of two holomorphic functions (for $\mathbf{C}^n$ this was proved by Poincaré in 1883). If Y is a closed submanifold of a Stein manifold X, every holomorphic function on Y is the restriction of a holomorphic function on X, and for every relatively compact open set U in X, $Y \cap U$ is defined by a finite number of equations $f_j = 0$, where the f_j are holomorphic on U. If X is a Stein manifold of (complex) dimension n, its homology groups $H_p(X, \mathbf{Z})$ are zero for $p > n$. Finally, if X is a Stein manifold and G a complex Lie group, the analytic isomorphism classes of holomorphic principal bundles with base X and group G are in canonical one–one correspondence with the topological isomorphism classes of topological principal bundles with base X and group G (B 71, 137; Stockholm (Grauert); [12]).

Continuation problems. Hartogs's theorem shows that for an analytic space X, there may exist a morphism $\alpha : X \to Y$ other than the identity such that the mapping $H^0(Y, \mathcal{O}_Y) \to H^0(X, \mathcal{O}_X)$ induced by α is bijective; in other words, if α is injective, such that *every* holomorphic function on X can be extended to a holomorphic function on Y. An *envelope of holomorphy* of X is an analytic space Z such that there exists a morphism $\omega : X \to Z$ having the above property and "universal" with respect to that property, i.e., for each morphism $\alpha : X \to Y$ of this type, there exists a morphism $\beta : Y \to Z$ such that $\omega = \beta \circ \alpha$. The existence of envelopes of holomorphy can be established for domains that are unramified coverings of a Stein manifold, and the envelope of holomorphy is again a Stein manifold [12]. As a simple example, the envelope of holomorphy of a "tube" is easily described: if $\mathbf{C}^n$ is written in the form $\mathbf{R}^n + i\mathbf{R}^n$, a tube is an open set of the form $B + i\mathbf{R}^n$, where B is open in $\mathbf{R}^n$, and its envelope of holomorphy is the tube $\Gamma(B) + i\mathbf{R}^n$, where $\Gamma(B)$ is the convex envelope of B in $\mathbf{R}^n$.

Instead of seeking to continue simultaneously *all* the holomorphic functions defined on a domain, we may limit attention to functions having particular properties. An example is the investigation of conditions under which functions f_j, holomorphic on tubes T_j in $\mathbf{C}^n$ whose bases B_j are open cones, are restrictions of the same entire function (the "edge of the wedge" problem: B 340). Other continuation theorems are related to the theory of hyperbolic analytic spaces (SAMS XXIX (Griffiths); [99], [186]).

Other extension or continuation problems relate to analytic subspaces and coherent sheaves: given an analytic subspace of an open subspace U in an analytic space X, is it the intersection with U of an analytic subspace of a larger open subspace (B 122)? For coherent sheaves, let Z be an analytic subspace of X and suppose we are given a coherent sheaf on X − Z; the problem is to obtain conditions under which this sheaf is induced on X − Z by a coherent sheaf on X (B 366; LN 172; [169]).

Properties of morphisms and automorphisms. The most important morphisms $f : X \to Y$ of analytic spaces are *proper* morphisms (the inverse image $f^{-1}(K)$ of each compact $K \subset Y$ is compact). The fundamental result about proper morphisms is Grauert's theorem on direct images: for each coherent sheaf $\mathscr{F}$ on X, the direct images $R^k f_*(\mathscr{F})$ (see **B** I) are coherent sheaves on Y (B 220, 404; LN 184).

This implies in particular that $f(X)$ is an analytic subspace of Y. Furthermore, it enables conditions to be given under which, when X is an analytic space and R is an equivalence relation on X such that the canonical mapping $X \to X/R$ is proper, the space X/R has a natural structure of an analytic space. This is always the case when X/R is the space of orbits of a group G of automorphisms of X such that the action of G on X is properly discontinuous [12].

If $f : X \to Y$ is any morphism of irreducible analytic spaces, the mapping $u \mapsto u \circ f$ is an isomorphism of the field K(Y) of meromorphic functions on Y onto a subfield of the field K(X) of meromorphic functions on X. If f is proper and surjective, K(X) is an extension of this subfield of transcendence degree $\leqslant \dim X - \dim Y$. Analogous results may be obtained by weakening in various ways the hypothesis that f is proper (LN 234).

The classical properties of entire and meromorphic functions of one complex variable that center on Picard's theorem do not generalize directly. For example, there exists an injective morphism $f : \mathbf{C}^2 \to \mathbf{C}^2$ whose image has a complement containing a nonempty open set (example of Fatou–Bieberbach). There is a satisfactory theory for a morphism $f: \mathbf{C}^m \to \mathbf{P}_n(\mathbf{C})$ by considering the variation of the inverse images $f^{-1}(D)$ where D runs through a family of hypersurfaces in $\mathbf{P}_n(\mathbf{C})$: for example, if $f(\mathbf{C}^m)$ is not contained in a linear subspace of dimension $<n$, then $f(\mathbf{C}^m)$ cannot lie in the complement of the union of $n + 1$ hyperplanes in general position (generalization of Picard's theorem). There is also a quantitative version of results of this type, generalizing Nevanlinna's theory (SAMS XXIX (Cornalba–Griffiths); BAMS 72 (S. Chern), 78 (Ph. Griffiths); LN 135; [186]).

The problem of "conformal representation," i.e., of the isomorphism of two analytic spaces, leads to very different results in higher dimensions, compared with the classical case of functions of one complex variable. Poincaré already remarked that there exists no biholomorphic mapping of the ball $|z_1|^2 + |z_2|^2 < 1$ onto the "bicylinder" $|z_1| < 1, |z_2| < 1$ (their automorphism groups, which are explicitly known, are not isomorphic); also examples are known of simply connected domains of holomorphy in $\mathbf{C}^n$ with no nontrivial automorphisms. Apart from the determination of groups of automorphisms of certain particular analytic spaces [12], the only general result known is an extension theorem: if D_1, D_2 are two strictly pseudo-convex domains in $\mathbf{C}^n$, any isomorphism of D_1 onto D_2 can be extended to a diffeomorphism of $\bar{D}_1$ onto $\bar{D}_2$ (B 463).

Singularities of analytic spaces. The study of an analytic space X in a neighborhood of a point is essentially an algebraic undertaking, centered on the study of the local rings $\mathcal{O}_x$ (the stalks of the sheaf $\mathcal{O}_X$) at the points of X, which are quotients of the ring of convergent power series in n variables. An important point is that this ring is Noetherian, so that the notions of dimension and depth (**C** II) are applicable (LN 25; C 1960–61).

An analytic space X is said to be *smooth* at a point if some open neighborhood of the point is isomorphic to an open set in $\mathbf{C}^n$. Points at which X is not smooth are the *singular points* of X. The space is said to be *normal* at the point x if the local ring $\mathcal{O}_x$ is integrally closed. The set of singular points is an analytic subspace, which is of codimension $\geqslant 2$ if the space is normal at each point. The example of algebraic varieties shows that the structure of an analytic space in a neighborhood of a singular point can be extremely complicated, and the only far-reaching investigations made so far are for isolated singular points, and especially for the structure near the origin of algebraic varieties $z_1^{\alpha_1} + z_2^{\alpha_2} + \cdots + z_n^{\alpha_n} = 0$ in $\mathbf{C}^n$, by considering the differential manifold that is the intersection of the variety with a hypersphere $\sum_{j=1}^{n} z_j \bar{z}_j = \varepsilon$, where ε is small and positive. The results depend on the values of the exponents α_j, and some of them are unexpected: for certain values of the α_j, manifolds diffeomorphic to "exotic" spheres (**A** I) are obtained; also the classification obtained is related to the classification of "root systems" [D, Chapter 21] of the theory of Lie algebras (B 250, 314; LN 57, 209, 815; [125]).

The most important result about singular points is Hironaka's desingularization theorem: for each analytic space X, there exists a smooth analytic space $\tilde{X}$ and a surjective proper morphism $f: \tilde{X} \to X$ such that if S is the set of singular points of X, the morphism $f^{-1}(X - S) \to X - S$, obtained by restriction of f, is an isomorphism; we can also require that $f^{-1}(S)$ is a union of hypersurfaces "with normal crossings," i.e., that at each point of $f^{-1}(S)$ there is a system of local coordinates z_j $(1 \leqslant j \leqslant n)$ in $\tilde{X}$ such that locally $f^{-1}(S)$ is defined by the equation $z_1 z_2 \cdots z_p = 0$ for some $p < n$ (Stockholm (Hironaka); Nice D 8 (Hironaka)).

The fundamental idea here (as in the analogous theorem of algebraic geometry (**A** IX)) is that of "blowing up." The simplest example is that of blowing up the origin in $\mathbf{C}^n$ ($n \geqslant 2$). Consider in $(\mathbf{C}^n - \{0\}) \times \mathbf{P}_{n-1}(\mathbf{C})$ the graph of the canonical morphism $\pi : \mathbf{C}^n - \{0\} \to \mathbf{P}_{n-1}(\mathbf{C})$, which maps each point $z \neq 0$ to the line $\{\lambda z : \lambda \in \mathbf{C}\}$. The closure X of this graph in $\mathbf{C}^n \times \mathbf{P}_{n-1}(\mathbf{C})$ is the analytic manifold obtained by blowing up the origin: the first projection $p : \mathrm{X} \to \mathbf{C}^n$ is a surjective proper morphism, its restriction to $\mathrm{X} - p^{-1}(0)$ is an isomorphism onto $\mathbf{C}^n - \{0\}$, and $p^{-1}(0)$ is isomorphic to $\mathbf{P}_{n-1}(\mathbf{C})$. If two curves in $\mathbf{C}^n - \{0\}$ approach the origin with distinct tangents, their inverse images under p approach $p^{-1}(0)$ at two *distinct* points. This notion can be generalized by replacing $\mathbf{C}^n$ by an arbitrary analytic space Y, and the point 0 by an analytic subspace S of Y; if S contains singular points, the effect of blowing up S is to "diminish" the singularities in the inverse image of S, in a certain sense (B 84).

The process "inverse" to blowing up is that of "blowing down" a compact analytic subset A (with no isolated points) in an analytic space X: this is a proper morphism $f : \mathrm{X} \to \mathrm{Y}$ such that $f(\mathrm{A})$ is a discrete set D, the restriction of f to X − A is an isomorphism onto Y − D, and for each open neighborhood U of D, every holomorphic function on $f^{-1}(\mathrm{U})$ is of the form $u \circ f$, where u is holomorphic on U. Such sets have been known for a long time in algebraic geometry under the name of "exceptional sets," and there are criteria that characterize them (**A** IX). For analytic spaces, there is the following general criterion: the subspace A is "exceptional" in X if there exists a strongly pseudoconvex neighborhood U of A such that A is maximal among the compact analytic subspaces of U with no isolated points (B 344; Stockholm (Grauert); [12]).

Singularities of analytic functions; residues. If X is an analytic space of dimension n, a closed subset A of X is said to consist of *singular* points of a holomorphic function f defined on X − A if f cannot be analytically continued to a function holomorphic at any point of A. Hartogs's theorem shows already that A cannot contain any isolated points if $n \geqslant 2$. In fact, A is necessarily an analytic subspace of (complex) dimension $n - 1$; it follows that if B is a differentiable submanifold of (real) dimension $\leqslant 2n - 3$ in a complex-analytic manifold of (complex) dimension n, every holomorphic function on X − B can be continued to a holomorphic function on X.

The fact that the singular points of an analytic function are not isolated when $n \geqslant 2$ shows that the *residue* of an analytic function cannot be defined in the same way as when $n = 1$. H. Poincaré was the first to show how this problem should be approached when $n = 2$. In fact, as G. de Rham showed later, the concept of residue has to be defined for a differential p-form on an analytic manifold ($p \leqslant n$), relative to the singular submanifolds of the coefficients of the form; the residue is then a $(p - 1)$-form carried by the singular submanifolds. This point of view was considerably developed by J. Leray, who elucidated its relationship with the homological properties of the singular submanifolds, and showed how it could be used in the theory of linear partial differential equations; his theory has since been generalized in various directions (B 183, 202; LN 205; [135] (El Zein)).

2. Compact analytic spaces; Kähler manifolds

Compact analytic spaces, and in particular compact complex manifolds, have many special properties. The most important class of compact analytic spaces consists of the projective algebraic varieties, defined by a finite number of homogeneous polynomial equations in a projective space $\mathbf{P}_n(\mathbf{C})$. In fact the theory of compact complex manifolds is closely related to the theory of nonsingular projective algebraic varieties, of which it is a generalization; on the other hand, following Riemann, Lefschetz, and Hodge, differential topology and the theory of elliptic partial differential equations (**A** V) play a preponderant role (BAMS 72 (Chern)).

Recall that if X is a compact analytic space, the cohomology spaces $\mathrm{H}^r(\mathrm{X}, \mathscr{F})$ are finite dimensional for all coherent $\mathscr{O}_\mathrm{X}$-Modules $\mathscr{F}$. On a compact connected complex manifold X, the most important sheaves are the sheaves $\mathscr{O}(\mathrm{E})$ of germs of holomorphic sections of *holomorphic* vector bundles E on X, defined by the condition that for each open subset U of X, the sections belonging to $\Gamma(\mathrm{U}, \mathscr{O}(\mathrm{E}))$ are the holomorphic sections of E over U. For these sheaves, Serre's duality theorem states that if $\check{\mathrm{E}}$ is the bundle dual to E [D, Chapter 16] and T^p the bundle of tangent p-covectors, the vector spaces $\mathrm{H}^r(\mathscr{O}(\mathrm{E}))$ and $\mathrm{H}^{n-r}(\mathscr{O}(\check{\mathrm{E}} \otimes \mathrm{T}^n))$ (where $n = \dim \mathrm{X}$) are canonically in duality (B 95).

An important category of compact complex-analytic manifolds consists of those on which a Hermitian metric $ds^2 = \sum_{j,k} h_{jk}\, dz_j\, d\bar{z}_k$ $(\bar{h}_{jk} = h_{kj})$ (in local coordinates) can be defined with the property that the imaginary part of the corresponding sesquilinear form, which is a real alternating form and can therefore be identified with an exterior differential 2-form Θ, is *closed* $(d\Theta = 0)$. A compact complex manifold carrying a metric with this property is called a *Kähler manifold*. Every analytic submanifold of a Kähler manifold is Kähler, and so is every manifold obtained by blowing up a Kähler manifold. The first example of a manifold which admits a Kähler structure is projective space $\mathbf{P}_n(\mathbf{C})$, and hence all nonsingular projective algebraic varieties are also Kähler manifolds; but there exist Kähler manifolds that are not isomorphic to algebraic varieties, for example, the tori $\mathbf{C}^n/\Gamma$ (where Γ is a lattice in $\mathbf{R}^{2n}$) that are not abelian varieties (**A** IX).

The importance of Kähler manifolds is due to their relations with Hodge theory (**A** V). The Hodge Laplacian (for the de Rham complex) commutes with the projection morphisms $T^p \to T^{r,s}$ $(r + s = p)$, where $T^{r,s}$ is the bundle whose sections are the C^∞ complex p-forms of type (r, s) (i.e., those expressed locally as linear combinations of exterior products of r forms dz_j and s forms $d\bar{z}_k$). If $\mathbf{H}^{r,s}$ is the space of harmonic forms of type (r, s), the space $\mathbf{H}^p$ of harmonic p-forms is the direct sum of the $\mathbf{H}^{r,s}$ such that $r + s = p$.

The space $\mathbf{H}^{p,0}$ is the space of *holomorphic* differential p-forms (or p-forms of the "first kind") that have played a fundamental role in analysis and algebraic geometry since the beginnings of the theory of elliptic functions.

More generally, there is a canonical isomorphism (Dolbeault)

$$\mathbf{H}^{r,s} \cong H^s(\mathcal{O}(T^r)), \tag{2}$$

from which it follows that the numbers $h^{r,s} = \dim(\mathbf{H}^{r,s})$ depend only on the analytic structure of X and not on the Kähler metric it carries. The Hodge–de Rham theorem relates these numbers to the topological invariants of X, because $\sum_{r+s=p} h^{r,s} = R_p$ is the pth Betti number. We have $h^{r,s} = h^{s,r}$, simply because if ω is a form of type (r, s), its complex conjugate $\bar{\omega}$ is of type (s, r). It follows that for odd p, the pth Betti number R_p must be even. On the other hand, if Θ^k is the exterior product of k copies of the canonical 2-form Θ, the Θ^k for $1 \leqslant k \leqslant n = \dim(X)$ are harmonic and nonzero, and Θ^n is up to a nonzero constant factor the "volume" $2n$-form on X [D, Chapter 20]. It follows that $\mathbf{H}^{2k} \neq 0$ for $1 \leqslant k \leqslant n$, hence that $R_{2k} \geqslant 1$.

Consider now the linear mapping $L: \omega \mapsto \Theta \wedge \omega$ for a Kähler manifold X; it can be shown to commute with the Laplacian, and therefore transforms harmonic forms into harmonic forms. If $r + s < n$, the mapping L is injective on $\mathbf{H}^{r,s}$, and $\mathbf{H}^{r+1,s+1}$ is the direct sum of $L(\mathbf{H}^{r,s})$ and the kernel $\mathbf{P}^{r+1,s+1}$ of $L^{n-r-s-1}$. If $\rho^{r+1,s+1}$ is the dimension of this kernel, it follows that $h^{r+1,s+1} = h^{r,s} + \rho^{r+1,s+1}$, whence the relation $R_p - R_{p-2} = \sum_{r+s=p} \rho^{r,s} \geqslant 0$ for $p \leqslant n$. We mention also the important fact that for $p < n$ the operator $L^{n-p}: \mathbf{H}^p \to \mathbf{H}^{2n-p}$ is an *isomorphism*, which is a sharper form of Poincaré duality for manifolds and is known as the "hard Lefschetz theorem" (**A** IX).

Hodge theory for compact Kähler manifolds also provides information on the bilinear form $I(\alpha, \beta) = \int_X \alpha \wedge \beta$ on the spaces $\mathbf{H}^r \times \mathbf{H}^{2n-r}$. If $p + q = r$ is even and $r \leqslant n$, and if α is a nonzero real form belonging to $\mathbf{P}^{p,q} \oplus \mathbf{P}^{q,p}$, we have $(-1)^p I(\alpha, L^{n-r}\alpha) > 0$ ([135] (Swinnerton-Dyer)).

Finally, the recent ideas of Sullivan on homotopy of polyhedra (**A** I) have established that the homotopy type over **R** of a compact Kähler manifold can be obtained from its real cohomology ring (B 475).

These necessary conditions show that there exist many compact complex manifolds that admit no Kähler structure (LN 154; SAMS XXIX (Cornalba–Griffiths); [191]).

The index formula of Atiyah–Singer (**A** V), applied to a suitable elliptic complex, gives an explicit formula for

$$\chi(E) = \dim H^0(\mathcal{O}(E)) - \dim H^1(\mathcal{O}(E)) + \cdots + (-1)^n \dim H^n(\mathcal{O}(E))$$

(where E is a line bundle over an *arbitrary* connected compact complex manifold X of dimension n) involving the Chern classes of X and E (Riemann–Roch–Hirzebruch formula). This formula is useful mainly for small values of the dimension n, and in situations where one has criteria that guarantee that $H^p(\mathcal{O}(E)) = 0$ for $p \geqslant 1$. One such criterion is that the first Chern class of the bundle $E \otimes \check{T}^n$ should be the cohomology class of a 2-form Θ coming from a Kähler metric on X.

This result, due to Kodaira, enabled him to obtain a fundamental criterion for a compact connected *Kähler* manifold X to be isomorphic to an algebraic subvariety of a projective space $\mathbf{P}_n(\mathbf{C})$ (or, equivalently, to a compact analytic submanifold of $\mathbf{P}_n(\mathbf{C})$, by virtue of a theorem of Chow): it is necessary and sufficient that there should exist a Kähler metric on X such that the cohomology class of the corresponding 2-form is *integral* (i.e., lies in $H^2(X, \mathbf{Z})$, not merely in $H^2(X, \mathbf{R})$) (B 114; LN 154). This criterion has been generalized to compact reduced analytic spaces by Grauert (Stockholm (Grauert); [12]).

Classification problems. It has been known since Riemann that connected compact complex manifolds of dimension 1 are isomorphic to nonsingular algebraic curves in projective space $\mathbf{P}_N(\mathbf{C})$, and Riemann already posed the problem of classifying such curves up to isomorphism; he introduced a numerical invariant, the genus g (equal to $\frac{1}{2}R_1$) and concluded by heuristic arguments that the isomorphism classes of curves of genus $g \geqslant 2$ depended on $3g - 3$ continuously varying complex parameters, which he called the "moduli." (When $g = 1$ this number reduces to 1, and when $g = 0$ it is 0.) It is only recently that it has been possible to give this statement a precise meaning and to show effectively that there exists an analytic space of dimension $3g - 3$ (called the "space of moduli") whose points correspond to the isomorphism classes of nonsingular curves of genus g (B 168; BAMS 71 (H. Rauch); C 1960–61).

Analogous problems can be formulated for compact connected complex-analytic manifolds (and more generally for reduced compact analytic spaces) of arbitrary dimension n: there are several numerical invariants (instead of only one, as in the case $n = 1$), and the theory has not got very far except for $n = 2$ (B 146, 506; LN 412, 439; [162]). It is necessary to consider invariants that are unchanged, more generally, by a "bimeromorphic" transformation (a generalization of the "birational" transformations of algebraic geometry (**A** IX)); this is a distinction that does not appear when $n = 1$, since every birational transformation of a nonsingular curve is an isomorphism.

An important "bimeromorphic" invariant of a reduced connected compact analytic space X is the transcendence degree over **C** of the field of meromorphic functions on X; this is an integer $a \leqslant n = \dim(X)$, that can take any value between 0 and n. An important particular case is that in which $a = n$; then X is said to be a Moishezon space, and there exists an algebraic variety X′ obtained from X by a finite sequence of blowings-up (B 344; Nice D 8 (Moishezon); [186] (R. Wells)).

3. Variations of complex structures and infinite-dimensional manifolds

Except for curves, there are few cases in which it is known how to define an analytic "space of moduli" whose points correspond to the isomorphism classes of compact analytic spaces having the same system of numerical invariants. When such a space exists, a continuous variation of a point in it represents a "continuous variation" of the structure of analytic space corresponding to the point. Even when the "space of moduli" cannot be constructed, one can at least study the "infinitesimal" aspect of such "variation of structure." For complex-analytic manifolds, the general idea is to consider a differential fiber bundle Z over a differential manifold S (the "parameter manifold") with projection $\pi : Z \to S$. Suppose that for each $s \in S$, the fiber $X_s = \pi^{-1}(s)$ is endowed with a structure of complex manifold, with a condition assuming that this structure varies differentiably. The study of such fiber bundles in a neighborhood of a fiber X_s is the theory of "deformations" of complex-analytic structures (B 277, 449; C 1960–61; LN 103 (C. Earle–J. Eells)).

A problem analogous to the problem of "moduli," but more accessible, is that of "parametrizing" the analytic submanifolds of a given analytic manifold X, in a "functorial" manner. Here it has been possible to define a space in which each point corresponds to an analytic submanifold and which in a neighborhood of each point has a structure of a finite-dimensional analytic space (B 296, 303).

This theory and the theory of "deformations" have shown the usefulness of enlarging the framework of the theory by introducing analytic spaces of infinite dimension, in which the "models" are no longer open sets in $\mathbf{C}^n$ (or analytic subspaces of these) but open sets in infinite-dimensional complex Banach spaces (or subspaces of such open sets, defined by the vanishing of families of holomorphic functions) (B 354; LN 410).

4. Real and *p*-adic analytic spaces

Since the notion of convergent power series remains meaningful when the coefficients and the variables belong to an arbitrary complete valued field, it is reasonable to try to generalize the theory of analytic spaces by replacing the field **C** of complex numbers by another complete valued field, in particular the field **R** of real numbers or a totally disconnected locally compact field, such as the field $\mathbf{Q}_p$ of *p*-adic numbers. In the case of real analytic spaces, the center of interest is their relations with complex analytic spaces; in particular, by virtue of the solution of Levi's problem it can be proved that every real analytic manifold is isomorphic to an analytic submanifold of some $\mathbf{R}^N$ (B 173; Stockholm (Grauert)). On the other hand, coherent sheaves on real analytic spaces can present pathological phenomena.

For analytic spaces over a totally disconnected field, it is necessary to modify the definition of "change of charts" in order to obtain an interesting theory, that of the "rigid analytic spaces," in which a good part of the theory of complex analytic spaces generalizes satisfactorily (B 327; LN 38).

5. Connections with the natural sciences

Several branches of quantum mechanics, in particular quantum field theory, employ the theory of analytic spaces and their singularities.

6. The originators

The main ideas of the theory of analytic spaces are due to the following mathematicians:

General theory. H. Poincaré (1854–1912), F. Hartogs (1874–1933), E. E. Levi (1883–1917), H. Weyl (1885–1955), H. Cartan, P. Thullen, K. Oka (1901–1978), K. Stein, J. P. Serre, H. Grauert, R. Remmert.

Singularities, residues. H. Hironaka, J. Leray.

Kähler manifolds. W. Hodge (1903–1975), K. Kodaira.

Moduli problems and deformations. O. Teichmüller (1913–1943), K. Kodaira, D. Spencer.

Infinite-dimensional manifolds. A. Douady.

p-adic manifolds. J. Tate.

The following have also made substantial contributions: S. Abhyankar, Y. Akizuki, A. Andreotti (1925–1980), M. Atiyah, T. Aubin, W. Baily, H. Behnke (1898–1979), S. Bergman (1899–1977), L. Bers, E. Bishop, A. Blanchard, S. Bochner, E. Bombieri, A. Borel, R. Bott, H. Bremermann, E. Brieskorn, F. Bruhat, L. Bungart, E. Calabi, C. Carathéodory (1873–1950), J. Carlson, E. Cartan (1869–1951), S. Chern, W. Chow, C. Clemens, G. Coeuré, M. Cornalba, P. Cousin (1867–1933), M. Cowen, P. Deligne, G. De Rham, P. Dolbeault, C. Earle, B. Eckmann, J. Eells, R. Elkik, L. Fantappié, J. Ferrier, G. Fischer, O. Forster, J. Frisch, H. Fujimoto, M. Green, R. Greene, P. Griffiths, A. Grothendieck, J. Guénot, R. Gunning, G. Henkin, A. Hirschowitz, F. Hirzebruch, H. Holmann, H. Hopf (1894–1971), L. Hörmander, J. Igusa, S. Iitaka, E. Kähler, M. Kashiwara, M. Kato, N. Katz, W. Kaup, S. Kawai, H. Kerner, R. Kiehl, P. Kiernan, J. King, A. Knapp, S. Kobayashi, J. Kohn, M. Kuranishi, M. Kwack, Lê Dung Trang, P. Lelong, A. Lichnerowicz, I. Lieb, D. Lieberman, S. Łojasiewicz, B. Malgrange, Ju. Manin, A. Martineau, E. Martinelli, Y. Matsushima, P. Mazet, Z. Mebkhout, J. Milnor, B. Moishezon, A. Morimoto, L. Nachbin, R. Narasimhan, I. Nakamura, S. Nakano, Y. Namikawa, A. Newlander, L. Nirenberg, F. Norguet, P. Noverraz, F. Pham, H. Popp, I. Pyatetskii-Shapiro, E. Ramirez, J. Ramis, H. Rauch, O. Riemenschneider, H. Röhrl, H. Rossi, W. Rothstein, H. Royden, W. Rudin, G. Ruget, I. Satake, M. Sato, P. Schapira, G. Scheja, W. Schmid, I. Shafarevich, N. Sibony, Y. Siu, H. Skoda, W. Stoll, G. Stolzenberg, B. Shiffman, B. Teissier, W. Thimm, A. Tjurin, G. Trautman, K. Ueno, A. Van de Ven, J. L. Verdier, E. Vesentini, H. C. Wang (1919–1978), A. Weil, R. Wells, J. Wolf, H. Wu, S. Yau.

References

B: 71, 84, 95, 114, 115, 122, 137, 146, 150, 168, 173, 183, 202, 220, 234, 250, 270, 277, 296, 303, 314, 327, 340, 344, 354, 366, 404, 449, 463, 475, 495, 500, 506, 507, 517, 523, 581.

LN: 25, 38, 57, 103, 135, 154, 172, 184, 205, 209, 234, 409, 410, 412, 432, 439, 538, 600, 603, 633, 670, 683, 699, 705, 777, 807, 815.

BAMS: 70 (Kohn), 71 (Rauch), 72 (Chern), 78 (Griffiths), 82 (Kobayashi), 83 (Stoll).

SAMS: XXIX, XXX.

Astérisque: 7, 8, 10, 16, 17, 36, 37, 54, 58.

[12], [27], [84], [99], [135], [162], [169], [169 *bis*], [186], [191], [214], [222].

A IX

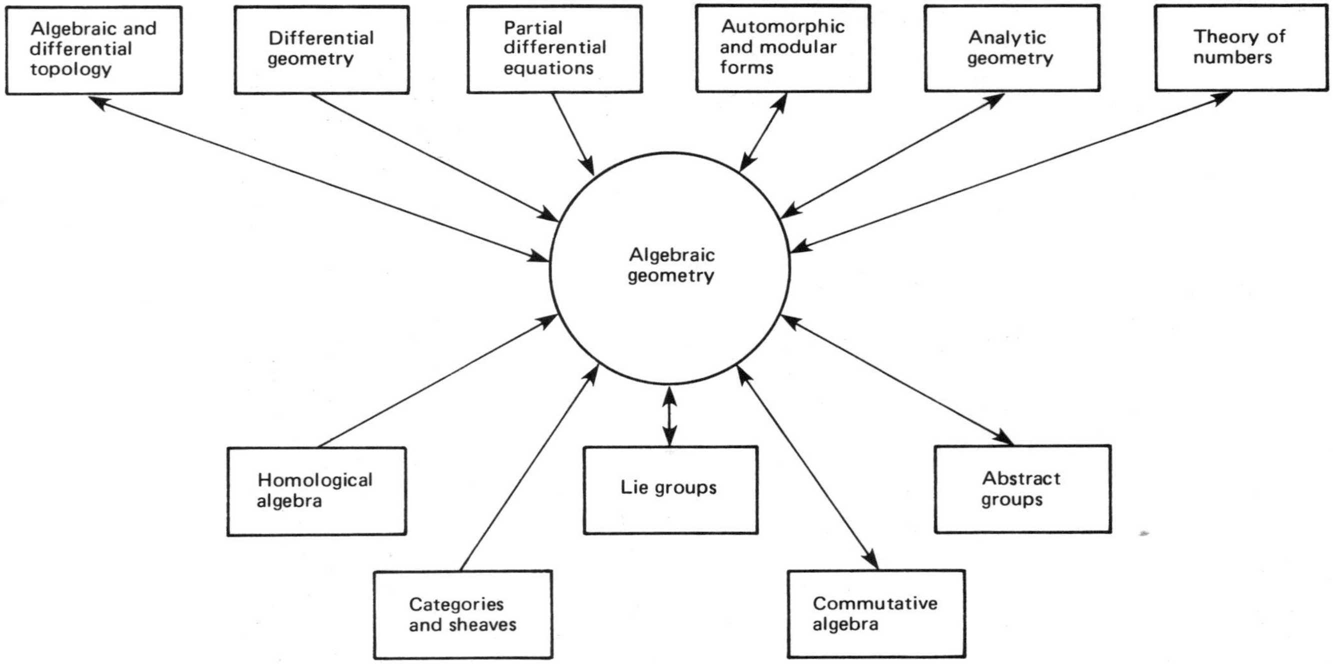
Algebraic and differential topology
Differential geometry
Partial differential equations
Automorphic and modular forms
Analytic geometry
Theory of numbers
Algebraic geometry
Homological algebra
Lie groups
Abstract groups
Categories and sheaves
Commutative algebra

A IX

Algebraic geometry

1. The modern framework of algebraic geometry

Algebraic geometry was born with the invention of cartesian coordinates, and at first consisted of the study of properties particular to sets of points (in $\mathbf{R}^2$ or $\mathbf{R}^3$) defined by polynomial equations in the coordinates. It developed around classification problems (on the model of the classical theory of conics), the search for invariants vis-à-vis certain transformations of the plane or of three-dimensional space, intersection problems, the study of families of points on a curve and families of curves on a surface, etc. But the context of these investigations has undergone considerable evolution since the beginning of the 19th century.

(1) The increasingly widespread use in the 18th century of complex numbers in analysis led to the concept of points with complex coordinates: such a point lies on an algebraic variety if it satisfies the equations of the variety. This is the first example of *extension of the ground field.*

(2) The introduction of general notions of "abstract" algebra from the beginning of the 20th century led immediately to a first natural generalization of algebraic geometry: if k is any field, an *affine algebraic k-variety* is the set V of points $(x_1, \ldots, x_n) \in k^n$ that satisfy a family of polynomial equations $P_\lambda(x_1, \ldots, x_n) = 0$ $(\lambda \in L)$, where the P_λ are an arbitrary family of polynomials with coefficients in k.

(3) From Riemann onward, the *functions* of a certain type on an affine algebraic k-variety have played an increasingly important part. The simplest of these are the restrictions to V of functions (defined on k^n)

$$(x_1, \ldots, x_n) \mapsto Q(x_1, \ldots, x_n),$$

where Q is a *polynomial* in $k[T_1, \ldots, T_n]$: these are the *regular* functions on V. The set $\mathfrak{J}$ of all polynomials $Q \in k[T_1, \ldots, T_n]$ that vanish at every point of V is an *ideal* in the k-algebra $k[T_1, \ldots, T_n]$, and the regular functions on V form a k-algebra A(V) isomorphic to $k[T_1, \ldots, T_n)/\mathfrak{J}$. If A(V) is an integral domain (in which case V is said to be *irreducible*), its field of fractions R(V) is called the field of *rational functions* on V, and was introduced by Riemann; its transcendence degree over k is called the *dimension* of V. A variety of dimension 1 (resp. 2) is called a *curve* (resp. a *surface*). Two irreducible algebraic varieties having the same field of rational functions are said to be *birationally equivalent*.

(4) Experience of geometry over the field of complex numbers suggests that in order to obtain simple results one should consider more particularly algebraic geometry over an *algebraically closed* field k. The rings of regular functions A(V) associated as above with affine algebraic varieties V can then be completely characterized by the following two properties: they are finitely generated k-algebras and are *reduced* (i.e., they have no nilpotent elements $\neq 0$). The variety V is then in canonical bijective correspondence with the set of k-algebra homomorphisms $\chi : \mathrm{A(V)} \to k$ that send identity element to identity element; the point $x \in \mathrm{V}$ corresponds to the homomorphism $\chi_x : f \mapsto f(x)$. The variety V is also in canonical bijective correspondence with the set of maximal ideals of A(V), which are the kernels of the homomorphisms χ_x.

(5) The fact that, when $k = \mathbf{C}$, affine algebraic varieties are particular cases of analytic varieties, and the definition of analytic varieties as *ringed spaces* (**A** VIII), suggest that one should seek to formulate an analogous definition for affine algebraic varieties over any algebraically closed field. This requires first defining a *topology* on an affine algebraic variety; for this purpose, we associate with each *ideal* $\mathfrak{a}$ of $\mathrm{A} = \mathrm{A(V)}$ the set $\mathrm{V}(\mathfrak{a})$ of points $x \in \mathrm{V}$ such that $f(x) = 0$ for all $f \in \mathfrak{a}$; these sets $\mathrm{V}(\mathfrak{a})$ are the closed sets of a topology on V called the *Zariski topology*. For each $t \in \mathrm{A}$, let $\mathrm{D}(t)$ denote the complement of the closed set $\mathrm{V}(t)$ corresponding to the principal ideal $\mathrm{A}t$, so that $\mathrm{D}(t)$ is the set of $x \in \mathrm{V}$ at which $t(x) \neq 0$; the $\mathrm{D}(t)$ form a basis of open sets for the Zariski topology. Also let A_t denote the ring of mappings $x \mapsto g(x)/t(x)^n$ (where n is any integer $\geqslant 0$ and g is any element of A) of $\mathrm{D}(t)$ into k; then it can be shown that there is a well-defined *sheaf of commutative rings* on V(**C** I), denoted by $\mathcal{O}_V$, such that $\mathcal{O}_V(\mathrm{D}(t)) = \mathrm{A}_t$ for all $t \in \mathrm{A}$.

If V and W are two affine algebraic varieties over k, the *morphisms of ringed spaces* (**C** I) $u : \mathrm{V} \to \mathrm{W}$ correspond bijectively to the k-algebra homomorphisms

$$\mathrm{A}(u) : \mathrm{A(W)} = \Gamma(\mathrm{W}, \mathcal{O}_\mathrm{W}) \to \Gamma(\mathrm{V}, \mathcal{O}_\mathrm{V}) = \mathrm{A(V)}$$

sending a section $g \in \Gamma(\mathrm{W}, \mathcal{O}_\mathrm{W})$ to the section $g \circ u \in \Gamma(\mathrm{V}, \mathcal{O}_\mathrm{V})$.

Conversely, if V (resp. W) is identified with the set of maximal ideals of A(V) (resp. A(W)), the image under u of a maximal ideal $\mathfrak{m}$ of A(V) is the inverse image $\mathrm{A}(u)^{-1}(\mathfrak{m})$ of $\mathfrak{m}$ under $\mathrm{A}(u)$ [40].

(6) Since the beginning of the 19th century it has been realized that the most significant results of algebraic geometry over the field of complex numbers concern not affine algebraic varieties (subsets of $\mathbf{C}^n$) but *projective* algebraic varieties (subsets of a projective space $\mathbf{P}_n(\mathbf{C})$). One way of looking at $\mathbf{P}_n(\mathbf{C})$ is to consider the complements U_j $(0 \leqslant j \leqslant n)$ in $\mathbf{P}_n(\mathbf{C})$ of the hyperplanes $x_j = 0$; each U_j can be canonically identified with affine space $\mathbf{C}^n$, so that $\mathbf{P}_n(\mathbf{C})$ is the result of "gluing together" $n + 1$ copies of $\mathbf{C}^n$. Since the notion of a ringed space is by design adapted to the operation of gluing together, we may pass from the notion of affine algebraic variety to the general notion of a *prevariety* (over k): a prevariety is defined to be a ringed space that admits a *finite* covering by open sets which (with their induced structures of ringed spaces) are affine algebraic varieties [40].

(7) The final step consists of abandoning the various restrictions made in the previous stages. In the first place, we want to be able to consider *any* commutative ring A (with identity element) as a ring of "regular functions." In order to preserve the relationship between morphisms of ringed spaces and homomorphisms of rings, it is no longer sufficient to consider only the maximal ideals of A, because for a ring homomorphism $h: A \to B$, the inverse image $h^{-1}(\mathfrak{m})$ of a maximal ideal is not in general maximal, but only prime. We therefore associate with each ring A the set Spec(A) of its prime ideals (called the *spectrum* of A), and we define the Zariski topology on Spec(A) by taking as closed sets the sets $V(\mathfrak{a})$, where for each ideal $\mathfrak{a}$ of A, $V(\mathfrak{a})$ is the set of prime ideals containing $\mathfrak{a}$. The definition of $D(t)$ for $t \in A$ is the same as before, and the $D(t)$ again form a basis of the topology of Spec(A). The ring A_t is defined to be the *ring of fractions* of A with respect to the multiplicatively stable subset of A consisting of the powers t^n $(n \geqslant 0)$ (**C** II). There again exists on $X = \text{Spec}(A)$ a sheaf of rings $\mathcal{O}_X$ such that $\mathcal{O}_X(D(t)) = A_t$ for all $t \in A$. It can then be verified that the morphisms of ringed spaces $\text{Spec}(A) \to \text{Spec}(B)$, for any two rings A, B, again correspond bijectively to the ring homomorphisms $B \to A$. Ringed spaces isomorphic to those of the form Spec(A) are called *affine schemes*; they form a "concrete" category equivalent to the opposite of the category of commutative rings (**C** I). Finally we define a *scheme* to be a ringed space admitting a covering (finite or not) by open sets which (with the induced structures of ringed spaces) are affine schemes (and are called "affine open sets").

In general, the topology of a scheme is not Hausdorff, nor are the one-point subsets closed in general. The k-prevarieties (for k algebraically closed) fit into the context of schemes in the following way: they correspond to schemes that admit a *finite* covering by affine open sets, each of which is the spectrum of a finitely generated reduced k-algebra; the prevariety is then the set of *closed* points of the scheme.

2. The fundamental notions of the theory of schemes ([40], [41], [69], [128], [130], [161])

(a) *Local properties and global properties.* If X is a scheme, the sheaf $\mathcal{O}_X$ has at each point $x \in X$ a *stalk* $\mathcal{O}_x$ (**C** I) that is a *local* ring (**C** II); if $\mathfrak{m}_x$ is its maximal ideal, we denote by $\kappa(x)$ the residue field $\mathcal{O}_x/\mathfrak{m}_x$. When $X = \operatorname{Spec}(A)$, a point $x \in X$ is just a prime ideal $\mathfrak{p}$ of A; $\mathcal{O}_x$ is the local ring $A_\mathfrak{p}$, $\mathfrak{m}_x$ its maximal ideal $\mathfrak{p}A_\mathfrak{p}$, and $\kappa(x)$ the field of fractions of the integral domain $A/\mathfrak{p}$. The scheme X is said to be *reduced* (resp. *normal*, resp. *regular*) at the point x if $\mathcal{O}_x$ is a reduced ring (resp. an integrally closed integral domain, resp. a regular local ring (**C** II)). For algebraic varieties over an algebraically closed field k, the notion of a regular point is the same as the classical notion of a "simple point."

The underlying topological space of a scheme X is said to be *irreducible* if every nonempty open set in X is dense; X is said to be *integral* if it is irreducible and reduced at each point, in which case every nonempty affine open set $U \subset X$ is of the form $U = \operatorname{Spec}(A)$ where A is an integral domain: the point $\xi \in U$ corresponding to the prime ideal (0) of A is the same for all nonempty affine open subsets of X, and is called the *generic* point of X. Its closure is the whole of X, and its local ring $\mathcal{O}_\xi = \kappa(\xi)$ is a field, denoted by R(X) and called the *field of rational functions* on X.

(b) *Quasi-coherent Modules and subschemes.* To the notion of a module over a commutative ring there corresponds in the theory of schemes the notion of a *quasi-coherent* Module. If $X = \operatorname{Spec}(A)$ and if M is an A-module, there exists an $\mathcal{O}_X$-Module $\mathcal{F}$ (**C** I) such that for each $t \in A$ we have $\mathcal{F}(D(t)) = M_t$, the module of fractions of M (equal to $M \otimes_A A_t$). The sheaf $\mathcal{F}$ is said to be the quasi-coherent $\mathcal{O}_X$-Module defined by M. If X is an arbitrary scheme, an $\mathcal{O}_X$-Module $\mathcal{F}$ is said to be quasi-coherent if for each affine open $U \subset X$ the restriction of $\mathcal{F}$ to U is a quasi-coherent $\mathcal{O}_U$-Module.

To the notion of an ideal in a ring there corresponds that of a *quasi-coherent Ideal* of $\mathcal{O}_X$, which is a quasi-coherent sub-$\mathcal{O}_X$-Module $\mathcal{J}$ of $\mathcal{O}_X$ considered as an $\mathcal{O}_X$-Module. For each $x \in X$, the stalk $\mathcal{J}_x$ is an ideal in $\mathcal{O}_x$, the set Y of $x \in X$ such that $\mathcal{J}_x \neq \mathcal{O}_x$ is closed in X, and $\mathcal{O}_X/\mathcal{J}$ may be considered as a sheaf of rings *on* Y. The ringed space $(Y, \mathcal{O}_X/\mathcal{J})$ is a scheme, called the *closed subscheme* of $(X, \mathcal{O}_X)$ defined by the quasi-coherent Ideal $\mathcal{J}$. The canonical injection $Y \to X$ and the canonical homomorphism $\mathcal{O}_X \to \mathcal{O}_X/\mathcal{J}$ define a morphism called the *canonical immersion* of the subscheme $(Y, \mathcal{O}_X/\mathcal{J})$ in $(X, \mathcal{O}_X)$. When $X = \operatorname{Spec}(A)$ is affine, $\mathcal{J}$ corresponds to an ideal $\mathfrak{a}$ of A, and $Y = \operatorname{Spec}(A/\mathfrak{a})$ has $V(\mathfrak{a})$ as underlying space.

Conversely, for each closed subset Y of X, there exists at least one subscheme of X having Y as underlying subspace. Among the quasi-coherent

Ideals of $\mathcal{O}_X$ that define these subschemes there is a largest Ideal, for which the corresponding subscheme is *reduced.*

(c) *Relativization and base change.* In the theory of schemes the emphasis is on properties of morphisms rather than on properties of the schemes themselves. In the majority of questions, one fixes a "base scheme" S, and the objects of study are S-*schemes*, i.e., schemes X endowed with a morphism $X \to S$ (the *structural* morphism). The S-schemes form a category ***Sch***/S: an S-morphism $u : X \to Y$ of S-schemes is by definition a morphism of schemes such that the diagram

$$\begin{array}{ccc} X & \xrightarrow{u} & Y \\ & {\scriptstyle f}\searrow \quad \swarrow{\scriptstyle g} & \\ & S & \end{array}$$

is commutative, where f and g are the structural morphisms. If $S = \text{Spec}(A)$, where A is a ring, we speak of A-*schemes*; every scheme may be considered as a **Z**-scheme. If k is a field, the k-schemes include algebraic k-varieties as special cases. For each point x of a k-scheme X, the field $\kappa(x)$ is an extension of k; for x to be a *closed* point, it is necessary and sufficient that $\kappa(x)$ should be a finite algebraic extension of k. The points x such that $\kappa(x) = k$ are said to be *rational* over k.

In each category ***Sch***/S, products (**C** I) exist (equivalently, *fiber* products exist in the category of all schemes). The product of two S-schemes X, Y is denoted by $X \times_S Y$. If $S = \text{Spec}(A)$, $X = \text{Spec}(B)$, $Y = \text{Spec}(C)$, we have $X \times_S Y = \text{Spec}(B \otimes_A C)$.

This notion is most frequently employed in the study of a morphism $f : X \to S$, by replacing the "base" S by an S-scheme S′; we write $X_{(S')}$ in place of $X \times_S S'$, and in the commutative diagram

$$\begin{array}{ccc} X & \longleftarrow & X_{(S')} \\ {\scriptstyle f}\downarrow & & \downarrow{\scriptstyle f_{(S')}} \\ S & \longleftarrow & S' \end{array}$$

$X_{(S')}$ and $f_{(S')}$ are said to be induced from X and f by the *base change* $S' \to S$. This is the general formulation of the idea of "extension of scalars," which has countless applications: for example, if $S = \text{Spec}(A)$, where A is a local ring, we may take S′ to be the spectrum of the completion $\hat{A}$, or of the Henselization ${}^hA$ of A (**C** II); if A is a field k, we may take S′ to be the spectrum of an algebraic closure of k, etc.

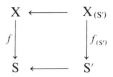

Often it occurs that a property of X or of f is easier to prove for $X_{(S')}$ or $f_{(S')}$, after a suitably chosen base change $S' \to S$; one then has to see whether the corresponding property of X or f can be inferred. This is the problem of "*descent*," which plays a considerable technical role, and for which it is important to have usable criteria (B 190, 195).

For each point $s \in S$, there is a canonical morphism $\mathrm{Spec}(\kappa(s)) \to S$, and the $\kappa(s)$-scheme $X_s = X \times_S \mathrm{Spec}(\kappa(s))$, obtained from an S-scheme X by the base change $\mathrm{Spec}(\kappa(s)) \to S$, has as its underlying space the fiber $f^{-1}(s)$ (with the induced topology). In a certain sense, an S-scheme may therefore be considered as a family of $\kappa(s)$-schemes X_s, parametrized by S.

(d) *The various types of morphisms.* To obtain substantial results in the theory of schemes, it is necessary to make supplementary hypotheses of various types on the morphisms under consideration.

One important class of morphisms is the *flat* morphisms. A morphism $f: X \to S$ is said to be flat if for each $x \in X$ the local ring $\mathcal{O}_x$ is a flat $\mathcal{O}_{f(x)}$-module (**C** II). One of the consequences of this assumption is that, for a flat morphism, the behavior of the fibers X_s cannot "jump" as s varies in S. Flatness also plays a "connecting" role for the fibers X_s, and it is often possible to deduce from properties of the fibers X_s the corresponding properties of X. Finally, "descent" is particularly well-behaved for base changes $S' \to S$ that are *faithfully flat*, i.e., flat and surjective.

The notion of a flat morphism enables two other types of morphisms to be defined, which correspond in algebraic geometry to the notions of fibration (*smooth* morphisms) and covering space (*étale* morphisms) in the theory of differential manifolds. These are flat morphisms; in addition an étale morphism $f: X \to S$ is such that each fiber $f^{-1}(s)$ consists of isolated points, at each of which the residue field $\kappa(x)$ is a finite separable extension of $\kappa(s)$. A smooth morphism $f: X \to S$ is such that for each $x \in X$, there exists an open neighborhood V of x and an affine open neighborhood $U = \mathrm{Spec}(A)$ of $s = f(x)$ such that $f(V) \subset U$ and such that the morphism $V \to U$ obtained by restricting f factorizes as

$$V \xrightarrow{h} \mathrm{Spec}(A[T_1, \ldots, T_r]) \xrightarrow{g} \mathrm{Spec}(A) = U,$$

where h is étale and g corresponds to the canonical homomorphism of A into the polynomial ring $A[T_1, \ldots, T_r]$: the spectrum of this polynomial ring corresponds to the idea of a "vector bundle" over Spec(A).

Other conditions on morphisms are *finiteness* conditions. Affine open sets are always quasi-compact (i.e., satisfy the Heine–Borel property but are not Hausdorff). A morphism $f: X \to S$ is said to be *quasi-compact* if for each affine open $U \subset S$, $f^{-1}(U)$ is quasi-compact. The morphism f is said to be *of finite type* (resp. *of finite presentation*) if, taking $U = \mathrm{Spec}(A)$, $f^{-1}(U)$ is a finite union of open sets V_j each of which is the spectrum of an A-algebra of finite type (resp. finite presentation) (**C** II). An even more restricted class of morphisms is the class of *finite* morphisms, which are such that for each affine open $U = \mathrm{Spec}(A) \subset S$, $f^{-1}(U)$ is the spectrum of a finite A-algebra (**C** II); all the fibers $f^{-1}(s)$ are then finite sets (but the converse is not true).

The third type of conditions involves the topology of the underlying spaces. A *closed immersion* $f : X \to S$ is an isomorphism of X onto a closed subscheme of S, followed by the canonical immersion. A morphism $f : X \to S$ is said to be *separated* if the "diagonal" morphism $X \to X \times_S X$ is a closed immersion. A separated k-scheme X (i.e., such that the structural morphism is separated) permits the usual arguments based on "density": if two k-morphisms u, v of a k-scheme Z into X agree on a dense open subset of Z, then they are equal. An *algebraic k-variety* over an algebraically closed field k consists of the closed points of a k-scheme that is *reduced, separated, and of finite type* over k.

One of the most important notions is that of a *proper* morphism: such a morphism $f : X \to S$ is separated and of finite type, and is such that for all base changes $S' \to S$ the morphism $f_{(S')} : X_{(S')} \to S'$ is *closed*, i.e., the image of each closed subset of $X_{(S')}$ is a closed subset of S′ (B 152). A k-scheme X whose structural morphism is proper is also said to be *complete*: such schemes play a role in algebraic geometry comparable to that played by compact spaces in topology.

(e) *Techniques of construction and representable functors.* If A is a finitely generated reduced algebra over an algebraically closed field k, we have seen that the corresponding algebraic k-variety V may be considered as the set of closed points of Spec(A), or equivalently as the set of k-homomorphisms $A \to k$. If K is an algebraically closed extension field of k, the variety obtained from V by "extending the ground field to K" is therefore the set of "points of V with values in K," i.e., the set of K-homomorphisms $A \otimes_k K \to K$, which correspond one-to-one with the k-homomorphisms $A \to K$, or equivalently to the Spec(k)-morphisms $\mathrm{Spec}(K) \to \mathrm{Spec}(A)$. This notion can be generalized to arbitrary schemes: given an S-scheme X, the "points of X with values in an S-scheme T" are by definition the S-morphisms $T \to X$; they are in one–one correspondence (**C** I) with the T-*sections* of $X \times_S T$, i.e., the morphisms $T \to X \times_S T$, which when composed with the structural morphism $X \times_S T \to T$ give the identity morphism of T. For each point $s \in S$, let $\{\bar{s}\}$ denote the spectrum of the algebraic closure of $\kappa(s)$; then $X_{\bar{s}} = X \times_{\mathrm{Spec}(\kappa(s))} \{\bar{s}\}$ is called the *geometric fiber* of s in X, and a point of this fiber is called a *geometrical point* over its projection in X.

In this way the canonical covariant functor **h** of the theory of categories (**C** I) enters the picture naturally: it associates to each S-scheme X the contravariant functor $\mathbf{h}_X : (\boldsymbol{Sch}/S)^\circ \to \boldsymbol{Ens}$ such that $\mathbf{h}_X(T) = \mathrm{Mor}_S(T, X)$, which is *representable* by the S-scheme X.

A fundamental idea of the theory of schemes introduced by Grothendieck is that in various constructions which attach canonically to an S-scheme X another S-scheme $\Phi(X)$, the natural method of proceeding is first to define the *functor* that is to be represented by the S-scheme $\Phi(X)$. For example, to generalize to any ring A the construction that, for a field k, defines the n-dimensional projective space $\mathbf{P}_n(k)$, we start from the geometrical idea that for an overfield K of k, the points of $\mathbf{P}_n(K)$ are in one–one correspondence with the hyperplanes in K^{n+1}, or equivalently with the kernels of the K-linear mappings $K^{n+1} \to K$. For an arbitrary commutative A-algebra **B**, we therefore consider the set $\mathrm{Hyp}(B^{n+1})$ of kernels of B-linear mappings $B^{n+1} \to B$, and so obtain a functor $B \mapsto \mathrm{Hyp}(B^{n+1})$. This definition can be generalized: for any scheme S and quasi-coherent $\mathcal{O}_S$-Module $\mathcal{E}$, we can define in the same way a "projective scheme $\mathbf{P}(\mathcal{E})$ associated with $\mathcal{E}$." This then enables us to define the notion of a *projective* S-*scheme* as a *closed* subscheme of $\mathbf{P}(\mathcal{E})$ for a suitable $\mathcal{E}$, and the notion of a *projective morphism*, which is the structural morphism of a projective S-scheme. Projective morphisms are proper, but not all proper morphisms are projective. There is another definition of projective schemes that is closer to the definition in classical algebraic geometry in terms of graded ideals (**C** II): if $A = \bigoplus_{n \geq 0} A_n$ is a graded ring, we define Proj(A) to be the subspace of Spec(A) consisting of the *graded* prime ideals contained in $A_+ = \bigoplus_{n \geq 1} A_n$, endowed with a sheaf of rings defined in a natural way ([41], [128]); for a ring **B**, $\mathbf{P}_n(\mathrm{B})$ is $\mathrm{Proj}(\mathrm{B}[T_0, \ldots, T_n])$.

If k is an algebraically closed field, a *projective k-variety* is a *closed* algebraic subvariety of a projective space $\mathbf{P}_n(k)$.

If in the construction of $\mathbf{P}_n(A)$ we replace the "hyperplanes" by the kernels of surjective linear mappings $B^{n+1} \to B^m$, we obtain the definition of *Grassmannians* $\mathbf{G}_m(A)$ (and more generally $\mathbf{G}_m(\mathcal{E})$ for a quasi-coherent $\mathcal{O}_S$-Module $\mathcal{E}$), which generalize the classical Grassmann varieties ([D, Chapter 16] and [41]).

A more intricate construction problem is the definition of the *Hilbert scheme* of an S-scheme X. Here we seek an S-scheme that "parametrizes" the closed subschemes Z of X that are *flat* over S (if S = Spec(k) where k is a field, this condition is automatically satisfied). The functor to be represented must take each S-scheme T to the set of closed subschemes of $X \times_S T$ that are flat over T. There are examples of complete k-varieties for which this functor is not representable; however, it is representable when S is the spectrum of a Noetherian ring and X is a projective S-scheme (**B** 221). The S-scheme $\mathbf{Hilb}_{X/S}$ that represents this functor is called the Hilbert scheme of X, and is the disjoint sum of connected projective S-schemes (**B** 283). For projective varieties over an algebraically closed field, there is an earlier method for associating with each closed subvariety a point in a projective space, called the "Chow point" of the subvariety; when X is a k-variety, there is a canonical morphism of $\mathbf{Hilb}_{X/k}$ into the "Chow variety" of X.

The same idea of defining schemes as representing functors also serves to define additional structures on a scheme X. For example, to define a notion of "equivalence relation" on an S-scheme X, we consider on each set $\mathrm{Mor}_S(T, X)$ an equivalence relation that "depends functorially" on T; this equivalence relation defines a quotient set, and by associating this quotient with T we have a functor that (if it is representable) will provide a definition of the "quotient scheme" of X by an equivalence relation (B 212). It is also by this method that algebraic structures on S-schemes are defined (group-schemes, etc.; cf. (**C** I) and see later).

It is therefore important to have criteria for the representability of a contravariant functor $(\mathbf{\mathit{Sch}}/S)^{\circ} \to \mathbf{\mathit{Ens}}$ (B 294). The fact that these criteria are not always satisfied has led to the consideration of a category which is larger than the category of schemes, namely, the *algebraic spaces* of M. Artin, which may be described as "quotients" of schemes by "equivalence relations" that may not possess "quotient schemes." Most of the properties of schemes extend to these more general objects, and the constructions mentioned above which encounter difficulties in the category of schemes can be carried out without inconvenient restrictions in the category of algebraic spaces (B 363; LN 203; Nice B 5 (M. Artin)).

3. The study of singularities

For an algebraic variety X over an algebraically closed field k, the *tangent space* $T_x(X)$ at each point $x \in X$ can be defined in a purely algebraic manner: if $\mathfrak{m}_x$ is the maximal ideal of the local ring $\mathcal{O}_x$, then $\mathcal{O}_x/\mathfrak{m}_x$ is canonically isomorphic to k, and $T_x(X)$ is the k-vector space dual to the k-vector space $\mathfrak{m}_x/\mathfrak{m}_x^2$. If X is an irreducible variety, a simple point of X is a point at which the dimension of $T_x(X)$ (or of $\mathfrak{m}_x/\mathfrak{m}_x^2$) is equal to that of X [40]. A variety all of whose points are simple is said to be *smooth* or *nonsingular*. The problem of "desingularization" for k-varieties takes the same form as in analytic geometry (**A** VIII), namely, to show that for a given algebraic variety X, there exists a smooth variety Y, a proper morphism $f: Y \to X$, and a dense open subset U of X such that the restriction $f^{-1}(U) \to U$ is an isomorphism. If k has characteristic 0, this theorem has been proved by Hironaka; if k has characteristic $p > 0$, it has been proved by Abhyankar for surfaces, and when $p \neq 2, 3, 5$ also for varieties of dimension 3 (B 320; SAMS XXIX (Lipman)). Hironaka has also extended his theorem to the case where X is an affine scheme Spec(A), where A is an excellent reduced Noetherian ring

(**C** II) whose residue fields are of characteristic 0; in this situation, Y is a scheme all of whose points are regular. Abhyankar's theorems generalize in the same way. The proofs depend on the technique of *blowing up*, just as in analytic geometry. There is a general definition of blowing up a scheme along a closed subscheme: if for example X = Spec(A), and the subscheme X′ of X is defined by an ideal $\mathfrak{a}$ of A, the blow-up of X along X′ is the scheme $\mathrm{Proj}\left(\bigoplus_{n \geqslant 0} \mathfrak{a}^n\right)$. The study of singular points has been pursued mainly for isolated singular points, and runs parallel to the analogous theory for complex analytic spaces (B 250; [135] (Hironaka); [113]). It is the same for the type of nonisolated singularities investigated by Zariski under the name of "equisingularity": the singular points in a neighborhood of one of them are situated on a nonsingular subvariety, and are "of the same type" along this subvariety (BAMS 77 (Zariski); SAMS XXIX (Teissier)).

4. The "transcendental" theory of algebraic varieties

Modern algebraic geometry was inaugurated by Riemann, to whom are due the first notions and fundamental results on nonsingular projective algebraic curves V over the field **C**: results obtained by studying the meromorphic functions and differential forms on the complex manifold V (of real dimension 2) in relation to the topology of V (which he was the first to define). The successors of Riemann, seeking to extend his results to algebraic surfaces, began by studying mainly the differential forms and their integrals, but Poincaré and above all Lefschetz perceived that the majority of the results so obtained were in fact purely topological theorems. The topological properties of projective algebraic varieties (closed subvarieties of $\mathbf{P}_n(\mathbf{C})$) are mainly due to three particular properties: (1) such a variety V (with arbitrary singularities) is triangulable (SAMS XXIX (Hironaka)); (2) V is orientable, and if V is irreducible and of (complex) dimension r, it is a $2r$-*cycle* (not merely a $2r$-chain) (**A** I); (3) if C, C′ are two irreducible subvarieties of V, of complementary dimensions p and q (i.e., $p + q = r$) and in "general position" (which means here that each of the points of intersection is nonsingular on C and on C′, and that the tangent spaces to C and C′ at each such point meet only in a point), then the coefficient of each point of intersection in the calculation of the 0-cycle $C \cdot C'$ is $+1$, so that the "intersection number" $(C \cdot C')$ in the sense of algebraic topology (the degree of the 0-cycle $C \cdot C'$) (**A** I) is in fact the number of points of the set $C \cap C'$.

Monodromy. A fundamental method used first by Picard and taken up again more generally by Lefschetz is induction on the dimension. For example, given an irreducible nonsingular surface $S \subset \mathbf{P}_3(\mathbf{C})$, with nonhomogeneous equation $F(x, y, z) = 0$, consider for each $y_0 \in \mathbf{C}$ the curve C_{y_0} which is the intersection of S and the plane $y = y_0$, with equation $F(x, y_0, z) = 0$ in x and z. The curve C_y is (provided that the axes of coordinates are in "general position") irreducible, nonsingular, and of constant genus p, except for a finite number of points y_j $(1 \leqslant j \leqslant \mu)$ at which C_{y_j} acquires one double point with distinct tangents, thus lowering the genus by 1. For a value a of y not equal to any y_j, let γ be an arbitrary 1-cycle on C_a, and consider on each C_y a 1-cycle which varies continuously with y and coincides with γ when $y = a$. As y describes a loop in $\mathbf{C}$ with origin a, encircling y_j, the cycle γ is changed into say $\tau_j(\gamma)$, homologous to $\gamma + (\gamma \cdot \delta_j)\delta_j$, where δ_j is a 1-cycle in C_a whose class in $H_1(C_a, \mathbf{Z})$ is independent of the choice of γ. Moreover, δ_j is a "vanishing cycle" in the following sense: if we join a to y_j by an arc l_j, there exists a 2-chain Δ_j in $\mathrm{pr}_2^{-1}(l_j)$ such that (i) $\partial\Delta_j = \Delta_j \cap C_a = \delta_j$, (ii) $\Delta_j \cap C_y$ is a 1-cycle obtained from δ_j by continuous variation as y runs along l_j, and finally (iii) $\Delta_j \cap C_{y_j}$ is the double point of C_{y_j}. In this way we define a homomorphism of the fundamental group of $\mathbf{C} - \{y_j\}$ (or of the complement in $\mathbf{C}$ of a nonempty subset of $\{y_1, \ldots, y_\mu\}$) into $H_1(C_a, \mathbf{Z})$, called the *monodromy homomorphism.* The analogy of this method with the study of singular points of linear differential equations in the complex domain (Riemann–Fuchs method; see LN 163) should be noted.

Lefschetz generalized this procedure to the case in which C_y is replaced by a variable fiber X_s of a morphism $X \to S$, where S is an algebraic curve and X is a nonsingular projective algebraic variety of arbitrary dimension; in this way he established the homological properties of nonsingular projective algebraic varieties (over $\mathbf{C}$) which have since been generalized to compact Kähler manifolds **A** VIII by means of Hodge theory.

More recently, the same idea has been extended to the situation where X is neither projective nor nonsingular, the morphism $X \to S$ being assumed to be proper and smooth. Here each fiber X_s is endowed with a "Hodge structure" E_s, a notion that subsumes in axiomatic form the main properties of Hodge theory; monodromy is now a homomorphism of the fundamental group $\pi_1(S, s_0)$ into the group of automorphisms of E_{s_0} (B 376; BAMS 76 (Griffiths); SAMS XXIX (Cornalba–Griffiths)). This notion is related to the generalization to varieties of arbitrary dimension (over $\mathbf{C}$) of the notion of meromorphic differential forms "of the second kind" (SAMS XXIX (Messing)).

Topology of subvarieties. In $\mathbf{P}_n(\mathbf{C})$, a closed subvariety X of codimension s is said to be a *complete intersection* (in the strong sense) if it is the intersection of s hypersurfaces H_j $(1 \leqslant j \leqslant s)$ such that at each point of X the tangent hyperplanes to these hypersurfaces are in general position. One of the results of the theory of Lefschetz is that if $X \subset \mathbf{P}_n(\mathbf{C})$ is irreducible, nonsingular, and a complete intersection, the canonical homomorphism $H^j(\mathbf{P}_n(\mathbf{C}), \mathbf{Z}) \to H^j(X, \mathbf{Z})$ is bijective for $j < \dim(X)$ and injective for $j = \dim(X)$. If $\dim(X) > n/2$, we have isomorphisms for $j \leqslant 2\dim(X) - n$ without assuming that X is a complete intersection, and in addition X is simply connected (B 458; BAMS 80 (Hartshorne), SAMS XXIX (Hartshorne, Barth)).

Algebraic cycles. Riemann's successors were led to interpret his results on algebraic curves with the aid of the notion of a *divisor*, which can be generalized to varieties of any dimension. With the introduction of the notions of algebraic topology it came to be realized that this notion was closely related to that of a *cycle*, and that divisor class groups were related to homology groups. If X is a nonsingular irreducible projective variety of dimension n over **C**, an *algebraic cycle* of codimension r is an element of the free abelian group generated by the irreducible closed subvarieties of X (possibly with singularities) of codimension r. This group is denoted by $C^r(X)$; of itself it is of little interest, but on it there are defined various important *equivalence relations*: the general idea is to consider two cycles as "equivalent" if it is possible to "deform" one into the other in a certain way. Two cycles Z_1, Z_2 in $C^r(X)$ are said to be *rationally equivalent* if there exists a cycle Z on $X \times D$ (where D is the affine line, i.e., the field **C** itself) such that the intersection of Z and $X \times \{t\}$ is a cycle of codimension r in $X \times \{t\}$ for all $t \in D$, and such that Z_1 (resp. Z_2) is the intersection of Z with $X \times \{0\}$ (resp. $X \times \{1\}$). The definition of *algebraically equivalent* cycles is obtained by replacing D in the preceding definition by an arbitrary irreducible curve, and 0 and 1 by two points of this curve. The subgroups $C^r_{\text{rat}}(X)$ and $C^r_{\text{alg}}(X)$ of $C^r(X)$ are then defined to consist of the cycles that are rationally (resp. algebraically) equivalent to 0. We denote by $C^r_{\text{tor}}(X)$ the group of cycles some integer multiple of which lies in $C^r_{\text{alg}}(X)$. Next we define $C^r_{\text{hom}}(X)$ to be the group of algebraic cycles homologous to 0 in $H_{2n-2r}(X, \mathbf{C})$, and $C^r_{\text{num}}(X)$ to consist of the cycles Z such that $(Y \cdot Z) = 0$ for all irreducible subvarieties Y of dimension r in X. We have then the following inclusions:

$$C^r_{\text{rat}} \subset C^r_{\text{alg}} \subset C^r_{\text{tor}} \subset C^r_{\text{hom}} \subset C^r_{\text{num}} \subset C^r.$$

The case most studied, and the simplest, is $r = 1$, in which case algebraic cycles are called *divisors*; rational equivalence is called *linear* equivalence and may be defined in another way, by considering certain discrete valuations (**C** II) on the field R(X) of rational functions on X. If V is an irreducible subvariety of codimension 1 in X, the associated valuation v_V is such that $v_V(f) \geqslant 0$ for functions $f \in R(X)$ defined at all points of V, and $v_V(f) > 0$

for $f \in R(X)$ which vanish at all points of V. For a rational function $f \neq 0$ in R(X), the *principal divisor* (f) is the linear combination $\sum_j n_j V_j$ where $n_j = v_{V_j}(f)$, and $C^1_{lin}(X)$ $(= C^1_{rat}(X))$ is the group of principal divisors. (When X is a curve, the V_j are points, and $v_{V_j}(f)$ is the *order* of the meromorphic function f at the point V_j). The group $C^1(X)/C^1_{lin}(X)$ is called the *Picard group* of X, written Pic(X). We have in addition $C^1_{tor}(X) = C^1_{hom}(X) = C^1_{num}(X)$; $C^1(X)/C^1_{alg}(X)$ is a finitely generated abelian group, called the *Néron–Severi group* of X, which may be identified with a subgroup of $H^2(X, \mathbf{Z})$, and its (finite) torsion group is $C^1_{tor}(X)/C^1_{alg}(X)$; hence $C^1(X)/C^1_{tor}(X)$ is a free abelian group $\mathbf{Z}^\rho$ whose rank ρ is called the *Picard number* of X (B 53).

For cycles of arbitrary codimension, it is known that $C^r(X)/C^r_{num}(X)$ is again a free abelian group $\mathbf{Z}^\rho$; it is conjectured that $C^r_{num}(X) = C^r_{hom}(X)$ in all cases, but this is established only when $r = 0, 1, 2, n - 1$, and n (where $n = \dim(X)$). An example due to Griffiths shows that it can happen that $C^r_{hom}(X) \neq C^r_{tor}(X)$, but it is not known whether $C^r_{hom}(X)/C^r_{tor}(X)$ is always finitely generated, nor whether $C^r_{tor}(X)/C^r_{alg}(X)$ is always finite (SAMS XXIX (Hartshorne); [135] (Kleiman)).

Divisors and abelian varieties. The concept of a divisor can be generalized to any complex manifold X. If D is a divisor on an algebraic variety X, there exists an open covering (U_α) of X such that the restriction of D to each U_α is a principal divisor (h_α), and for two sets U_α, U_β of the covering, the quotient h_α/h_β on $U_\alpha \cap U_\beta$ is holomorphic and $\neq 0$. If $\mathscr{M}^*_X$ is the sheaf of germs $\neq 0$ of meromorphic functions, and $\mathscr{O}^*_X$ the subsheaf of germs $\neq 0$ of holomorphic functions, it follows that D may be identified with a global section of the quotient sheaf (of multiplicative groups) $\mathscr{M}^*_X/\mathscr{O}^*_X$, and this definition makes sense for any complex manifold X. In the cohomology exact sequence (**B** I)

$$0 \to H^0(X, \mathscr{O}^*_X) \to H^0(X, \mathscr{M}^*_X) \to H^0(X, \mathscr{M}^*_X/\mathscr{O}^*_X) \to H^1(X, \mathscr{O}^*_X) \to H^1(X, \mathscr{M}^*_X) \to \cdots$$

it can be shown that $H^1(X, \mathscr{M}^*_X) = 0$, and that the image of $H^0(X, \mathscr{M}^*_X)$ in $C^1(X) = H^0(X, \mathscr{M}^*_X/\mathscr{O}^*_X)$ is the subgroup $C^1_{lin}(X)$, so that we have a canonical isomorphism $C^1(X)/C^1_{lin}(X) = \mathrm{Pic}(X) \xrightarrow{\sim} H^1(X, \mathscr{O}^*_X)$. On the other hand, the exact sequence of the multiplicative Cousin problem (**A** VIII, (1))

$$0 \to H^1(X, \mathbf{Z}) \to H^1(X, \mathscr{O}_X) \to H^1(X, \mathscr{O}^*_X) \to H^2(X, \mathbf{Z}) \to H^2(X, \mathscr{O}_X) \to \cdots$$

shows that $H^1(X, \mathscr{O}_X)/H^1(X, \mathbf{Z})$ is isomorphic to the kernel of the homomorphism $H^1(X, \mathscr{O}^*_X) \to H^2(X, \mathbf{Z})$. For a projective algebraic variety X, this kernel is isomorphic to $C^1_{\text{alg}}(X)/C^1_{\text{lin}}(X)$; on the other hand, there is an isomorphism $H^1(X, \mathcal{O}_X) \simeq H^1(X, \mathbf{R})$ (see below), so that $C^1_{\text{alg}}(X)/C^1_{\text{lin}}(X)$ is isomorphic to $H^1(X, \mathbf{R})/H^1(X, \mathbf{Z})$. Now Hodge theory defines on $H^1(X, \mathbf{R})$ (for any compact Kähler manifold X) a canonical complex vector-space structure, in which $H^1(X, \mathbf{Z})$ is a lattice; hence $C^1_{\text{alg}}(X)/C^1_{\text{lin}}(X)$, for a projective algebraic variety X, is a *complex torus* isomorphic to $\mathbf{C}^g/\mathbf{Z}^{2g}$. Moreover, this torus, called the *Picard variety* of X, can be *embedded* in a complex projective space, and is therefore a torus of a particular type, called an *abelian variety* over **C**. When X is an algebraic curve, its Picard variety, denoted by J(X), is called the *Jacobian* of X, and is of complex dimension g equal to the genus of X. Its definition and its main properties are due in substance to Riemann ([40], [107]). If we fix a point P_0 of X, the mapping which takes $P \in X$ to the class of the divisor $P - P_0 \in C^1_{\text{alg}}(X)$ is an embedding of X in its Jacobian, and J(X) together with an embedding in a projective space (i.e., a *polarization* of the abelian variety J(X)) determines X up to isomorphism (B 151).

For an arbitrary projective algebraic variety X, it may be asked whether there exists a canonical structure of abelian variety on $C^r_{\text{alg}}(X)/C^r_{\text{rat}}(X)$ (or on a suitable quotient of this group). This is known to be the case when $r = n = \dim(X)$; the corresponding abelian variety Alb(X) canonically associated with X is called the *Albanese variety* of X and is characterized by the following universal property: if P_0 is a point of X, and if φ is the mapping $X \to \text{Alb}(X)$ such that $\varphi(P)$ is the class of the 0-cycle $P - P_0$, then every morphism $f : U \to A$ of an open set U of X into an abelian variety A factorizes uniquely as $f = \lambda \circ \varphi + c$, where $\lambda : \text{Alb}(X) \to A$ is a morphism of algebraic varieties and a homomorphism of groups, and c is an element of A.

In general, every complex torus E/Δ, where E is a finite-dimensional complex vector space and Δ is a lattice in E, admits a *dual* torus E'/Δ', where E' is the dual of E and Δ' the lattice which is the Pontrjagin dual of E/Δ (**B** IV); E/Δ is the torus dual to E'/Δ', and if E/Δ is an abelian variety so also is E'/Δ'. The Picard and Albanese varieties of a projective algebraic variety are duals of each other [131].

The problem of the existence of "intermediate" abelian varieties in between the Albanese and Picard varieties is not completely solved, and in any case it is known that the Albanese variety is not always isomorphic to $C^n_{\text{alg}}(X)/C^n_{\text{rat}}(X)$, but only to some quotient of this group (B 72; SAMS XXIX (Hartshorne); [135] (Lieberman)).

Divisors and vector bundles. An algebraic cycle $Z \in C^r(X)$ is said to be *positive* if it is a linear combination of irreducible subvarieties with positive integer coefficients. The problem that led Riemann to the notion of a divisor was that of the existence, on a nonsingular projective algebraic curve X, of a function $f \in R(X)$ having poles of orders $\leqslant m_j$ at given points P_j. If D is the divisor $-\sum_j m_j P_j$, this condition is expressed as $(f) + D \geqslant 0$ in the group $C^1(X)$. So to each divisor D on a nonsingular irreducible projective algebraic variety X we attach the vector space L(D) of functions $f \in R(X)$ such that $(f) + D \geqslant 0$.

This space L(D) (which is finite dimensional) can be interpreted as the space of holomorphic global sections of a *holomorphic line bundle* B(D) over X, associated with D. To define B(D), choose an open covering (U_α) of X such that the restriction of D to each U_α is a principal divisor (h_α), and then "glue together" [D, Chapter 16] the complex manifolds $U_\alpha \times \mathbf{C}$ and $U_\beta \times \mathbf{C}$ by taking as "transition function" the function

$$(x, z) \mapsto (x, (h_\beta(x)/h_\alpha(x))z),$$

which is holomorphic on $(U_\alpha \cap U_\beta) \times \mathbf{C}$. If s is a holomorphic section of B(D), its restrictions $s_\alpha = s|U_\alpha$ therefore satisfy $s_\beta = (h_\beta/h_\alpha)s_\alpha$ on $U_\alpha \cap U_\beta$, and hence there is a meromorphic function f on X such that $f|U_\alpha$ is equal to s_α/h_α for all α, and this condition is equivalent to $(f) + D \geqslant 0$. For example, if $X = \mathbf{P}_n(\mathbf{C})$ and D is a *hyperplane* $H \subset \mathbf{P}_n(\mathbf{C})$, then $L(H) = \Gamma(B(H))$ is the vector space of all linear forms on $\mathbf{C}^{n+1}$. Conversely, it can be shown that every holomorphic line bundle on X is isomorphic to B(D) for some divisor D, and B(D), B(D′) are isomorphic if and only if $D' - D \in C^1_{\text{lin}}(X)$ (B 82).

We are thus led to associate with a divisor D the sheaf $\mathcal{O}(B(D))$ of germs of sections of the line bundle B(D). This sheaf is denoted by $\mathcal{O}_X(D)$; it is an *invertible* $\mathcal{O}_X$-Module, that is to say, it is locally isomorphic to $\mathcal{O}_X$; conversely, every invertible $\mathcal{O}_X$-Module is isomorphic to an $\mathcal{O}_X(D)$, where the divisor D is determined up to linear equivalence. We have $\mathcal{O}_X(D + D') = \mathcal{O}_X(D) \otimes \mathcal{O}_X(D')$ for two divisors D, D′, and $\mathcal{O}_X(-D) = \mathcal{O}_X(D)^\vee$ (the dual of $\mathcal{O}_X(D)$, also written $\mathcal{O}_X(D)^{-1}$).

These remarks and parallel developments in analytic geometry (**A** VIII) have led to an enlargement of the conceptions of Riemann's immediate successors, by the consideration of vector bundles of arbitrary rank over an algebraic variety X (B 154, 316, 473) and the corresponding sheaves of germs of sections, which are precisely the *locally free* $\mathcal{O}_X$-Modules, i.e., those that are locally isomorphic to a direct sum $\mathcal{O}_X^k$. More generally still, as in analytic geometry, one is led to study coherent $\mathcal{O}_X$-Modules and their cohomology.

It has come to be realized that in fact most of the invariants that have been attached to nonsingular projective algebraic varieties over **C** can be expressed in terms of sheaf cohomology. To such a variety X, regarded as a complex manifold, there are associated the bundles of tangent p-covectors and the corresponding locally free sheaves Ω^p; when $p = n = \dim(X)$, the sheaf Ω^n is invertible, and the corresponding divisor Δ has from Riemann onwards played a fundamental role in algebraic geometry, under the name of *canonical divisor*. The number

$$p_g = \dim(H^0(\Omega^n)) = \dim(H^0(\mathcal{O}_X(\Delta)))$$

is called the *geometric genus* of X (the maximum number of linearly independent holomorphic differential n-forms), and the numbers

$$P_k = \dim(H^0(\mathcal{O}_X(k \cdot \Delta))),$$

where k is an integer $\geqslant 2$, are called the *plurigenera* of X. A series of analogous invariants are given by the numbers $\dim(H^s(\Omega^r))$ which, for a nonsingular projective variety, coincide with the numbers $h^{r,s}$ of Hodge theory (Dolbeault isomorphism (**A** VIII)). The alternating sum

$$p_a = \dim H^n(\mathcal{O}_X) - \dim H^{n-1}(\mathcal{O}_X) + \cdots + (-1)^{n-1} \dim H^1(\mathcal{O}_X)$$

is called the *arithmetic genus* of X. More generally, we define for each *coherent* $\mathcal{O}_X$-Module $\mathcal{F}$ (**C** I) its "Euler–Poincaré characteristic"

$$(1) \qquad \chi(\mathcal{F}) = \dim H^0(\mathcal{F}) - \dim H^1(\mathcal{F}) + \cdots + (-1)^n \dim H^n(\mathcal{F}).$$

If D is a divisor, $\chi(\mathcal{O}_X(D))$ (also written $\chi(D)$) is expressed in terms of the Chern classes of X and the Chern classes of the bundle B(D) by the Riemann–Roch–Hirzebruch formula (**A** VIII).

For a projective algebraic variety X of dimension n, the hard Lefschetz theorem from Hodge theory (**A** VIII) is interpreted as follows: the operator $L : H^p(X, \mathbf{C}) \to H^{p+2}(X, \mathbf{C})$ is multiplication (in the cohomology ring) by the class $\theta \in H^2(X, \mathbf{C})$ which is the canonical image of the homology class in $H_{2n-2}(X, \mathbf{C})$ of a hyperplane section of X.

Ample divisors and projective embeddings. Let $X \subset P_N(\mathbf{C})$ be a nonsingular irreducible projective variety, and let D be a divisor on X such that the vector space L(D) has dimension $r + 1 > 0$. By definition, the functions $f \in L(D)$ are the restrictions to X of functions of the form $\left(\sum_{j=0}^{r} \lambda_j P_j\right)\Big/Q$, where the P_j and Q are homogeneous polynomials of the same degree in the homogeneous coordinates, with no common factor. The divisors $(f) + D$ linearly equivalent to D are therefore expressible in the form

$$\left(\sum_{j=0}^{r} \lambda_j P_j\right) - (Q) + D.$$

In other words, we are led to associate with D a variable family of positive divisors, defined as hypersurfaces in X that are the intersections of X with the *linear* family of hypersurfaces in projective space with equations $\sum_{j=0}^{r} \lambda_j P_j = 0$. Conversely, if we are given $r+1$ linearly independent homogeneous polynomials P_j of the same degree which do not vanish identically on X, consider the positive divisors $\left(\sum_{j=0}^{r} \lambda_j P_j\right)$, where the λ_j are variable complex numbers, not all zero. If D is one of these divisors, corresponding to particular values λ_j^0 of the parameters λ_j, we may write $\left(\sum_{j=0}^{r} \lambda_j P_j\right) = (f) + D$, where f is the rational function obtained by restricting $\sum_j \lambda_j P_j \Big/ \sum_j \lambda_j^0 P_j$ to X. Hence the divisors $\left(\sum_{j=0}^{r} \lambda_j P_j\right)$ form a *projective linear variety* in the projective space $\mathbf{P}(L(D))$, also denoted by $|D|$. Such a variety of dimension r is called a *linear series* of dimension r on X; it is *complete* if it is the whole of $|D|$. The study of linear series is thus essentially equivalent to the study of divisors, and was developed in this more geometrical form long before the invention of sheaves [40].

The existence of appropriate linear series on X enables us to define morphisms of X (or of dense open subsets of X) into projective spaces; namely, a point $M \in X$ is mapped to the point in $\mathbf{P}_r(\mathbf{C})$ with homogeneous coordinates $P_j(M)$ $(0 \leqslant j \leqslant r)$; this makes sense whenever M is a point at which not all the P_j vanish. The most interesting case is that in which a point in general position in the image X′ is the image of only one point of X, in which case X′ is birationally equivalent to X; this leads in particular to the study of numerous remarkable algebraic varieties such as the Del Pezzo surfaces, and to the theory of birational transformations of a projective space into itself, called "Cremona transformations" (B 413; [117]).

A particular linear series on X is that in which the hypersurfaces $\sum_j \lambda_j P_j = 0$ are *hyperplanes* H in the ambient projective space; the corresponding invertible $\mathcal{O}_X$-Module is denoted by $\mathcal{O}_X(1)$. Whenever the procedure described above, starting with a divisor D, produces a variety X′ birationally equivalent to X, the image of D in X′ is a divisor corresponding to the linear system of hyperplane sections of X′ (which are irreducible for a hyperplane in general position (B 49)).

We write $\mathcal{O}_X(1)^{\otimes m} = \mathcal{O}_X(m)$ for all integers $m \in \mathbf{Z}$, and

$$\mathscr{F}(m) = \mathscr{F} \otimes_{\mathcal{O}_X} \mathcal{O}_X(m)$$

for an $\mathcal{O}_X$-Module $\mathscr{F}$. If $\mathscr{F} = \mathcal{O}_X(D)$ for a divisor D on X, then $\mathscr{F}(m) = \mathcal{O}_X(D + mH)$. If $\mathscr{F}$ is a coherent $\mathcal{O}_X$-Module, $\chi(\mathscr{F}(m))$ is a *polynomial* in m

for all values $m \in \mathbf{Z}$; moreover, if m is sufficiently large and positive, we have $H^q(\mathscr{F}(m)) = 0$ for all $q \geqslant 1$ (see B 94), so that $\chi(\mathscr{F}(m)) = \dim H^0(\mathscr{F}(m))$ for these values of m, and $\chi(\mathscr{F}(m))$ is precisely the Hilbert polynomial corresponding to the graded ideal $\mathfrak{a}$ of homogeneous polynomials that vanish on X (**C** II).

Consider now an *arbitrary* algebraic variety X over **C** (defined as the set of closed points of a **C**-scheme) and an invertible $\mathcal{O}_X$-Module $\mathscr{L}$: we can define directly a projective variety that corresponds to the variety X′ obtained by the classical construction described above, by forming the graded ring $R = \bigoplus_{m \geqslant 0} H^0(X, \mathscr{L}^{\otimes m})$ and taking $X' = \operatorname{Proj}(R)$. If X′ is isomorphic to X, the sheaf $\mathscr{L}$ is said to be *very ample*, and $\mathscr{L}$ is said to be *ample* if some sufficiently high tensor power $\mathscr{L}^{\otimes k}$ (k a positive integer) is very ample. Since X may have singularities, we define a divisor D directly as a global section of $\mathscr{M}_X^*/\mathcal{O}_X^*$, and we associate with D an invertible $\mathcal{O}_X$-Module $\mathcal{O}_X(D)$ as described earlier. For each subvariety Y of X, the restriction to Y of an invertible $\mathcal{O}_X$-Module is an invertible $\mathcal{O}_Y$-Module, and for a divisor D on X we denote by $\mathcal{O}_Y(D)$ the restriction of $\mathcal{O}_X(D)$ to Y. If $D_1, \ldots, D_s$ are any divisors on X, and Y is a subvariety of X of dimension s, we put

$$(2) \quad ((D_1 D_2 \cdots D_s) \cdot Y) = \sum_{t=0}^{s} (-1)^{s-t} \sum_{j_1 < \cdots < j_t} \chi(\mathcal{O}_Y(D_{j_1} + \cdots + D_{j_t}));$$

then we have the following remarkable ampleness criterion of Nakai–Moishezon: for $\mathcal{O}_X(D)$ to be ample, it is necessary and sufficient that $(D^s \cdot Y) > 0$ for all integers $s \geqslant 0$ and all subvarieties Y of dimension s. From this follows a criterion for a complete variety X to be projective: it is necessary and sufficient that every finite subset of X should be contained in an affine open set (B 301). If X is projective and nonsingular and $\mathscr{L}$ is an ample $\mathcal{O}_X$-Module, the smallest exponent k such that $\mathscr{L}^{\otimes k}$ is very ample depends only on the polynomial $m \mapsto \chi(\mathscr{L}^{\otimes m})$ (B 493; BAMS 80 (Matsusaka), SAMS XXIX (Lieberman–Mumford)).

5. Cohomology of schemes

For 50 years, the central problem of algebraic geometry has been to generalize the properties of classical varieties (defined over **C**) to varieties defined over an *arbitrary* field. The impulse for this generalization comes mainly from Diophantine geometry (**A** X), notably from the standard procedure in arithmetic of "reduction" modulo a prime number or an ideal, thereby inevitably introducing fields *of characteristic* >0. Although the preponderant role of topology in the study of algebraic varieties over **C** was universally recognized, Weil's calculations of zeta functions, in which

Betti numbers appeared quite unexpectedly, led him to suspect that this role in reality masked deeper properties of a purely algebraic nature (SAMS XXIX (Mazur)). The introduction by Serre of sheaf-theoretic techniques for the Zariski topology on an algebraic variety over an algebraically closed field of arbitrary characteristic was another step in the same direction: he showed that for a nonsingular projective variety X over **C**, if $\mathscr{F}$ is a coherent $\mathscr{O}_X$-Module (with respect to the Zariski topology) and if we define a sheaf (in the sense of the theory of complex manifolds) $\mathscr{F}^h = \mathscr{F} \otimes_{\mathscr{O}_X} \mathscr{H}$, where $\mathscr{H}$ is the sheaf of germs of holomorphic functions, then the mapping $\mathscr{F} \mapsto \mathscr{F}^h$ gives isomorphisms for the cohomology groups ([153], [135] (Hartshorne)).

The discovery of cohomological notions adequate for the desired extensions is due above all to A. Grothendieck and his school. Although the most important applications concern algebraic varieties, the use of various techniques of "base change" and "descent" requires the context of the theory of schemes. A complete exposition of the notions and results of these cohomology theories at present requires several thousand pages, and it is impossible to give in a short space even an idea of the techniques used.

The various cohomologies. The results of the classical theory that can be expressed in terms of sheaf cohomology (in the sense of analytic geometry (**A** VIII)) and that have been described above can in large part be extended to nonsingular projective varieties over any algebraically closed field, by using the cohomology of coherent sheaves for the Zariski topology: Serre's duality theorem (which generalizes even to singular varieties (B 149; LN 20, 146)), properties of the $\mathscr{F}(m)$, the theorem of coherence of the higher direct images of coherent Modules under a proper morphism (the analog of Grauert's theorem in analytic geometry (**A** VIII)), the Riemann–Roch–Hirzebruch theorem (Grothendieck–Washnitzer) (B 177; [21]), the theory of surfaces [130]. It is also possible to define, by use of the theory of abelian varieties over an arbitrary field k (see later), the Albanese and Picard varieties of a projective variety over k, and indeed for certain S-schemes X a *Picard scheme* $\mathbf{Pic}_{X/S}$ can be defined, which "parametrizes" the isomorphism classes of invertible $\mathscr{O}_X$-Modules. However, a part of the results of the classical theory, which are proved through Hodge theory, lose their validity. For example, it is still possible to define in general the sheaves Ω^r of germs of differential r-forms, and hence to define the Hodge numbers $h^{r,s} = \dim H^s(\Omega^r)$; but it can happen that $h^{s,r} \neq h^{r,s}$, the sum $h^{0,1} + h^{1,0}$ may be different from 2 dim(A), where A is the Albanese variety, and it can also happen that $\dim(A) \neq \dim(H^1(\mathscr{O}_X))$ ([130], [198]; SAMS XXIX (Berthelot, Mazur)).

To these results have been added (always with respect to the Zariski topology) others concerning *local cohomology*, the purpose of which is to study the cohomology of a subvariety in relation to that of its "neighborhoods" (reminiscent of the use of "tubular neighborhoods" in differential topology), using formal schemes (see later) (B 182, 453, 458; LN 41; [44]).

Another variant is the *de Rham cohomology*, which consists of taking the hypercohomology (**B** I) of the complex of sheaves Ω^r; this can be extended (in characteristic 0) to singular varieties, by considering them as subvarieties of a nonsingular variety and showing that the results obtained are independent of the embedding (LN 156; [75]).

All these definitions provide cohomology spaces over the field k over which the variety is defined. An entirely different idea, which leads to spaces over fields *of characteristic* 0, is to use sheaves with respect to appropriate Grothendieck topologies (**C** I). In the most frequently used cases, we take as covering families of morphisms of schemes either the faithfully flat, quasi-compact morphisms (the *fpqc* topology), or the faithfully flat morphisms of finite presentation (the *fppf* topology), or finally the étale morphisms (the étale topology). The most complete results are for the étale topology: it is necessary first of all to work only with torsion sheaves, which are $(\mathbf{Z}/l^\nu)$-modules (where l is a prime number distinct from the characteristics of the residue fields of the scheme, and ν is an arbitrary positive integer); from the cohomology groups so obtained, we pass to the inverse limit by letting ν tend to $+\infty$, so obtaining $\mathbf{Z}_l$-modules; and then by tensoring with the l-adic field $\mathbf{Q}_l$ we finally obtain *l-adic cohomology spaces* $H^j(X_{et}; \mathbf{Q}_l)$ over the field $\mathbf{Q}_l$ (LN 269, 270, 305). For a nonsingular projective variety over an arbitrary algebraically closed field k, this cohomology has properties very close to those of ordinary cohomology when $k = \mathbf{C}$: it vanishes for $j > 2n$ (where $n = \dim(X)$), obeys a Poincaré duality and a Künneth formula, and to each algebraic cycle of dimension j there corresponds a cohomology class of dimension $2(n - j)$. This enables one to prove for this cohomology the weak Lefschetz theorem and the Lefschetz trace formula (**A** I) for the number of fixed points of a morphism. We have $\dim H^1(X_{et}; \mathbf{Q}_l) = 2 \dim A$, where A is the Albanese variety of X. Finally, when $k = \mathbf{C}$, $H^j(X_{et}; \mathbf{Q}_l)$ is canonically isomorphic to the topological cohomology $H^j(X_{an}, \mathbf{Q}_l)$ of the analytic manifold X_{an} underlying X (B 279; [44]). So far there is no result involving positive definite quadratic forms, as in Hodge theory (**A** VIII); but Deligne has been able to establish the hard Lefschetz theorem, by an extraordinary proof which combines the properties of étale cohomology, his theorem on the zeros of zeta functions (the "Weil conjectures," **A** X), the theory of semisimple Lie groups and the procedure of Hadamard–de la Vallée Poussin for proving that the Riemann zeta function $\zeta(s)$ does not vanish on the line $\mathscr{R}s = 1$ (SAMS XXIX (Messing); [221]).

We remark also that the relation between the Brauer group and Galois 2-cohomology (**B** I) generalizes to schemes, but it is étale cohomology that is involved (B 290, 297; [44]).

Another Grothendieck topology gives rise to *crystalline cohomology*, which, when k is a field of characteristic $p > 0$, gives cohomology spaces *over the field* $\mathbf{Q}_p$ (and not over $\mathbf{Q}_l$, $l \neq p$). This cohomology is related to the theory of formal groups (see later) (B 456; LN 370, 407; Nice B 5 (Grothendieck); BAMS 78 (Mazur); SAMS XXIX (Berthelot, Illusie)).

Finally, the fact that for an algebraic curve, its Jacobian can take the place of the *integral* cohomology group of degree 1 has led to the idea that there should exist a cohomology theory of varieties of arbitrary dimension which would provide richer information than cohomology over the fields $\mathbf{Q}_l$ or $\mathbf{Q}_p$. This is the theory of "motives" or "motivic cohomology," in which it is thought that the definitions are the good ones, but the expected results are still conjectural (B 365; [135] (Kleiman)).

Intersection multiplicities and homology. A purely algebraic definition of the intersection multiplicity of two algebraic cycles has required much effort. It is by use of homological algebra that it has finally been possible to generalize the definition, known since the 19th century, for two plane curves: if these curves V, W intersect at a point P and if $\mathfrak{p}_V$, $\mathfrak{p}_W$ are the corresponding prime ideals in the local ring A at the point P (in the plane k^2), the intersection multiplicity is the length of the A-module $A/(\mathfrak{p}_V + \mathfrak{p}_W)$. In the general case of two subvarieties V, W of a nonsingular variety X of dimension n, the multiplicity of their intersection $V \cap W$ at a point P of this intersection has to be "corrected": it is defined to be the sum

$$\sum_{j=0}^{n} (-1)^j \operatorname{length}(\operatorname{Tor}_j^A(A/\mathfrak{p}_V, A/\mathfrak{p}_W)),$$

where $\mathfrak{p}_V$ and $\mathfrak{p}_W$ are again the prime ideals corresponding to V and W in the local ring A of X at the point P (LN 11). We have thus one of the ingredients for establishing a calculus of algebraic cycles on a nonsingular variety X over an arbitrary algebraically closed field, on the model of the classical homology ring (**A** I); the other ingredient is the notion of *rational equivalence* of cycles, which substitutes for homological equivalence, and for which it is necessary to prove a lemma (Chow's "moving lemma") that will guarantee that any two cycles may be replaced by rationally equivalent cycles that are in "general position" ([135] (Roberts)). In this way we obtain what is called the (graded) *Chow ring* $A_{.}X$, which can in fact be defined also for singular projective varieties [58]. This leads to a generalization of the Riemann–Roch theorem in the form given to it by Grothendieck for nonsingular varieties: the Grothendieck group $K_0(X)$ is defined to be the quotient of the **Z**-module of formal linear combinations $\sum_j n_j[\mathscr{F}_j]$ of coherent $\mathscr{O}_X$-Modules by the submodule generated by the combinations $[\mathscr{F}] - [\mathscr{F}'] - [\mathscr{F}'']$ for each exact sequence $0 \to \mathscr{F}' \to \mathscr{F} \to \mathscr{F}'' \to 0$, and the theorem gives a natural transformation $K_0(X) \to A\ X \otimes_{\mathbf{Z}} \mathbf{Q}$ (B 464; LN 225; SAMS XXIX (Fulton)).

The fundamental group and monodromy. The algebraic definition of the fundamental group of a scheme S is another example of the use of representable functors. Consider the category $\boldsymbol{C}$ of étale coverings of S and the functor F that associates to each $X \in \mathrm{Ob}\boldsymbol{C}$ the set of geometrical points of X lying over $a \in S$. The functor F can be "represented" not by an object of $\boldsymbol{C}$ but by a "pro-object" (which may be thought of as an inverse limit (**C** I) of objects of $\boldsymbol{C}$ in a larger category), the "universal covering" of S; the fundamental group $\pi_1(S, a)$ is then the group of automorphisms of this pro-object. This definition agrees with that of the (topological) Galois group of the algebraic closure of a field k, when $S = \mathrm{Spec}(k)$. It gives rather different results from the classical theories: for example, for a projective algebraic curve having a double point with distinct tangents, the fundamental group is the completion $\hat{\mathbf{Z}}$ of $\mathbf{Z}$ with respect to the topology for which the subgroups of finite index form a fundamental system of neighborhoods of 0, whereas for a curve with a cusp, the fundamental group is 0 (B 204, 543; LN 176, 208, 224). Algebraic curves over a field of characteristic $p > 0$ can be "lifted" to curves over a field of characteristic 0, and this fact can be exploited to obtain more precise information about their fundamental groups, by using the topological theory of coverings [D, Chapter 16].

It is then possible to develop machinery that enables one to define, in the context of nonsingular projective varieties over an arbitrary field k, a "monodromy transformation," which is an action of an element of the fundamental group $\pi_1(U, u)$, where U is an open set in the affine line and $u \in U$, on an étale cohomology group $H^j((X_u)_{et}, \mathbf{Q}_l)$ of the fiber X_u of a morphism $X \to U$ at the point u (LN 163, 288, 340). This is one of the principal tools in Deligne's proofs (B 446; SAMS XXIX (Messing), [221]).

6. Classification problems

The process inverse to that of "blowing up" a subvariety (**A** VIII) also exists in algebraic geometry: for example, on a nonsingular projective algebraic surface, an irreducible curve C can be "blown down" to a point if and only if $(C \cdot C) = -1$ and the genus of C is zero (Castelnuovo's criterion in the classical case, which is valid also over fields of characteristic $\neq 0$). Such curves are called "exceptional curves of the first kind," and a surface is said to be *minimal* if it possesses none. On every projective surface, the exceptional curves can be "blown down" so as to obtain a *minimal model*, which is unique up to isomorphism, except for ruled surfaces ([160], [199]).

The classification of surfaces. These phenomena (in the classical case) led the Italian geometers (especially Enriques) to seek to establish a classification of minimal models of algebraic surfaces based on their various numerical invariants. This classification has been extended in two directions: to arbitrary compact holomorphic surfaces, by Kodaira, and to algebraic surfaces over an arbitrary field; this latter classification is now almost complete (B 500, 506; SAMS XXIX (Bombieri–Husemoller)) and a part of the results generalize to varieties of higher dimension (LN 412, 439).

"*Moduli*" *problems.* The "problem of the moduli" of Riemann, i.e., the "parametrization" of the set of isomorphism classes of nonsingular projective algebraic curves over **C** by the points of an algebraic variety (**A** VIII) can be posed in the same terms in algebraic geometry over an arbitrary algebraically closed field. It has been solved by Mumford, who has constructed a "scheme of moduli" M for curves of a given genus g, having the following property: for any algebraically closed field k, the closed points of the scheme $M \otimes_{\mathbf{Z}} k$ obtained from M by the base change $\mathrm{Spec}(k) \to \mathrm{Spec}(\mathbf{Z})$ are in functorial one–one correspondence with the isomorphism classes of nonsingular irreducible projective curves of genus g over the field k. The proof is in several steps and begins by constructing, for n sufficiently large, a closed subscheme H of the Hilbert scheme of $\mathbf{P}_n(\mathbf{Z})$ such that to each curve of genus g over k is associated a point of $H \otimes_{\mathbf{Z}} k$, and such that two points corresponding to isomorphic curves are obtained one from the other by a projective transformation of $\mathbf{P}_n(k)$. The problem is now to define M as an "orbit scheme" of the group scheme $\mathbf{PGL}(n)$ acting on the scheme H. Invariant theory over a field of characteristic 0 (see later) enables Mumford to obtain an orbit scheme for $H \otimes_{\mathbf{Z}} \mathbf{Q}$, which must therefore be $M \otimes_{\mathbf{Z}} \mathbf{Q}$. To obtain M itself, he has to go *via* a "moduli scheme" for abelian varieties equipped with certain supplementary structures, which is easier to construct than that for curves; finally he shows that the set of orbits of H can be identified with a subscheme of this latter scheme, by virtue of the identification of a curve (up to isomorphism) with its polarized Jacobian (see later) (Nice B 5 (Mumford, Seshadri); SAMS

XXIX (Seshadri); [129]). The study of the scheme M has scarcely begun; all that is known is that $M \otimes_{\mathbf{Z}} k$ is irreducible for each algebraically closed field k (B 385).

There are no analogous results for varieties of dimension $\geqslant 2$, except for certain vector bundles over curves, and abelian varieties (B 338). However, there are algebraic results corresponding to the theory of "local" deformations of complex manifolds (**A** VIII), depending on the notion of a formal scheme (see later) (SAMS XXIX (Seshadri); [135] (Kleiman–Landolfi); LN 239, 283).

7. Algebraic groups

We have seen earlier how to define, for an arbitrary scheme S, the notion of a *group scheme over* S. Equivalently, a group scheme over S consists of an S-scheme X and two morphisms $m: X \times_S X \to X$ and $i: X \to X$ satisfying the formal properties of multiplication and inversion in group theory: for example, associativity is expressed by the commutativity of the diagram

$$\begin{array}{ccc} X \times_S X \times_S X & \xrightarrow{m \times 1} & X \times_S X \\ {\scriptstyle 1 \times m}\downarrow & & \downarrow{\scriptstyle m} \\ X \times_S X & \xrightarrow[m]{} & X \end{array} \qquad (3)$$

A *homomorphism* $u: X \to Y$ of group schemes over S is an S-morphism such that the following diagram is commutative:

$$\begin{array}{ccc} X \times_S X & \xrightarrow{u \times u} & Y \times_S Y \\ {\scriptstyle m_X}\downarrow & & \downarrow{\scriptstyle m_Y} \\ X & \xrightarrow[u]{} & Y \end{array} \qquad (4)$$

It should be observed that if X is a group scheme over S, the underlying set X is *not* a group (although one often speaks of X as if it were a group): it is the set X_T of "points of X with values in T" that *is* a group, for every S-scheme T. In the case where $S = \operatorname{Spec}(A)$ and $X = \operatorname{Spec}(B)$ are affine, so that B is an A-algebra, the morphism m corresponds to an A-*homomorphism* $\Delta: B \to B \otimes_A B$ satisfying the condition corresponding to (3), i.e., $(\Delta \otimes 1) \circ \Delta = (1 \otimes \Delta) \circ \Delta$. The other conditions on m and i are translated in the same way, and an A-algebra B with this additional structure is called an A-*bigebra* [42]. For example, the *additive group* $\mathbf{G}_a(A)$ is the scheme Spec(A[T]) of the algebra A[T] of polynomials in one variable, where

$\Delta(T) = 1 \otimes T + T \otimes 1$. If $A \to k$ is a homomorphism of A into an algebraically closed field k, the points of $\mathbf{G}_a(A)$ with values in k are in one-one correspondence with the homomorphisms $\chi_x : A[T] \to k$ such that $\chi_x(T) = x \in k$, and the points of the product $\mathbf{G}_a(A) \times_S \mathbf{G}_a(A)$ with values in k are in one-one correspondence with the homomorphisms

$$\chi_{(x,y)} : A[T] \otimes_A A[T] \to k$$

such that $\chi_{(x,y)}(T \otimes 1) = x$ and $\chi_{(x,y)}(1 \otimes T) = y$; since $\chi_{(x,y)} \circ \Delta = \chi_{x+y}$, the name "additive group" is justified. Likewise, the *multiplicative group* $\mathbf{G}_m(A)$ is the scheme $\mathrm{Spec}(A[T, T^{-1}])$, with

$$\Delta(T) = 1 \otimes T + T \otimes 1 + T \otimes T.$$

Already there appears a very clear difference between the notion of group scheme and the notions of "abstract" group or Lie group: not only are $\mathbf{G}_a$ and $\mathbf{G}_m$ not isomorphic, but there is no nontrivial homomorphism of one into the other.

The theory of group schemes is built up on the model of the classical theory of abstract groups, by defining subgroups, normal subgroups, kernels and images of homomorphisms, quotient groups, the center, commutator subgroup, etc.; of course, "subgroup" always means "group subscheme" (LN 15, 119, 151, 152, 153; [38]; [135] (Oort)). Here again new phenomena present themselves. For example, if k is an algebraically closed field, the only homomorphisms u_n of $\mathbf{G}_m(k)$ into itself correspond to the homomorphisms v_n of $k[T, T^{-1}]$ into itself such that $v_n(T) = T^n$, for some positive or negative integer n. The "kernel" of this homomorphism u_n is the subscheme $\mathrm{Spec}(k[T]/(T^n - 1))$: if n is not a multiple of the characteristic p of k, this scheme has an underlying set consisting of n points, at each of which the local ring is isomorphic to k; but if $n = p$, we have $T^p - 1 = (T - 1)^p$ and the underlying set consists of a single point, with a *nonreduced* local ring (which, in passing, shows the necessity of admitting such rings into the theory), so that we have an "infinitesimal" kernel (see later).

The most interesting case is that of *algebraic groups* (**B** 145): if k is an algebraically closed field, such a group is an algebraic variety G over k that consists of the closed points of a group scheme X over k (reduced, separated, and of finite type). Equivalently, G is an algebraic variety endowed with a group structure such that the mappings $(x, y) \mapsto xy$ and $x \mapsto x^{-1}$ are morphisms of varieties (the product set $G \times G$ consists of the closed points of the scheme $X \times_k X$ because k is algebraically closed). If X is obtained by extension of scalars to k of a group scheme X_0 over k_0 (where k is an extension of k_0), we say that G is *defined over* k_0, or is a k_0*-group*, and the homomorphisms obtained in the same way by extension of scalars from homomorphisms $X_0 \to X'_0$ of group schemes over k_0 are called k_0-*homomorphisms*. In this case, for each extension K of k_0 we may consider the group G_K of points of G *with values in* K; the group G, defined over k_0 (but consisting of points with values in k), should not be confused with the group G_{k_0} of points with values in k_0 (which may well be a finite group, whereas G itself is infinite).

So long as one is not concerned with problems of "descent" for subfields of an algebraically closed field k, one can usually ignore the "infinitesimal" phenomena mentioned above, and regard algebraic groups over k simply as sets of points. An important notion in the theory is that of *isogeny*: this is a morphism $f: G_1 \to G_2$ of algebraic groups over k that is surjective with finite kernel. It should be remarked that a bijective isogeny need not be an isomorphism. If there exists an isogeny $G_1 \to G_2$, the group G_2 is said to be *isogenous* to G_1.

Abelian varieties. The theory of abelian varieties over an arbitrary algebraically closed field k was created by A. Weil. Here one cannot start from groups such as $\mathbf{C}^g$; an abelian variety A over k is an algebraic group for which the underlying algebraic variety is connected (in the Zariski topology) and *complete*, which implies that A must be *commutative*. The theory of abelian varieties is based on the study of the divisors on A and the effect of a translation of the group on the divisors. In this way it can be shown (generalizing a theorem of Poincaré on classical abelian varieties) that every abelian variety is isogenous to a product of *simple* abelian varieties, where "simple" means containing no proper abelian subvariety of dimension >0. The *dual* A′ of an abelian variety A is defined as the Picard variety of A, and it can be shown that (A′)′ is canonically isomorphic to A. Moreover, every abelian variety is a projective variety (B 104, 106, 156, 164, 286; LN 326; [131]; [135] (Oort)).

In the theory of schemes there is a notion that generalizes that of an abelian variety: a group scheme X over S is said to be *abelian* if the structural morphism $X \to S$ is smooth and proper and its geometric fibers are connected. It should be remarked that X is no longer necessarily commutative [129]. When $S = \operatorname{Spec}(A)$, where A is a discrete valuation ring with maximal ideal $\mathfrak{m}$, there is a notion of "minimal model" for abelian schemes X over S such that $X \times_S \operatorname{Spec}(A/\mathfrak{m})$ is a given abelian variety X_0 over the field $A/\mathfrak{m}$, analogous to the notion of minimal models of algebraic surfaces, and called the "Néron model" (B 227).

Linear algebraic groups. A linear algebraic group over an algebraically closed field k is an algebraic group G whose underlying algebraic variety is an *affine* algebraic variety. The prototype of such groups is the general linear group $\mathbf{GL}(n, k)$, and every linear algebraic group is isomorphic to a closed subgroup of some $\mathbf{GL}(N, k)$. The identity component G_0 of G (with respect to the Zariski topology) is a linear algebraic subgroup of finite index $(G : G_0)$. The method of investigation (for a *connected* group G) is related to the study of compact connected Lie groups (**B** II), based on the consideration of their maximal tori [D, Chap. 21]. Here the tori $\mathbf{T}^n = \mathbf{R}^n/\mathbf{Z}^n$ of Lie group theory are replaced by "algebraic tori," isomorphic to the groups $\mathbf{G}_m^n$, but Lie algebras can no longer be used in the same way (see later). An essential notion is that of a *maximal connected solvable subgroup*, also called a *Borel subgroup* (for A. Borel). Any two maximal tori are conjugate in G: each maximal torus T is its own centralizer, and its normalizer $\mathcal{N}(T)$ is such that the group $\mathcal{N}(T)/T = W$, the *Weyl group* of T, is *finite*. Any two Borel subgroups are conjugate in G, and each Borel subgroup B is its own normalizer. For a given maximal torus T, the number of Borel subgroups containing T is finite, and the Weyl group W permutes them simply transitively. There is also a unique largest connected closed solvable normal subgroup R, called the *radical* of G, which is also the intersection of all the Borel subgroups; the radical of G/R consists only of the identity element, and groups with this property are said to be *semisimple*. A connected linear algebraic group whose radical is a torus is said to be *reductive*.

If G is semisimple and T is a maximal torus in G, the set of one-dimensional tori (isomorphic to the group $\mathbf{G}_m$) contained in T is a torsion-free $\mathbf{Z}$-module $X_*(T)$, and the group W acts on the real vector space

$$H = X_*(T) \otimes_{\mathbf{Z}} \mathbf{R}.$$

As in the case of compact groups, it can be shown that there is a scalar product on H, with respect to which W is generated by reflections in a family of hyperplanes orthogonal to vectors forming a "reduced root system" [D, Chapter 21]. Finally, if $B \supset T$ is a Borel subgroup, G is the disjoint union of the double cosets BwB, where w runs through a system of representatives of W in $\mathcal{N}(T)$ (*Bruhat decomposition*). Using these properties, it can be shown that up to isogeny the semisimple algebraic groups over k have the *same* definitions as when $k = \mathbf{C}$ (B 121, 206; [18]; [29]; [86 *bis*]). In fact, it can be shown that they are obtained by extension of scalars from group schemes *over* $\mathbf{Z}$ (B 219; LN 131, 153), which explains their independence of the characteristic and the existence of Chevalley groups (**B** III).

Analogous methods are used to obtain, on the model of the linear representations of compact connected Lie groups (**B** II) [D, Chapter 21], linear representations $G \to \mathbf{GL}(E)$ defined over k, for a semisimple algebraic group G over an algebraically closed field k, where E is a finite-dimensional k-vector space. The problems relating to such representations are not completely solved when k has characteristic $p > 0$ (SAMS XXIX (Borel)).

If G is a semisimple algebraic group defined over a field $k_0 \subset k$, it can happen that the Borel subgroups and the maximal tori of G are not defined over k_0. The study of G_{k_0} in this situation has been carried through by Borel and Tits (B 313, 435; [22]): it again involves root systems, which are not the same as for G, and the *parabolic* subgroups, which are the subgroups $P \neq G$ containing a Borel subgroup. The case where k_0 is a local field (for example the p-adic field $\mathbf{Q}_p$) is particularly interesting, in view of arithmetical applications; here the Tits buildings (**B** III) play an important part (Vancouver (Tits)).

Apart from semisimple and reductive groups, the only other classes of linear algebraic groups over an algebraically closed field k that have been studied to any extent are the commutative groups and unipotent groups (i.e., groups which are conjugate in $\mathbf{GL}(N, k)$ to groups consisting of upper triangular matrices with 1's down the diagonal) (LN 434, 455; [38], [135] (Oort)). If k is algebraically closed of characteristic 0, every connected linear algebraic group over k is the semidirect product of its radical and a semisimple group (*Levi decomposition*).

Finally, if G is any algebraic group over k, there exists a normal subgroup L of G that is a linear algebraic group, such that G/L is an abelian variety (Chevalley's theorem). These groups have been studied only in particular cases, such as the "generalized Jacobians" corresponding to algebraic curves with singularities (B 75, 93; [154]).

Invariant theory. The classical theory of invariants was created in the 19th century in pursuit of a classification of algebraic subvarieties of projective space $\mathbf{P}_n(\mathbf{C})$, two varieties being placed in the same class if one could be obtained from the other by the action of an element of the group $\mathbf{PGL}(n + 1)$. With the development of the theory of linear representations of groups (**B** III), invariant theory came to be subsumed in this latter theory, in the following form. Consider a subgroup G of $\mathbf{GL}(n, k)$, where k is an algebraically closed field, and a space of tensors $T_q^p(k^n)$, on which G acts in the natural way: the problem is to decide whether this linear representation is completely reducible, and to determine as explicitly as possible its irreducible subrepresentations, in particular those of degree 1, which will provide the desired "invariants." This program has been accomplished with success for the classical groups over a field of characteristic 0 (B 395; [43], [54]). Latterly, the problem has been generalized to one of algebraic geometry: given an algebraic group G over an algebraically closed field k that acts on an algebraic variety X over k in such a way that the action of G on X is a morphism $G \times_k X \to X$ of algebraic varieties, can the orbit space X/G be canonically endowed with the structure of an algebraic variety? If X = Spec(A) is affine, G acts on A by automorphisms; if A^G is the subalgebra of G-invariant elements of A, the "orbit variety" ought to be $\mathrm{Spec}(A^G)$, which leads to the question whether A^G is a finitely generated k-algebra. This is known to be the case when k is of characteristic 0 and G is reductive (Hilbert's finiteness theorem), but there are examples due to Nagata (with k of characteristic 0) in which A^G is not finitely generated as a k-algebra (B 175). Recently, W. Haboush has proved that A^G is finitely generated when G is reductive and k of characteristic $p > 0$ (B 462; SAMS XXIX (Seshadri)). If X is a projective variety, it is not in general possible (even for $G = \mathbf{GL}(n, k)$) to define a structure of algebraic variety on the whole of X/G; it is necessary to eliminate certain orbits, and retain only those called "semistable" (Hilbert–Mumford) ([129], [135] (Mumford–Suominen)).

8. Formal schemes and formal groups

Let X be a scheme and $\mathscr{I}$ a quasi-coherent Ideal of $\mathscr{O}_X$. In addition to the closed subscheme X′ of X defined by $\mathscr{I}$, having $\mathscr{O}_X/\mathscr{I}$ as sheaf of rings, we may consider also the sheaves $\mathscr{O}_X/\mathscr{I}^{k+1}$ for all integers $k \geqslant 1$, which define closed subschemes X_k of X (having the same underlying space as X′) which may be thought of as the "infinitesimal neighborhoods of order k" of the subscheme X′.

Pursuing this idea, we are led to consider *simultaneously* all the sheaves $\mathscr{O}_X/\mathscr{I}^{k+1}$, which form an inverse system, and the inverse limit, which is a sheaf of topological rings. This defines on X′ (under certain conditions) a new type of structure, which is a particular case of what is called a *formal* scheme.

To see in what respects this structure differs from that of a scheme, let us first consider the affine case, where we have a ring A, an ideal $\mathfrak{J}$ in A, and the inverse limit of the rings $A/\mathfrak{J}^n$. For simplicity suppose that A is Noetherian (**C** II); then this inverse limit may be identified with the completion $\hat{A}$ of A with respect to the topology for which the $\mathfrak{J}^n$ form a fundamental system of neighborhoods of 0. The topology of $\hat{A}$ is Hausdorff, and the ideals $\mathfrak{J}^n\hat{A}$ form a fundamental system of neighborhoods of 0. The *formal spectrum* $\mathrm{Spf}(\hat{A})$ consists of the prime ideals that are *open* in this topology; the Zariski topology is induced by that of Spec(A), and we have to take an inverse limit of sheaves to obtain $\mathrm{Spf}(\hat{A})$ as a ringed space. From then on we proceed in the usual way (by "gluing together") to arrive at the general notion of a formal scheme [69].

Let us now return to the situation at the beginning of this section. If the scheme X is locally Noetherian (i.e., obtained by gluing together spectra of Noetherian rings) and $\mathscr{I}$ is coherent, the sections of the formal scheme X′ so defined play a role analogous to that of the holomorphic nonrational functions on a classical algebraic variety, and had been introduced by Zariski (for arbitrary algebraic varieties) in order to provide, in "abstract" algebraic geometry, an analytical tool capable of performing the same services (B 86, 158, 182; [69]). Grothendieck showed that formal schemes perform an analogous function in the general case, for the study of cohomology of schemes. For example, if $f: X \to Y$ is a proper morphism of spectra of Noetherian rings, f factorizes as $X \xrightarrow{h} Z \xrightarrow{g} Y$, where g is a finite morphism and the fibers of h are connected.

Formal schemes form a category, and we may therefore follow the usual procedure for defining algebraic structures on the objects of a category (**C** I) and define *formal groups* to be group objects in the category of formal schemes (LN 151). For affine formal schemes of the type $\mathrm{Spf}(\hat{A})$, we see that as in the case of group schemes a structure of formal group is defined by continuous homomorphisms $\Delta: \hat{A} \to \hat{A} \hat{\otimes} \hat{A}$ and $a: \hat{A} \to \hat{A}$ satisfying conditions which express the group axioms (the sign $\hat{\otimes}$ indicates the "completion" of the usual tensor product (see [42])). The simplest case ("naive" formal groups) is that in which $\hat{A}$ is the completion of a polynomial ring $R[T_1, \ldots, T_n]$, i.e., a formal power series ring $R[[T_1, \ldots, T_n]]$ over a commutative ring R (**C** II); then $\hat{A} \hat{\otimes} \hat{A}$ is a ring of formal power series in $2n$ indeterminates $R[[U_1, \ldots, U_n, V_1, \ldots, V_n]]$, and Δ is determined by n formal power series $\Delta(T_j) = \varphi_j(U_1, \ldots, V_n)$. It can be verified that the conditions on the φ_j that correspond to the group axioms are (writing $U = (U_1, \ldots, U_n)$ and $V = (V_1, \ldots, V_n)$ for brevity): (1) $\varphi_j(U, V) = U_j + V_j + \psi_j(U, V)$, where the terms of the series ψ_j are of degree $\geqslant 1$ in the U_k and in the V_k; (2) the associativity relation $\varphi(\varphi U, V), W) = \varphi(U, \varphi(V, W))$, where $\varphi(U, V)$ denotes the system of n series $\varphi_j(U, V)$. Apart from the fact that the coefficients lie in an arbitrary commutative ring R, we are in the same algebraic situation as for the local expression of a Lie group law [D, Chapter 19], and we may therefore associate with a formal group, as in the classical case, an associative "infinitesimal R-algebra" $\mathfrak{G}$ with a basis (Z_α) over R, where the multi-index α runs through $\mathbf{N}^n$. The Z_α such that $|\alpha| = 1$ form a Lie subalgebra $\mathfrak{g}$ of $\mathfrak{G}$; but if for example R is a field of characteristic $p > 0$, the associative subalgebra generated by $\mathfrak{g}$ is not the whole of $\mathfrak{G}$ (it is finite dimensional!).

If now G is a group scheme over $S = \mathrm{Spec}(A)$, where A is a Noetherian ring, the mechanism of constructing a formal scheme from the closed subscheme of G corresponding to the notion of the "identity element" gives rise to a formal group and hence to an "infinitesimal algebra" that is the analog of the "universal enveloping algebra" of the Lie algebra of a Lie group; inside this associative algebra there is a Lie subalgebra that plays the role of the Lie algebra of the group scheme G, but does not in general generate the whole infinitesimal algebra: so that it is only from the infinitesimal algebra, and not from the Lie algebra, that one can hope to obtain results on the structure of the group scheme. This hope has so far been justified by the study of abelian varieties and the group schemes which generalize them (B 352).

This is a consequence of the fact that the commutative formal groups are well known, and the study of them reduces to problems of linear algebra. For a "naive" commutative formal group of the type considered above, we consider systems $f(\mathrm{T}) = (f_1(\mathrm{T}), \ldots, f_n(\mathrm{T}))$ of n formal power series in R[[T]] with no constant terms, which compose according to the formal group law $(f + g)(\mathrm{T}) = \varphi(f(\mathrm{T}), g(\mathrm{T}))$ and hence form a commutative group. If in addition the ring R is for example $\mathbf{Z}_p$ (or a quotient of this), we can introduce in a natural way a noncommutative ring C acting on this commutative group, which thereby becomes a C-module (the elements of which are called "typical curves"). It turns out that the structure of this C-module completely determines that of the formal group; these C-modules are particularly well known when R is an algebraically closed field of characteristic $p > 0$ (B 318, 359, 409; LN 74, 264, 302, 443; [42]).

9. Connections with the natural sciences

Only very recently have interesting applications of algebraic geometry appeared, notably in the theory of elementary particles (Yang–Mills equations) and in the theory of the Korteweg–de Vries equation, where abelian varieties are involved (Ju. Manin, V. Arnold, Mumford, etc.).

10. The originators

The main ideas in algebraic geometry are due to the following mathematicians:

Classical algebraic geometry. N. Abel (1802–1829), C. Jacobi (1804–1851), B. Riemann (1826–1866), R. Dedekind (1831–1916), H. Weber (1842–1913), L. Kronecker (1823–1891), E. Picard (1856–1941), H. Poincaré (1854–1912), G. Castelnuovo (1864–1952), F. Enriques (1871–1946), F. Severi (1879–1961), S. Lefschetz (1884–1972), W. Hodge (1903–1975), K. Kodaira, J. P. Serre, F. Hirzebruch.

Algebraic varieties over an arbitrary field and the theory of schemes. B. L. van der Waerden, O. Zariski, A. Weil, J. P. Serre, A. Grothendieck, H. Hironaka, P. Deligne.

Algebraic groups. A. Weil, C. Chevalley, A. Borel.

Invariant theory. A. Cayley (1821–1895), D. Hilbert (1862–1943), M. Nagata, D. Mumford, W. Haboush.

Formal groups. M. Lazard, P. Cartier, J. Lubin.

The following mathematicians have also made substantial contributions: S. Abhyankar, S. Akbuhut, G. Albanese (1890–1947), A. Andreotti (1925–1980), V. Arnold, S. Aronhold (1819–1884), M. Artin, M. Atiyah, I. Barsotti, W. Barth, P. Baum, L. Bers, P. Berthelot, E. Bertini (1846–1933), A. Bielanycki-Birula, S. Bloch, E. Bombieri, J. Boutot, A. von Brill (1842–1935), W. Chow, R. Clebsch (1833–1872), C. Clemens, W. Clifford (1845–1879), M. Cornalba, L. Cremona (1830–1903), P. Del Pezzo (1859–1936), M. Demazure, P. Du Val, B. Dwork, M. Eger (1922–1952), R. Elkik, J. Fogarty, J. Fontaine, T. Frankel, W. Fulton, P. Gabriel, L. Godeaux (1887–1975), A. Göpel (1812–1847), J. Goodman, P. Gordan (1837–1912), H. Grauert, P. Griffiths, L. Gruson, G. Harder, R. Hartshorne, M. Hazewinkel, C. Hermite (1822–1901), H. Hijikata, G. Hochschild, A. Hurwitz (1859–1919), J. Igusa, S. Iitaka, L. Illusie, V. Iskovski, N. Iwahori, J. P. Jouanolou, H. Jung (1876–1953), N. Katz, G. Kempf, H. King, S. Kleiman, M. Kneser, A. Landman, S. Lang, Le Dung Trang, J. Le Potier, S. Lichtenbaum, D. Lieberman, J. Lipman, S. Lubkin, I. G. Macdonald, R. Macpherson, Ju. Manin, T. Matsusaka, A. Mattuck, B. Mazur, W. Messing, J. Milne, Y. Miyaoka, B. Moishezon, P. Monsky, J. Morgan, S. Mori, G. Mostow, J. P. Murre, Y. Nakai, M. Narasimhan, J. Nash, A. Néron, E. Netto (1846–1919), E. Noether (1882–1935), M. Noether (1841–1921), T. Oda, A. Ogg, A. Ogus, F. Oort, P. Orlik, C. Peskine, V. Platonov, V. Puiseux (1820–1883), S. Ramanan, C. Ramanujam, M. Rapoport, M. Raynaud, R. Richardson, J. Roberts, G. Roch (1839–1866), A. Roitman, J. Rosenhain (1816–1887), M. Rosenlicht, G. C. Rota, P. Samuel, W. Schmid, F. K. Schmidt, M. Schlessinger, H. Schubert (1848–1911), B. Segre (1903–1977), C. Segre (1863–1924), A. Seidenberg, C. Seshadri, I. Shafarevich, E. Snapper, T. Springer, R. Steinberg, J. Sylvester (1814–1897), L. Szpiro, J. Tate, O. Teichmüller (1913–1943), J. Tits, A. Tjurin, J. A. Todd, A. Tognoli, R. Torelli (1884–1915), K. Ueno, A. van de Ven, J. L. Verdier, G. Veronese (1857–1917), E. Vesentini, P. Wagreich, R. Walker, A. Wallace, G. Washnitzer, K. Weierstrass (1815–1897), V. Yančevskii, H. Zeuthen (1839–1920).

References

B: 72, 75, 82, 86, 93, 94, 104, 106, 121, 145, 149, 151, 152, 154, 156, 158, 164, 168, 177, 182, 190, 195, 204, 206, 212, 219, 221, 227, 232, 236, 248, 250, 279, 283, 286, 290, 294, 297, 301, 313, 316, 318, 320, 338, 352, 359, 363, 365, 376, 385, 395, 409, 413, 435, 446, 453, 456, 458, 464, 473, 493, 500, 505, 506, 519, 543, 544, 548.

LN: 11, 15, 20, 41, 74, 119, 131, 146, 151, 152, 153, 156, 163, 174, 176, 203, 208, 224, 225, 239, 264, 269, 270, 283, 288, 302, 305, 326, 340, 349, 370, 407, 412, 414, 439, 443, 455, 462, 569, 585, 589, 592, 603, 614, 620, 632, 687, 708, 732, 777, 815.

BAMS: 76 (Griffiths), 77 (Zariski), 78 (Mazur), 80 (Hartshorne, Matsusaka).

SAMS: XXIX.

Astérisque: 20, 47–48, 54, 63–65.

[18], [21], [22], [38], [40], [41], [42], [43], [44], [54], [58], [69], [70], [75], [86 *bis*], [107], [113], [117], [128], [129], [130], [131], [135], [153], [154], [160], [161], [162], [198], [199], [207], [208], [214], [221], [222].

A X

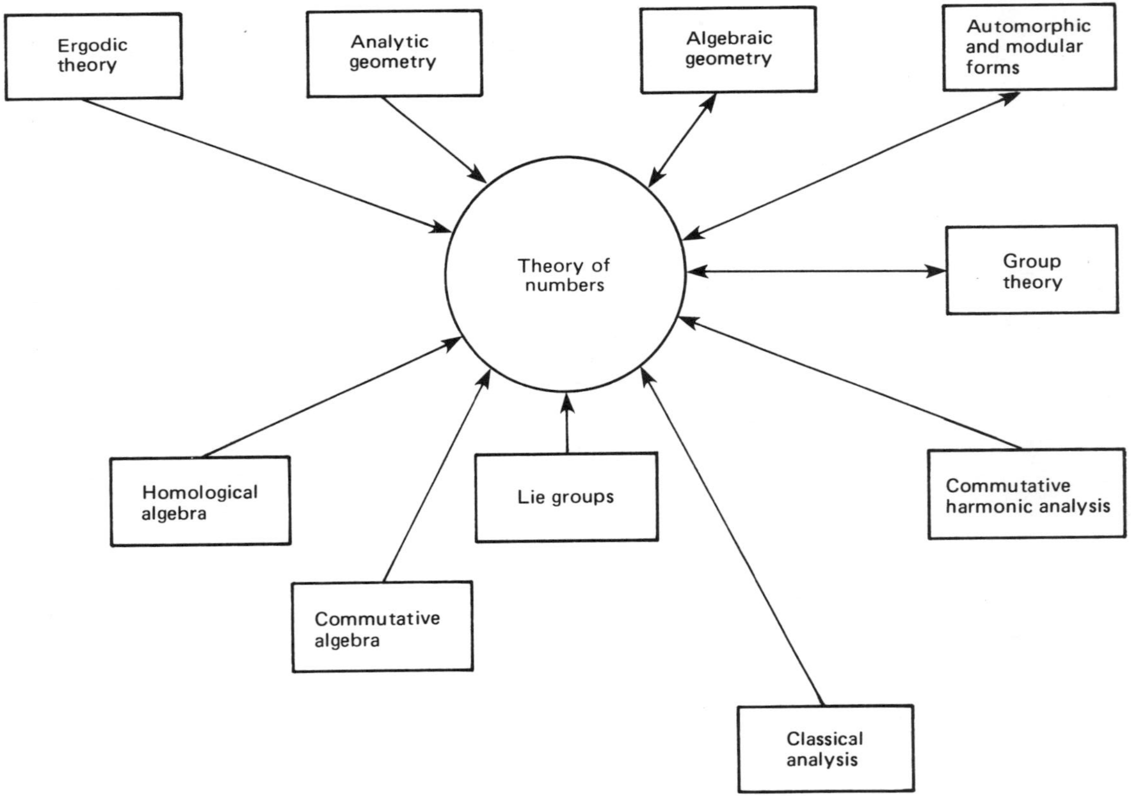

Ergodic theory
Analytic geometry
Algebraic geometry
Automorphic and modular forms
Theory of numbers
Group theory
Homological algebra
Lie groups
Commutative harmonic analysis
Commutative algebra
Classical analysis

A X

Theory of numbers

1. The modern viewpoint in number theory

The influence of algebraic geometry and the theory of analytic functions on the traditional problems of the theory of numbers have led to the point of view that the greater part of number theory is a chapter in algebraic geometry, distinguished by the very special properties of the ground fields or rings involved, especially the field **Q** of rational numbers and its finite algebraic extensions (which are called "algebraic number fields" or simply "number fields"). These fundamental properties are:

(1) Such a field admits a countable infinity of inequivalent absolute values (**C** II), all but a finite number of which are *ultrametric* with *finite* residue fields, and therefore correspond to discrete valuation rings whose completions are *compact*.

(2) The remaining absolute values (finite in number) are archimedean and provide canonical *embeddings* of the field into the field **C** of complex numbers or the field **R** of real numbers.

The ultrametric absolute values play the largest role in questions of *divisibility*, whereas the archimedean absolute values are preponderant in questions of *diophantine approximation*, the *geometry of numbers*, and in the study of *transcendental numbers*. But the deepest results are obtained only by taking account *simultaneously* of both types of absolute values, and the fundamental concept of *adèles* and *idèles* provides the appropriate setting.

Local fields, adèles and idèles. Let K be an algebraic number field, hence an algebraic extension of **Q** of finite degree $n = [\mathrm{K} : \mathbf{Q}]$; let S be the set of its absolute values or "places" (there is a canonical procedure for choosing one absolute value in each class of equivalent absolute values) and let S_∞ denote the set of archimedean absolute values (or "places at infinity"). Let K_v denote the completion of K at $v \in \mathrm{S}$ (**C** II); if $v \in \mathrm{S}_\infty$, K_v is either **R** or **C**, and we denote by r_1 (resp. r_2) the number of $v \in \mathrm{S}_\infty$ for which $\mathrm{K}_v = \mathbf{R}$ (resp.

$K_v = \mathbf{C}$); we have $r_1 + 2r_2 = n$. For $v \in S - S_\infty$ (the "finite places"), K_v is an extension of degree $\leqslant n$ of a p-adic field $\mathbf{Q}_p$; let $\mathfrak{o}_v$ denote the discrete valuation ring defined by $|z|_v \leqslant 1$ in K_v, and $\mathfrak{p}_v$ its maximal ideal (defined by $|z|_v < 1$), N_v the number of elements in the residue field $\mathfrak{o}_v/\mathfrak{p}_v$ (**C** II).

Just as in modern commutative algebra we associate with each element of a commutative ring A its images in the local rings $A_\mathfrak{p}$ for all prime ideals $\mathfrak{p}$ of A (**C** II), so we associate with each element $x \in K$ its canonical images $x_v \in K_v$, or equivalently the point (x_v) in the product $\prod_{v \in S} K_v$. Now for each $x \in K$ we have $x_v \in \mathfrak{o}_v$ for all but finitely many $v \in S - S_\infty$; we are therefore led to replace $\prod_{v \in S} K_v$, which is too big, by the subset K_A of this product consisting of the (z_v) such that $z_v \in \mathfrak{o}_v$ for all but a finite set of places $v \in S - S_\infty$. The elements of K_A are called the *adèles* of K. An essential fact is that K_A can be canonically endowed with a *locally compact topology* compatible with its ring structure. A fundamental system of neighborhoods of 0 for this topology is provided by the neighborhoods of 0 in the subring $\mathfrak{o}(S_\infty) = \prod_{v \in S_\infty} K_v \times \prod_{v \in S - S_\infty} \mathfrak{o}_v$, endowed with the product topology (the $\mathfrak{o}_v$ for $v \in S - S_\infty$ being compact and totally disconnected). With respect to this topology, the field K (embedded canonically in K_A by the "diagonal" mapping $x \mapsto (x_v)$) is *discrete*, and the quotient K_A/K is a *compact* abelian group.

The units of the ring K_A are called *idèles*; they form a multiplicative group $K_A^\times$ that is again locally compact with respect to a topology finer than that induced by the topology of K_A (it may be defined by the condition that the mapping $z \mapsto (z, z^{-1})$ of $K_A^\times$ into $K_A \times K_A$ should be a homeomorphism onto its image). For each idèle $z = (z_v)$, the product $|z|_A = \prod_{v \in S} |z_v|_v$ is finite, and $z \mapsto |z|_A$ is a continuous homomorphism of $K_A^\times$ into $\mathbf{R}_+^\times$; its kernel K_A^1 contains the multiplicative group $K^\times = K - \{0\}$, and $K_A^\times/K_A^1$ is isomorphic to $\mathbf{R}_+^\times$. Furthermore, $K^\times$ is *discrete* and the quotient $K_A^1/K^\times$ is *compact*. For each finite subset $P \supset S_\infty$ of S, let $\Omega(P) = \prod_{v \in P} K_v^\times \times \prod_{v \notin P} \mathfrak{o}_v^\times$, where $\mathfrak{o}_v^\times$ is the group of units of the ring $\mathfrak{o}_v$. Then the quotient $K_A^\times/K^\times\Omega(P)$ is *finite*, and the group $E(P) = K^\times \cap \Omega(P)$ is isomorphic to $E \times \mathbf{Z}^s$, where E is the group of roots of unity contained in K, and $s = \mathrm{Card}(P) - 1$.

These results imply classical theorems of algebraic number theory. The ring $\mathfrak{o} = K \cap \mathfrak{o}(S_\infty)$ (also denoted by $\mathfrak{o}_K$) is the ring of algebraic integers of K, and $E(S_\infty)$ its group of units. To each idèle z there corresponds a fractional ideal $\mathfrak{a}(z)$ in K, defined as the set of $x \in K$ such that $|x|_v \leqslant |z_v|_v$ for all places $v \in S - S_\infty$; we have $\mathfrak{a}(zz') = \mathfrak{a}(z)\mathfrak{a}(z')$, and every fractional ideal $\neq 0$ is obtained in this way; the prime ideals of $\mathfrak{o}$ correspond to the idèles z such that $z_v = 1$ except for one absolute value $v \in S - S_\infty$, at which z_v is a generator of

$\mathfrak{p}_v$. The finite group $K_A^\times/K^\times\Omega(S_\infty)$ is isomorphic to the quotient of the group of nonzero fractional ideals of K by the group of nonzero principal ideals, i.e., it is the *ideal class group* of K. The group $C_K = K_A^\times/K^\times$ is called the *idèle class group*; its identity component D_K is isomorphic to $\mathbf{R} \times \mathbf{T}^{r_2} \times S^{r_1+r_2-1}$, where S is the "solenoid" dual (**B** IV) to the discrete additive group **Q** (B 103; [31], [105], [6], [192]).

Zeta functions and L-*functions.* The fact that the idèle group $K_A^\times$ is a locally compact abelian group implies that we can apply the results of harmonic analysis, and in particular the Poisson formula (**B** IV); in this way we obtain a unified and simplified version of the classical theory of zeta functions and L-functions attached to the field K.

There exists a distinguished choice of Haar measure on $K_A^\times$, called the *Tamagawa measure* (see later); with respect to this measure, the volume of the compact group $K_A^1/K^\times$ is given by the formula

$$\kappa = \frac{2^{r_1}(2\pi)^{r_2}hR}{wd^{1/2}},$$

where d is the absolute value of the discriminant of K, w the order of the group E of roots of unity in K, h the number of ideal classes, and $R = \det(\log|\varepsilon_j|_{v_k})$ is the *regulator* of K (the numbers ε_j $(1 \leqslant j \leqslant r_1 + r_2 - 1)$ generate a free subgroup of $E(S_\infty)$ supplementary to E, and the v_k are $r_1 + r_2 - 1$ of the archimedean absolute values).

The continuous homomorphisms of the group $C_K = K_A^\times/K^\times$ into the group $\mathbf{C}^\times$, also called *quasi-characters*, may be identified with the mappings $z \mapsto c(z) = \chi(z)|z|_A^s$ of $K_A^\times$ into $\mathbf{C}^\times$, where χ is a character (**B** IV) of the group $K_A^\times$ that is equal to 1 on $K^\times$, and s is a complex number. For such a quasi-character c and a function f on K_A which together with its Fourier transform $\hat{f}$ satisfies certain regularity conditions, the general *zeta function* (J. Tate) is defined by

(1) $$\zeta(f, c) = \int_{K_A^\times} f(z)c(z)\, d^\times z,$$

the integration being with respect to the Tamagawa measure. For a given function f, we consider ζ as an analytic function of c (for each given χ, the set of corresponding quasi-characters may be regarded as a complex manifold isomorphic to **C**); this function has two simple poles at c_0 and c_1, where $c_0(z) = 1$ and $c_1(z) = |z|_A$, with respective residues $-\kappa f(0)$ and $\kappa\hat{f}(0)$. Furthermore, there is the fundamental functional equation

(2) $$\zeta(f, c) = \zeta(\hat{f}, \hat{c}),$$

where $\hat{c}(z) = |z|_A c^{-1}(z)$ (B 312; [31], [105]).

By specializing f and χ we obtain the L-functions defined by Dedekind and Hecke, and their functional equations. To obtain Dedekind's L-functions, we take a character χ of the group of fractional ideals (which we can identify with a character of C_K equal to 1 on the image of $K^\times\Omega(S_\infty)$) and form the infinite product

$$\text{(3)} \qquad L(s, \chi) = \prod_{\mathfrak{p} \notin S_\chi} \left(1 - \frac{\chi(\mathfrak{p})}{N\mathfrak{p}^s}\right)^{-1}$$

in which S_χ is the finite set of prime ideals such that χ is not equal to 1 on the group $\mathfrak{o}_v^\times$ of units of the corresponding $\mathfrak{p}$-adic ring, and $N\mathfrak{p}$ is the number of elements in $\mathfrak{o}/\mathfrak{p}$. For a suitable choice of f, the function $\zeta(f, c)$ is the product of a constant, some exponential factors, some gamma factors and $L(s, \chi)$; if we denote it by $\Lambda(s, \chi)$, the functional equation (2) takes the form

$$\text{(4)} \qquad W(\chi)\Lambda(s, \chi) = \Lambda(1 - s, \bar{\chi}),$$

where $W(\chi)$ is a constant. For example, if χ_0 is the trivial character, we have

$$\text{(5)} \qquad \Lambda(s, \chi_0) = (2^{-2r_2}\pi^{-n}d)^{s/2}\Gamma(\tfrac{1}{2}s)^{r_1}\Gamma(s)^{r_2}\zeta_K(s),$$

where $\zeta_K(s)$, the zeta function of the field K, is given for $\mathscr{R}s > 1$ by the series $\sum_{\mathfrak{a}} N\mathfrak{a}^{-s}$ summed over all ideals $\mathfrak{a} \neq 0$ contained in $\mathfrak{o}$, where $N\mathfrak{a}$ is the number of elements of the ring $\mathfrak{o}/\mathfrak{a}$; when $K = \mathbf{Q}$, it is Riemann's zeta function.

The importance of the L-functions lies in their relations with the invariant κ described above, which lead to significant information on the numbers h and R. The most remarkable result in this direction is Siegel's theorem: if an infinite sequence of number fields is such that $n/\log d \to 0$, then $\log(hR) \sim \log d^{1/2}$ [106]. In the case of quadratic extensions $\mathbf{Q}(\sqrt{d})$ of $\mathbf{Q}$, consideration of L-functions led Dirichlet to explicit formulas for the class number h. Siegel's theorem shows that for $d < 0$, there cannot be more than a finite number of values of d for which h is fixed; in particular, the number of these fields for which $h = 1$ (i.e., in which every ideal is principal) is finite. These fields have been determined explicitly only recently (there are nine of them, corresponding to $-d = 1, 2, 3, 7, 11, 19, 43, 67, 163$) by using relations between several L-functions corresponding to different characters χ, and properties of diophantine approximation related to the theory of transcendental numbers; the same methods have also been used to determine the numbers $d < 0$ for which $h = 2$ (B 335; BAMS 77 (Baker); SAMS XX (Stark)).

Local fields and global fields. There are other fields whose absolute values are all ultrametric, with finite residue fields: namely, finite algebraic extensions of fields $\mathbf{F}_q(X)$, i.e., fields of $\mathbf{F}_q$-rational functions on algebraic curves defined over the finite field $\mathbf{F}_q$ (**A** IX). For these fields all the preceding notions can be defined: adèles, idèles, zeta functions, and the results can be extended with very few modifications; in fact they are simpler because of the absence of archimedean absolute values, and often the methods of algebraic geometry enable properties of these fields to be proved which then lead one to conjecture the analogous properties (usually much harder to establish) for number fields (B 394; Nice I (Tate), B 4 (Iwasawa); SAMS XXIV (Coates)).

For this reason, the algebraic extensions of $\mathbf{Q}$ and of $\mathbf{F}_p(X)$ are collectively known as *global fields*. The study of such fields K is inseparable from that of the local fields K_v obtained by completing K with respect to its various absolute values, and the approach to a question about K is often to "localize" by considering first the corresponding question for a local field, and then to "globalize" the results obtained for the various K_v.

2. Class-field theory

During the course of the 19th century, the study of reciprocity laws on the one hand, and of complex multiplication (LN 21) on the other, indicated relations between the ideal class group of an algebraic number field K and the Galois groups of its unramified abelian extensions (i.e., extensions in which no finite place of K is ramified (**C** II)). The conjectures were formulated in precise terms by Weber and Hilbert, and were proved during the period 1900–1930 by Furtwängler, Takagi, and E. Artin, thereby creating *class-field theory*. The modern exposition of this theory for global fields is accompanied by a parallel theory for local fields.

The objects of study in local class-field theory are the finite abelian extensions L of an ultrametric local field K, and the fundamental theorem is the existence of a *canonical isomorphism*

$$K^\times / N_{L/K} L^\times \simeq \mathrm{Gal}\,(L/K) = G \tag{6}$$

of the quotient of $K^\times$ by the group of norms of elements of $L^\times$ onto the (abelian) Galois group G of L/K. If L/K is unramified, G is cyclic with a distinguished generator called the *Frobenius substitution* F, which is characterized by the fact that for an integral element z of L we have $F \cdot z \equiv z^q \pmod{\mathfrak{p}}$, where $\mathfrak{p}$ is the maximal ideal of the ring of integers of L and q is the number of elements in the residue field; the isomorphism (6) is induced by the homomorphism $x \mapsto F^{v(x)}$ of $K^\times$ into G, where v is the normalized valuation of K. When L is an arbitrary abelian extension of K, the definition of the isomorphism (6) is less direct, and depends on a study of the cohomology groups of G acting on $L^\times$ (B 42, 77; [105], [31]). For a finite Galois (not necessarily abelian) extension L of K, the group $H^2(G, L^\times)$ is canonically isomorphic to $\mathrm{Hom}(G, K^\times/N_{L/K}L^\times)$ and is cyclic of order $n = [L:K]$; on the other hand, there is a canonical injection $H^2(G, L^\times) \to \mathbf{Q}/\mathbf{Z}$, and the inverse of the isomorphism (6) is the element of $\mathrm{Hom}(G, K^\times/N_{L/K}L^\times)$ that corresponds canonically to $1/n$ in $\mathbf{Q}/\mathbf{Z}$. The fundamental theorem is completed by a *characterization* of the subgroups of $K^\times$ of the form $N_{L/K}L^\times$, to each of which corresponds an extension L that is unique up to isomorphism: they are precisely the *open* subgroups of *finite* index in $K^\times$.

This theory can be generalized to the case in which K is a field that is complete with respect to a discrete valuation, with algebraically closed residue field k: the abelian extensions of K are in one–one correspondence with the isogenies of the group of units of K (B 185).

Global class-field theory likewise is concerned with the finite abelian extensions L of a global field K. First it is necessary to define a "norm" mapping for idèles: $N_{L/K}: L_A^\times \to K_A^\times$. For each idèle $(z_w) \in L_A^\times$, we take the norm $N_{L_w/K_v} z_w$ of z_w in the local field K_v of which L_w is the extension, and then for each v form the product x_v of the norms $N_{L_w/K_v} z_w$ over all the places w of L lying above v; the idèle (x_v) is by definition the norm of the idèle (z_w). By passing to quotients we obtain a homomorphism $N_{L/K}: C_L \to C_K$ of the idèle class group of L into that of K. The fundamental theorem is the existence of a *canonical isomorphism*

$$C_K/N_{L/K}C_L \xrightarrow{\sim} \mathrm{Gal}(L/K). \tag{7}$$

This isomorphism is obtained by passing to the quotient from a canonical homomorphism $\psi_{L/K}: K_A^\times \to \mathrm{Gal}(L/K)$, called the *Artin homomorphism*, which is characterized by the following properties: (1) $\psi(x) = 1$ for $x \in K^\times$; (2) for each finite place v of K unramified in L, and each idèle $z \in K_A^\times$ of which all the components are 1 except the component $z_v \in K_v^\times$, we have $\psi(z) = F_{L/K}(v)^{v(z_v)}$: in this formula, $F_{L/K}(v)$ is the Frobenius substitution in the Galois group of one of the extensions L_w of K_v, identified with the subgroup of G which fixes w; because L/K is abelian, this subgroup is independent of the choice of w lying over v. Here again, the fundamental theorem is completed by a characterization of the subgroups of C_K that are of the form $N_{L/K}C_L$: they are again the open subgroups of finite index in C_K, and their intersection is D_K, which shows that C_K/D_K is isomorphic to the (topological) Galois group (**C** II) of the maximal abelian extension K_{ab} of K.

If L is a finite Galois extension of a global field K and v is a finite place of K unramified (**C** II) in L, the degree f of the places w of L lying over v is equal to the order in Gal(L/K) of any of the Frobenius substitutions corresponding to the places w. If L/K is abelian, this degree (and hence also the number g of places w, because $fg = [L:K]$) is therefore known if one knows the order of the class of the prime ideal $\mathfrak{p}$ corresponding to v in the group $C_K/N_{L/K}C_L$. An important particular case is that in which this quotient group is the ideal class group of K; the corresponding field L is called the *absolute class-field* (or the Hilbert class-field) of K, and is unramified over K; the number f is then the order, in the ideal class group, of the class of $\mathfrak{p}$. A particular property of the absolute class-field L is that every ideal of K generates a *principal* ideal in L. This leads naturally to the consideration of the "class-field tower" $K = K_0 \subset K_1 \subset \cdots \subset K_m \subset \cdots$, in which each K_m is the absolute class-field of K_{m-1}; if this "tower" is finite, the last term is a field in which all ideals are principal; however, Golod and Shafarevich have given examples of fields K for which the "tower" is infinite [31].

We remark finally that the determination of the equivalence classes of quadratic forms over a number field is solved by the use of class-field theory, which provides invariants characterizing these classes (Minkowski–Hasse theory; see [138], [201]).

Particular class-fields. The maximal abelian extension $\mathbf{Q}_{ab}$ of the field $\mathbf{Q}$ of rational numbers is the field generated by all roots of unity (Kronecker–Weber theorem). This fact leads to information about the ideal class groups of finite abelian extensions of $\mathbf{Q}$, by means of the Dirichlet series $L(s, \chi)$, where χ is a character of $(\mathbf{Z}/m\mathbf{Z})^\times$ for some integer $m > 1$ (B 325).

If K is an imaginary quadratic extension of $\mathbf{Q}$, the maximal abelian extension K_{ab} of K can be generated by values of elliptic or modular functions corresponding to ratios of periods τ that are integers of K (B 138; LN 21; [31]).

Iwasawa has made a deep study of the (infinite) abelian extensions L of a number field K such that Gal(L/K) is isomorphic to the additive group $\mathbf{Z}_p$ of p-adic integers, for some prime number p, and of unramified abelian extensions of L whose Galois group over L is a p-group. From this he has obtained remarkable results on the ideal class group of the field K_n generated by the p^{n+1}th roots of unity: if p^{e_n} is the largest power of p dividing the class number of K_n, there exist three integers $\lambda \geqslant 0$, $\mu \geqslant 0$, and ν, independent of n, such that $e_n = \lambda p^n + \mu n + \nu$. Iwasawa's theory also provides information on the ideal class groups of other abelian extensions of $\mathbf{Q}$; it is related to the problem in K-theory (**B** I) of calculating the groups K_2F for number fields F (B 174, 325, 394, 575; BAMS 65 (Iwasawa); SAMS XX (Birch), XXIV (Coates); Nice I (Tate), B 4 (Iwasawa)).

Galois extensions of local and global fields. When the Galois group is not abelian, there are only partial and scattered results on Galois extensions of local and global fields (see **A** VII). There is a description of the Galois group of the maximal p-extension of a p-adic field K (i.e., the composition of all the Galois extensions of K with a p-group as Galois group), where p is the characteristic of the residue field of K. If K is a number field and K_{ab}, K_{res} are respectively the maximal abelian extension and the maximal solvable extension of K, the Galois group $\mathrm{Gal}(K_{res}/K_{ab})$ can be described (B 128).

The most interesting general results are cohomological. We have already observed above that if K is a local field, L a finite Galois extension of K of degree n and G the Galois group Gal(L/K), then $H^2(G, L^\times)$ is cyclic of order n. If now K is a global field, L a finite Galois extension of degree n, and G = Gal(L/K), the most interesting cohomology groups are the groups $H^j(G, C_L)$ corresponding to the natural action of G on the idèles of L; the fundamental result is that $H^1(G, C_L) = 0$ and that $H^2(G, C_L)$ is cyclic of order n (B 77; [6], [31]). Moreover, there is a canonical injective homomorphism of $H^2(G, C_L)$ into $\mathbf{Q}/\mathbf{Z}$ and a distinguished generator $u_{L/K}$ of $H^2(G, C_L)$ whose image under this homomorphism is $1/n$; to this cohomology class there corresponds a group W(L/K) (the Weil group of L/K), which is an extension of G by the group C_L, unique up to isomorphism, and which appears in the theory of automorphic forms (B 83, 466). The interpretation of the group $H^2(G, L^\times)$ as the Brauer group of classes of simple algebras (**B** I) enables class-field theory (local and global) to be based on the theory of simple algebras, together with the theory of zeta-functions of such algebras, which are defined in a similar way to the zeta-functions of local and global fields, and have analogous properties (LN 260; [192]).

Under the same conditions, E. Artin showed how to associate to each character χ of G a meromorphic function $s \mapsto \Lambda(s, \chi)$ which again satisfies a functional equation of the form (4). The properties of these functions can be used to prove the only known result on the places of L, namely, Tchebotareff's density theorem. The places of K unramified in L are divided into types in the following way: for each conjugacy class $\mathscr{C}$ in G, the places v of type $\mathscr{C}$ are those for which the Frobenius substitutions at the places w of L lying over v belong to $\mathscr{C}$. If $\pi(x)$ is the number of places v such that $N_v \leqslant x$, and $\pi_{\mathscr{C}}(x)$ the number of these places which are of type $\mathscr{C}$, then the quotient $\pi_{\mathscr{C}}(x)/\pi(x)$ tends to $\mathrm{Card}(\mathscr{C})/\mathrm{Card}(G)$ as $x \to \infty$.

The determination of the constant $W(\chi)$ in (4) for an Artin L-function is related to the existence of normal bases of the ring of integers $\mathfrak{o}_L$ of L (considered as an $\mathfrak{o}_K$-module) (B 450).

3. Diophantine approximations and transcendental numbers

The problems of Diophantine approximation concern estimation of the differences $\alpha - \dfrac{p}{q}$ between an irrational number α and a rational number $\dfrac{p}{q}$ (where p and q are coprime integers), or again the distribution of the numbers $q\alpha$ modulo 1 for $q \in \mathbf{N}$; the problem is to evaluate $\|q\alpha\|$, where $\|x\|$ denotes the distance from $x \in \mathbf{R}$ to the nearest integer. An elementary result of Dirichlet shows that there always exist infinitely many integers q such that $\|q\alpha\| < 1/q$. If $\psi(q)$ is an increasing function such that $\psi(q)/q$ tends to $+\infty$ with q, one may ask which $\alpha \in \mathbf{R}$ have the property that there exist infinitely many integers q such that $\|q\alpha\| \leqslant 1/\psi(q)$. It is easy to construct such numbers α for each function ψ; but it is remarkable that these numbers (if irrational) cannot be *algebraic*. For if α is an algebraic irrational, then for each $\varepsilon > 0$ there are only finitely many integers q such that $\|q\alpha\| \leqslant q^{-1-\varepsilon}$ (Roth's theorem). This result may be generalized to simultaneous approximations: if $\alpha_1, \ldots, \alpha_n$ are real numbers such that $1, \alpha_1, \ldots, \alpha_n$ are linearly independent over $\mathbf{Q}$, then there are infinitely many integers q such that $\|q\alpha_j\| \leqslant q^{-1/n}$ for $1 \leqslant j \leqslant n$; but if the α_j are algebraic, then for each $\varepsilon > 0$ there are only finitely many integers q such that $\|q\alpha_j\| \leqslant q^{-(1/n)-\varepsilon}$ for $1 \leqslant j \leqslant n$. Also there are only finitely many systems of n nonzero integers $q_1, \ldots, q_n$ such that $\|q_1\alpha_1 + \cdots + q_n\alpha_n\| \leqslant |q_1 q_2 \cdots q_n|^{-1-\varepsilon}$ (W. Schmidt's theorems) (B 400; BAMS 77 (Lang); [30]).

It has been known since Hermite and Lindemann that e and π are transcendental numbers, and Gelfond and Schneider proved that α^β is transcendental if α and β are algebraic, $\alpha \neq 0, 1$, and β is irrational. These results have been considerably generalized recently by A. Baker, and can be attached to Diophantine inequalities. For a complex number x algebraic over $\mathbf{Q}$, consider the nontrivial equations $a_0 x^d + \cdots + a_d = 0$ with mutually prime coefficients $a_j \in \mathbf{Z}$; there is a unique (up to sign) such equation of minimal degree, and the corresponding integer $\sup_j |a_j|$ is called the *height* $h(x)$ of x. Now let L be the set of complex numbers of the form $\log \alpha$ for α algebraic over $\mathbf{Q}$ (allowing all determinations of the logarithm); if $l_1, \ldots, l_n \in \mathrm{L}$ and $\beta_0 \neq 0$, $\beta_1, \ldots, \beta_n$ are algebraic numbers, we have

$$|\beta_0 + \beta_1 l_1 + \cdots + \beta_n l_n| \geqslant \mathrm{C} \exp(-(\log \mathrm{H})^k),$$

where $\mathrm{H} = \sup_j h(\beta_j)$, $k > n + 1$, and C is a constant depending only on n, $k, l_1, \ldots, l_n$ and the maximum d of the degrees of the β_j, which can be minorized by an explicit expression involving only these quantities. In particular, if $\beta_1 l_1 + \cdots + \beta_n l_n$ is not zero (the β_j being algebraic numbers), it is transcendental. For example, $\pi + \log \alpha$ is transcendental if $\alpha \neq 0$ is algebraic; and if $\alpha_1, \ldots, \alpha_n, \beta_0, \beta_1, \ldots, \beta_n$ are nonzero algebraic numbers, the number $e^{\beta_0}\alpha_1^{\beta_1} \cdots \alpha_n^{\beta_n}$ is transcendental. There is an analogous inequality

$$|\beta_1 l_1 + \cdots + \beta_n l_n| \geqslant \mathrm{C}' \exp(-(\log \mathrm{H})^k)$$

when the l_j are linearly independent over $\mathbf{Q}$. This implies that $\alpha_1^{\beta_1} \cdots \alpha_n^{\beta_n}$ is transcendental when the α_j and β_j are algebraic, $\alpha_j \neq 0, 1$, and $1, \beta_1, \ldots, \beta_n$

are linearly independent over **Q** (B 368; BAMS 77 (Lang); SAMS XXIV (Baker); LN 402, 785).

The general idea of the proofs of these results, which are extremely technical, goes back to Siegel and Gelfond, and consists of a *reductio ad absurdum* by constructing a polynomial (in the case of diophantine approximations) or an entire function (in the case of transcendence theorems) in a large number of complex variables, having a large number of zeros in certain regions, or zeros of high orders at certain points. Using majorations obtained from algebra (in the case of polynomials) or from the maximum modulus principle (in the case of entire functions) the values at other points of the function constructed can be majorized. But the function can be so constructed that at these latter points the values of the function are algebraic numbers which can be minorized (by virtue of the initial hypothesis) if they are not zero. By comparing the upper and lower bounds obtained, it follows that the only possibility is that these numbers are zero, and in view of the construction, this leads to a contradiction.

The classical transcendence theorems admit interpretations which generalize them. For example, the fact that e^{α} is transcendental for α algebraic and $\neq 0$ (Hermite–Lindemann) is implied by the fact that an algebraic number field K cannot simultaneously contain α and e^{α}. It would then contain the numbers $m\alpha$ and $e^{m\alpha}$ for all integers m, and this would contradict a general theorem according to which, if f_j $(1 \leqslant j \leqslant \mathrm{N})$ are N meromorphic functions on **C**, the number of points $w \in \mathbf{C}$ such that $f_j(w) \in \mathrm{K}$ for $1 \leqslant j \leqslant \mathrm{N}$ is *finite*, under the following conditions: (i) the f_j are of finite order; (ii) the field $\mathrm{K}(f_1, \ldots, f_\mathrm{N})$ has transcendence degree $\geqslant 2$ over K; (iii) the derivatives of the f_j belong to the ring $\mathrm{K}[f_1, \ldots, f_\mathrm{N}]$. This same general theorem proves that α^{β} is transcendental, by taking $f_1(z) = e^z$, $f_2(z) = e^{\beta z}$; likewise, for the Weierstrass $\wp$-function defined in terms of algebraic invariants g_2, g_3, by taking $f_1 = \wp$ and $f_2 = \wp'$ it follows that $\wp(\alpha)$ is transcendental when α is algebraic (B 276). The generalization to functions of d complex variables is that the set of points $w \in \mathbf{C}^d$ such that $(f_1(w), \ldots, f_\mathrm{N}(w)) \in \mathrm{K}^\mathrm{N}$ is contained in an algebraic hypersurface, provided that the f_j are of finite order, the transcendence degree of $\mathrm{K}(f_1, \ldots, f_\mathrm{N})$ is $\geqslant d + 1$, and all the partial derivatives of the f_j belong to $\mathrm{K}[f_1, \ldots, f_\mathrm{N}]$ (B 384); this depends on delicate majorations from the theory of plurisubharmonic functions (B 384). For more recent progress (such as the fact that π and $\Gamma(\frac{1}{4})$ are algebraically independent), see (B 488).

With the use of these results, the fact that e^{α} is transcendental for α algebraic and $\neq 0$ can be generalized in another direction. Let G be an algebraic group (**A** IX) defined over an algebraic number field K, and let $\alpha \neq 0$ be a point of the Lie algebra $\mathfrak{g}$ of G, rational over K. Then if $t \mapsto \exp_\mathrm{G}(t\alpha)$ is not an algebraic function of t, the point $\exp_\mathrm{G}(\alpha)$ is transcendental over K. There are other results: for a homomorphism $\varphi : \mathbf{C}^d \to \mathrm{G}$ such that $\varphi(\mathbf{C}^d)$ is not an algebraic subgroup of G, the image $\varphi(\Gamma)$ of a discrete subgroup Γ of $\mathbf{C}^d$ containing d points linearly independent over $\mathbf{C}$ cannot be contained in the group of points of G algebraic over K (B 276, 305; BAMS 77 (Lang)).

By replacing rational numbers by p-adic numbers (the field $\mathbf{C}$ being then replaced by the completion of the algebraic closure of $\mathbf{Q}_p$) or by formal power series over $\mathbf{C}$, we can formulate analogous questions of transcendence and algebraic independence. For example, if $y_1, \ldots, y_n$ are formal power series without constant terms, belonging to $\mathbf{C}[[t_1, \ldots, t_m]]$ and linearly independent over $\mathbf{Q}$, then the field $\mathbf{Q}(y_1, \ldots, y_n, e^{y_1}, \ldots, e^{y_n})$ has transcendence degree $\geqslant n + 1$ over $\mathbf{Q}$. This result is a consequence of a theorem on algebraic groups that does not involve the field $\mathbf{Q}$ (B 382; Nice B 6 (Ax)).

4. Diophantine geometry

Classical Diophantine problems consisted in finding integral or rational solutions of systems of polynomial equations with integer coefficients. The influence of algebraic geometry led to the more general problem of studying, for an algebraic variety V defined over a field k (**A** IX), the points of V that are rational over k. When k is a global field, this question is inseparable from the same problem for the local fields k_v of k, because a point rational over k is also rational over each k_v. The variety V is said to satisfy the *Hasse principle* when, conversely, if there exist points of V rational over k_v for each place v, then there is at least one point of V rational over k. This principle is satisfied for V a projective quadric, but when $k = \mathbf{Q}$ there exist algebraic curves which do not satisfy it, for example, the cubic curve $3x^3 + 4y^3 + 5z^3 = 0$. Likewise, we are led to consider the same problem for a finite field, for if a polynomial equation $P(x_1, \ldots, x_n) = 0$ with coefficients in $\mathbf{Z}$ has a solution in $\mathbf{Z}^n$, this solution will also satisfy the congruences $P(x_1, \ldots, x_n) \equiv 0 \pmod{p}$ for each prime number p, so that by "reducing" the coefficients of P modulo p we obtain an equation with coefficients in $\mathbf{F}_p$ that has a solution in this field. In general, if V is a scheme over $\mathbf{Z}$ (**A** IX), a section of V over Spec($\mathbf{Z}$) (i.e., a morphism $u : \mathrm{Spec}(\mathbf{Z}) \to \mathrm{V}$ such that $\pi \circ u = 1_{\mathrm{V}}$, where $\pi : \mathrm{V} \to \mathrm{Spec}(\mathbf{Z})$ is the structural morphism) has for each $p \in \mathrm{Spec}(\mathbf{Z})$ a value in the fiber V_p that is a rational point over the residue field $\kappa(p) = \mathbf{F}_p$. When V is a scheme of finite type over $\mathbf{Z}$, the notion of the zeta-function of a global field may be generalized as follows: for each closed point $x \in \mathrm{V}$, the residue field $\kappa(x)$ is a finite algebraic extension of the field $\mathbf{F}_p$ (where $p = \pi(x)$); we denote by Nx the number of elements of $\kappa(x)$ and define

$$\zeta(\mathrm{V}, s) = \prod_x (1-(\mathrm{N}x)^{-s})^{-1}, \tag{8}$$

the product being taken over all the closed points of V (Hasse–Weil zeta-function). It can be shown that this product converges absolutely for

$\mathscr{R}s > \dim V$. It is conjectured that this function has an analytic continuation to a meromorphic function on $\mathbf{C}$, but in general the existence of such an analytic continuation has been established only for $\mathscr{R}s > \dim V - \frac{1}{2}$. If $V = \mathrm{Spec}(\mathfrak{o})$, where $\mathfrak{o}$ is the ring of integers of an algebraic number field K, then $\zeta(V, s)$ is equal to $\zeta_K(s)$ (and in particular is Riemann's zeta-function when $K = \mathbf{Q}$). If V is an algebraic curve over a field $\mathbf{F}_p$, we have $\pi(V) = \{p\}$, and $\zeta(V, s)$ is the zeta-function of the (global) field of rational functions on V. In general, for every scheme V of finite type over $\mathbf{Z}$, we have $\zeta(V, s) = \prod_p \zeta(V_p, s)$ (product over all prime numbers p). When a finite group G acts on V, we can also define L-functions that generalize Artin's L-functions, and which include $\zeta(V, s)$ as a particular case. These functions play an important role in questions of Diophantine geometry.

Diophantine geometry over a finite field. This is the case in which the results are at present most complete. If V is an algebraic variety defined over a finite field $\mathbf{F}_q$, the numbers $\mathrm{N}x$ in (8) are powers of q and we may therefore write $\zeta(V, s) = Z_V(u)$, where $u = q^{-s}$; it is then easily shown that if N'_ν is the number of points $x \in V$ such that $\kappa(x) = \mathbf{F}_{q^\nu}$ and $N_\nu = \sum_{\mu | \nu} N'_\mu$, we have

$$\text{(9)} \qquad \frac{uZ'_V(u)}{Z_V(u)} = \sum_{\nu=1}^{\infty} N_\nu u^\nu$$

so that knowledge of Z_V gives the number of points of V rational over $\mathbf{F}_{q^\nu}$ for *all integers* ν simultaneously.

The determination of Z_V is closely related to the étale cohomology (**A** IX) of V, by virtue of the observation of Hasse and Weil that N_ν is the number of fixed points of the νth iterate F^ν of the Frobenius morphism F of V, considered as acting on the set of closed points of the scheme $V \otimes_{\mathbf{F}_q} \overline{\mathbf{F}}_q$ (where $\overline{\mathbf{F}}_q$ is an algebraic closure of $\mathbf{F}_q$). If V is projective and nonsingular, so that this set of closed points is identified with a subset of $\mathbf{P}_n(\overline{\mathbf{F}}_q)$ defined by polynomial equations with coefficients in $\mathbf{F}_q$, the morphism F takes a point $x = (x_0, \ldots, x_n)$ to the point $Fx = (x_0^q, \ldots, x_n^q)$. Now the number of fixed points of F^ν may be obtained from the Lefschetz formula (**A** I, **A** IX) involving the traces of the endomorphisms $(F^\nu)^{(j)}$ induced by F^ν on the étale cohomology groups $H^j(V_{et}, \mathbf{Q}_l)$ (where l is a prime number distinct from the characteristic of $\mathbf{F}_q$) (**A** IX); in this way we obtain

$$\text{(10)} \qquad Z_V(u) = \frac{P_1(u)P_3(u)\cdots P_{2d-1}(u)}{P_0(u)P_2(u)\cdots P_{2d}(u)},$$

where $P_j(u) = \det(1 - u \cdot F^{(j)})$ for $0 \leqslant j \leqslant 2d$, d being the dimension of V. It follows that $Z_V(u)$ is a rational function of u, and Poincaré duality (in étale cohomology) gives rise to the functional equation

$$(11) \qquad Z_V\left(\frac{1}{q^d u}\right) = \pm q^{d\chi/2} u^{\chi} Z_V(u),$$

where $\chi = \sum_{j=0}^{2d} (-1)^j \dim H^j(V_{et}, \mathbf{Q}_l)$. These results were obtained by Dwork, Grothendieck, and Verdier; in 1973, Deligne proved that the polynomials P_j are independent of l and have rational integer coefficients, and that the zeros α_{jk} of P_j have absolute value $|\alpha_{jk}| = q^{j/2}$, thereby completely establishing the "Weil conjectures" (previously proved for curves of genus 1 by Hasse and for curves of genus $\geqslant 2$ by A. Weil) (B 39, 198, 279, 423, 446; SAMS XXIX (Mazur); [44] (Kleiman), [221]).

Knowledge of the zeta-functions enables an explicit description to be given of the abelian varieties over a finite field, up to isogeny, by using also the theory of complex multiplication and that of "p-divisible" groups (B 352; SAMS XX (Waterhouse–Milne)).

The study of zeta-functions of curves over a finite field also leads to the development of a theory parallel to global class-field theory, for abelian extensions of the field of rational functions K = R(V) of a nonsingular projective variety defined over a finite field k (B 133; [154]).

Abelian varieties defined over local and global fields. Let A be an abelian variety (**A** IX) defined over a field K which is a finitely generated extension of its prime field (for example, a global field). Then the subgroup A_K of A consisting of the K-rational points is finitely generated (Mordell–Weil theorem) (B 380; [106]). The study of this theorem has led to important notions, in the first place a notion of the height of a point of A_K when K is a global field: this is a generalization of the logarithm of the height of an algebraic number, defined earlier, and can be defined for K-rational points of any variety embedded in a projective space $\mathbf{P}_n$. For abelian varieties there is a *canonical* height function, defined independently of a projective embedding (B 274). On the other hand, it is conjectured that the rank r of the group A_K should be equal to the order of the pole of the function $\zeta(A, s)$ at the point $s = 1$, and the value of the limit of $\zeta(A, s)/(s - 1)^r$ as $s \to 1$ is the subject of other remarkable conjectures, related to obstructions to the "Hasse principle" for A, the Brauer–Grothendieck group Br(A) (**A** IX) and étale cohomology (B 156, 306, 503; SAMS XX (Birch); Stockholm (Cassels, Tate); Nice B 4 (Manin); [176], [179], [31] (Swinnerton–Dyer)). Some of these conjectures and certain partial results concern more general algebraic varieties than abelian varieties.

Among the abelian varieties defined over a number field, the best known are those that have properties generalizing those of elliptic curves with complex multiplication: if such a variety A has dimension n, there must exist a number field of degree $2n$ over $\mathbf{Q}$ whose ring of integers is isomorphic to a subring of End(A). For such varieties, the zeta-function can be calculated in terms of Hecke L-functions, and shown to satisfy the general conjectures on these functions (B 129, 136; [166]).

Diophantine geometry over a ring of algebraic integers. The only general result known about the integral points of algebraic varieties over number fields is a famous theorem of Siegel on *curves* of genus $\geqslant 1$. Such an affine curve, defined over a number field K, has only a *finite* number of points whose coordinates are integers of K. This result can be generalized to the case where K is finitely generated over $\mathbf{Q}$ and it is assumed only that the coordinates of the points under consideration are in a subring R of K, finitely generated over $\mathbf{Z}$. Siegel's method is to embed the curve in its Jacobian (**A** IX) and then to show, by means of the Mordell–Weil theorem and a theorem of Diophantine approximation, that the heights of the points are bounded, which implies that they form a finite set (B 247; [106]).

This is purely an existence theorem, but the methods of Baker lead in certain cases to effectively calculable bounds for the coordinates of integral points on curves with given equations (B 368; SAMS XX (Baker); XXIV (Baker)).

A conjecture of Mordell is that a curve of genus $\geqslant 2$ defined over a number field K has only a finite number of K-rational points. At present all that can be proved is an analogous result in which K is not a number field but a finitely generated extension of an algebraically closed field k, and the curve is assumed not to be birationally equivalent over K to a curve defined over k (B 287).

For algebraic varieties of dimension $\geqslant 2$, integral or rational points have been studied only in some particular cases, such as cubic surfaces (SAMS XX (Swinnerton-Dyer); [117]).

5. Arithmetic linear groups

Let G be a linear algebraic group (**A** IX), defined over the field $\mathbf{Q}$ of rational numbers. The group $G_{\mathbf{R}}$ of points of G rational over $\mathbf{R}$ is then a real Lie group. A subgroup Γ of $G_{\mathbf{R}}$ is called an *arithmetic group* if there exists an embedding $\rho : G \to \mathbf{GL}(n)$ defined over $\mathbf{Q}$ that maps Γ onto a subgroup of $\rho(G)$ commensurable with the subgroup $\rho(G) \cap \mathbf{GL}(n, \mathbf{Z})$ of integer matrices belonging to $\rho(G)$. The most interesting case is that in which G is semisimple; then the homogeneous space $G_{\mathbf{R}}/\Gamma$ has *finite* volume (with respect to the invariant measure on $G_{\mathbf{R}}/\Gamma$, which exists because Γ is a discrete subgroup of $G_{\mathbf{R}}$). Moreover, $G_{\mathbf{R}}/\Gamma$ is compact if and only if G has no **Q**-rational unipotent element other than the identity.

The *adelized group* $G_{\mathbf{A}}$ of a linear algebraic group G defined over **Q** is defined as follows. Supposing G embedded in **GL**(n), consider for each prime number p the subgroup $G_{\mathbf{Z}_p}$ of points of $G_{\mathbf{Q}_p}$ with coordinates in $\mathbf{Z}_p$, and take $G_{\mathbf{A}}$ to be the subgroup of the product $G_{\mathbf{R}} \times \prod_p G_{\mathbf{Q}_p}$ consisting of the points for which the $\mathbf{Q}_p$-components are in $G_{\mathbf{Z}_p}$ for all but finitely many primes p. The neighborhoods of the identity element in the topological product $G_{\mathbf{R}} \times \prod_p G_{\mathbf{Z}_p}$ are taken as a fundamental system of neighborhoods of the identity element in $G_{\mathbf{A}}$. It can be verified that, up to isomorphism, these definitions are independent of the choice of embedding $G \subset \mathbf{GL}(n)$. The topology of $G_{\mathbf{A}}$ is locally compact (when $G_{\mathbf{Q}} = \mathbf{Q}^{\times}$, we obtain the idèle group), and the subgroup $G_{\mathbf{Q}}$ is discrete in $G_{\mathbf{A}}$. To the properties of $G_{\mathbf{R}}/\Gamma$ stated above there correspond equivalent properties of $G_{\mathbf{A}}/G_{\mathbf{Q}}$: when G is semisimple, this homogeneous space has finite volume (with respect to its invariant measure), and $G_{\mathbf{A}}/G_{\mathbf{Q}}$ is compact if and only if G has no **Q**-rational unipotent element other than the identity.

These notions may be generalized by replacing **Q** by an arbitrary algebraic number field K, and **Z** by its ring of integers $\mathfrak{o}$; the quotient $G_{\mathbf{A}}/G_{K}$ of the adelized group by its group of K-rational points is again of finite volume when G is semisimple (B 235, 257; LN789; [19], [31]).

For a given embedding of G in **GL**(n), we may consider the particular arithmetic subgroups $\Gamma_{\mathfrak{q}}$ of G consisting of the elements of $G \cap \mathbf{GL}(n, \mathfrak{o})$ congruent to the unit matrix modulo an ideal $\mathfrak{q}$. Arithmetic subgroups that contain such a subgroup are called *congruence subgroups*, and it can be asked whether every arithmetic subgroup is a congruence subgroup (this condition is independent of the choice of embedding). It has been known since Klein that this is not the case when $G = \mathbf{SL}(2)$; but if G is simple, simply connected, split, and of rank $\geqslant 2$, every arithmetic subgroup of G is a congruence subgroup provided that the field K has at least one real conjugate; on the other hand, if K is totally imaginary, there exist arithmetic subgroups of **SL**(n) for $n \geqslant 3$ and of **Sp**($2n$) for $n \geqslant 2$ that are not congruence subgroups. The proofs of these results are related to the notion of "symbols" and to K-theory (B 330).

Another question that has only recently been answered is that of the converse of the finite volume property: if G is semisimple and defined over **Q**, are there discrete subgroups $\Gamma \subset G_{\mathbf{R}}$ other than arithmetic groups such that $G_{\mathbf{R}}/\Gamma$ has finite volume? The answer is negative when the simple components of G are groups of rank $\geqslant 2$ (Margulis's theorem, B 482, 559); the proof is difficult and uses, among other things, ergodic theory (**A** IV).

The arithmetic theory of quadratic forms. If G is semisimple, there exists on the homogeneous space G_A/G_K a distinguished invariant measure τ, called the *Tamagawa measure*; the number $\tau(G_A/G_K)$, which from the results above is finite, is called the *Tamagawa number* of G, denoted by $\tau(G)$. It is conjectured that $\tau(G) = 1$ when G is simply connected (**A** IX); this has been verified for most of the classical groups and some exceptional groups (B 186, 351).

When G is the special orthogonal group relative to a nondegenerate quadratic form over K in $n \geqslant 3$ variables, we have $\tau(G) = 2$, and this relation is equivalent to the theorem of Minkowski–Siegel on classes of quadratic forms with integer coefficients. Let us take $K = \mathbf{Q}$, and let S_1, S_2 be two $n \times n$ nonsingular symmetric matrices with coefficients in $\mathbf{Z}$; they are said to belong to the same *class* if there exists a nonsingular matrix X with coefficients in $\mathbf{Z}$ such that ${}^tXS_1X = S_2$, and they are said to belong to the same *genus* if, for each prime number p, this equation in X is satisfied by a matrix X_p with coefficients *in* $\mathbf{Z}_p$ and also has a solution X_∞ with coefficients *in* $\mathbf{R}$. Fix $S_1 = S$, and let G be the algebraic group, defined over $\mathbf{Q}$, of all matrices $X \in \mathbf{GL}(n)$ such that ${}^tXSX = S$ and $\det(X) = 1$. Let G_Ω be the open subgroup of $G_{\mathbf{A}}$ that is the product of the $G_{\mathbf{Z}_p}$ and $G_{\mathbf{R}}$; it can be shown that the classes of matrices belonging to the genus of S are in one–one correspondence with the *double cosets* $G_\Omega U_j G_{\mathbf{Q}}$ with respect to the subgroups G_Ω and $G_{\mathbf{Q}}$ of $G_{\mathbf{A}}$, which are finite in number. On the group G_Ω, the Tamagawa measure coincides with a product of Haar measures m_p on the $G_{\mathbf{Z}_p}$ and m_∞ on $G_{\mathbf{R}}$; if $G_0(U_j)$ is the discrete subgroup of $G_{\mathbf{R}}$ that is the projection of the group $(U_j^{-1}G_\Omega U_j) \cap G$, elementary considerations from the theory of Haar measure show that we have the relation

$$(12) \qquad 2 = \tau(G_{\mathbf{A}}/G_{\mathbf{Q}}) = \left(\prod_p m_p(G_{\mathbf{Z}_p})\right)\left(\sum_j m_\infty(G_{\mathbf{R}}/G_0(U_j))\right).$$

When the symmetric matrix S is positive definite, $m_\infty(G_{\mathbf{R}}/G_0(U_j))$ is equal to $1/N_j$, where N_j is the order of the orthogonal group corresponding to the matrix U_j, and the formula (12) is equivalent to Minkowski's formula for the "mean" $\sum_j 1/N_j$ of the reciprocals of the orders of the orthogonal groups of the various classes in the genus of S. In the same way we can recover Siegel's formulas for the numbers of representations of one quadratic form by another, when $\mathbf{Q}$ is replaced by an arbitrary number field K, together with the asymptotic formulas corresponding to the case when S is no longer positive definite, so that the orthogonal groups corresponding to the U_j are infinite ([31], [138]).

6. Connections with the natural sciences

There are hardly any direct applications of the theory of numbers, but certain methods used in this theory, such as the construction of "zeta-functions," have inspired analogous methods in subjects apparently very far removed from the theory of numbers, such as the theory of dynamical systems (**A** III).

7. The originators

The principal ideas in the theory of numbers are due to the following mathematicians:

Algebraic number theory. P. Fermat (1608–1665), L. Euler (1707–1783), J. L. Lagrange (1736–1813), C. F. Gauss (1777–1855), G. Lejeune-Dirichlet (1805–1859), C. G. Jacobi (1804–1851), E. Kummer (1810–1893), G. Eisenstein (1823–1852), C. Hermite (1822–1901), L. Kronecker (1823–1891), R. Dedekind (1831–1916), H. Weber (1842–1913), K. Hensel (1861–1941), D. Hilbert (1862–1943), E. Hecke (1887–1947), C. Siegel (1896–1981), E. Artin (1898–1962), N. Tchebotareff (1894–1947), T. Takagi (1875–1960), H. Hasse (1898–1979), C. Chevalley, A. Weil, K. Iwasawa, J. Tate.

Diophantine approximations and transcendental numbers. C. Hermite (1822–1901), A. Thue (1863–1922), C. Siegel (1896–1981), A. Gelfond (1906–1968), T. Schneider, K. Roth, A. Baker, W. Schmidt.

Diophantine geometry. L. Mordell (1888–1972), A. Weil, C. Siegel, (1896–1981) H. Hasse (1898–1979), A. Grothendieck, G. Shimura, P. Deligne.

Arithmetic groups. C. Hermite (1822–1901), H. J. S. Smith (1827–1883), G. Margulis, H. Minkowski (1864–1909), C. Siegel (1896–1981), A. Borel, Harish-Chandra, T. Tamagawa, A. Weil.

Geometry of numbers. H. Minkowski (1864–1909).

Analytic number theory. G. Lejeune-Dirichlet (1805–1859), B. Riemann (1826–1866), J. Hadamard (1865–1963), C. de la Vallée-Poussin (1866–1962), S. Ramanujan (1887–1920), G. Hardy (1877–1947), I. Vinogradov, J. E. Littlewood (1885–1977).

The following have also contributed substantially to these theories: M. Artin, J. Ax, A. Atkin, H. Bass, B. Birch, H. Blichfeldt (1873–1945),

E. Bombieri, A. Brumer, A. Bukhstab, J. Cassels, A. Cauchy (1789–1857), C. Chabauty, F. Chatelet, J. Chen, J. Coates, H. Davenport (1907–1969), V. Demjanenko, M. Deuring, L. Dickson (1874–1954), B. Dwork, M. Eichler, P. Erdös, N. Feldman, G. Frobenius (1849–1917), A. Fröhlich, R. Fueter (1880–1950), P. Furtwängler (1869–1940), P. Gallagher, H. Garland, E. Golod, H. Grauert, G. Halász, H. Heegner, H. Heilbronn (1909–1976), J. Herbrand (1908–1931), E. Hlawka, T. Honda, G. Hochschild, A. Hurwitz (1859–1919), J. Igusa, Y. Ihara, M. Ishida, H. Iwanieč, C. Jordan (1838–1922), N. Katz, M. Kneser, A. Korkine (1837–1908), M. Krasner, D. Kubert, T. Kubota, E. Landau (1877–1938), S. Lang, R. Langlands, A. Legendre (1752–1833), H. Leopoldt, D. Lewis, S. Lichtenbaum, C. Lindemann (1852–1939), Ju. Linnik (1915–1972), J. Liouville (1809–1882), J. Lubin, K. Mahler, H. Matsumoto, Ju. Manin, J. Mars, A. Mattuck, B. Mazur, J. Mennicke, J. Milne, J. Milnor, H. Montgomery, C. Moore, G. Mostow, T. Nakayama (1912–1964), A. Néron, T. Oda, T. Ono, C. Pisot, H. Poincaré (1854–1912), G. Poitou, R. Rankin, A. Rényi (1921–1970), C. Rogers, M. Raghunathan, S. Schanuel, A. Schinzel, F. K. Schmidt, W. Sierpinski (1882–1969), A. Selberg, E. Selmer, J. P. Serre, I. Shafarevich, T. Skolem (1887–1963), A. Speiser (1885–1970), H. Stark, S. Stepanov, L. Stickelberger (1850–1936), X. Stouff (1861–1903), H. Swinnerton-Dyer, Y. Taniyama (1927–1958), P. Turán (1910–1976), J. van der Corput (1890–1975), W. Waterhouse, M. Waldschmidt, G. Whaples, A. Wiles, E. Wirsing, R. Zimmer, G. Zolotareff (1847–1878).

References

B: 39, 42, 47, 77, 83, 103, 128, 129, 133, 136, 138, 156, 174, 185, 186, 198, 235, 247, 252, 257, 274, 276, 279, 287, 305, 306, 312, 325, 330, 335, 351, 352, 368, 380, 382, 384, 394, 400, 423, 430, 446, 450, 466, 469, 482, 488, 503, 511, 535, 559, 575, 576.

LN: 21, 227, 402, 437, 555, 601, 627, 776, 785, 789, 800.

BAMS: 65 (Iwasawa), 77 (Baker, Lang), 81 (Ogg, Stark).

SAMS: XX, XXIV, XXIX.

Astérisque: 18, 24–25, 41–42.

[6], [19], [30], [31], [44], [105], [106], [117], [138], [154], [157], [159], [166], [176], [179], [192], [201], [205], [206], [215], [221].

B I

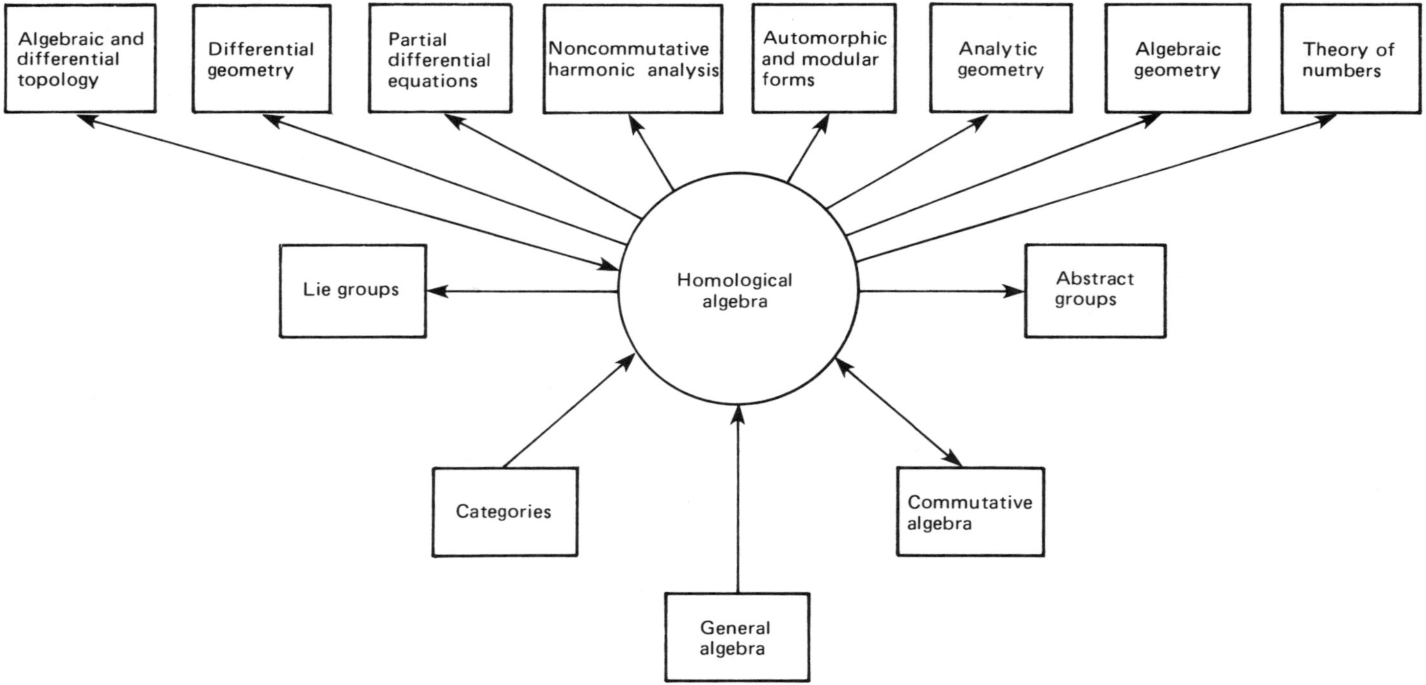
Algebraic and differential topology
Differential geometry
Partial differential equations
Noncommutative harmonic analysis
Automorphic and modular forms
Analytic geometry
Algebraic geometry
Theory of numbers
Lie groups
Homological algebra
Abstract groups
Categories
Commutative algebra
General algebra

B I

Homological algebra

The constructions of algebraic topology produce "invariants" of various kinds (groups, rings, numerical invariants, etc.) associated functorially (**C** I) with topological spaces. A study of the underlying mechanisms shows that it is possible to define in an analogous way "invariant" objects for every sort of objects of an algebraic or algebraico-topological nature.

1. Derived functors in abelian categories

The fundamental notions are those of a *complex* and *homology* of a complex. In an abelian category $\boldsymbol{C}$ (**C** I) a complex, or *chain complex*, is a sequence $X = (X_n, d_n)$ (in general infinite in both directions) of objects and morphisms of $\boldsymbol{C}$:

$$\cdots \leftarrow X_{n-3} \xleftarrow{d_{n-2}} X_{n-2} \xleftarrow{d_{n-1}} X_{n-1} \xleftarrow{d_n} X_n \leftarrow \cdots$$

such that $d_{n-1}d_n = 0$ for all n. A complex is said to be *bounded below* (resp. *bounded above*) if the X_n are all zero for $n \leqslant n_0$ (resp. $n \geqslant n_0$), in which case we write only the X_n for $n \geqslant n_0$ (resp. $n \leqslant n_0$). By definition we have $\operatorname{Im} d_{n+1} \subset \operatorname{Ker} d_n$, and the quotient object $H_n(X) = (\operatorname{Ker} d_n)/(\operatorname{Im} d_{n+1})$ is the nth *homology object* of X. The chain complexes over $\boldsymbol{C}$ form an abelian category, a morphism $f : X \to Y$ of chain complexes being defined as a sequence of morphisms $f_n : X_n \to Y_n$ in $\boldsymbol{C}$ such that the squares in the diagram

$$\begin{array}{ccccccc}
\cdots \leftarrow & X_{n-1} & \xleftarrow{d_n} & X_n & \xleftarrow{d_{n+1}} & X_{n+1} & \leftarrow \cdots \\
 & \downarrow{\scriptstyle f_{n-1}} & & \downarrow{\scriptstyle f_n} & & \downarrow{\scriptstyle f_{n+1}} & \\
\cdots \leftarrow & Y_{n-1} & \xleftarrow[d'_n]{} & Y_n & \xleftarrow[d'_{n+1}]{} & Y_{n+1} & \leftarrow \cdots
\end{array}$$

are commutative; the composition of two morphisms $f = (f_n) : X \to Y$ and $g = (g_n) : Y \to Z$ is defined to be $g \circ f = (g_n \circ f_n)$. We have

$$f_n(\operatorname{Ker} d_n) \subset \operatorname{Ker} d'_n \text{ and } f_n(\operatorname{Im} d_{n+1}) \subset \operatorname{Im} d'_{n+1},$$

so that on passing to the quotients f_n we obtain a morphism $H_n(f) : H_n(X) \to H_n(Y)$ for all n.

When the objects of $\boldsymbol{C}$ are sets, the elements of X_n are called *n-chains*, those of Ker d_n are *n-cycles*, those of Im d_{n+1} are *n-boundaries*, and the elements of $H_n(X)$ are called *homology classes*; two n-cycles are *homologous* if they are in the same homology class.

Two morphisms of complexes $f, g : X \to Y$ are called *homotopic* if for each n there exists a morphism $s_n : X_n \to Y_{n+1}$ such that

$$f_n - g_n = d'_{n+1}s_n + s_{n-1}d_n$$

for each n, in which case we have $H_n(f) = H_n(g)$ for all n.

If $0 \to X \xrightarrow{f} Y \xrightarrow{g} Z \to 0$ is an exact sequence of chain complexes over $\boldsymbol{C}$, for each n there is a well-defined morphism $\partial_n : H_n(Z) \to H_{n-1}(X)$ such that the *homology sequence*

(1) $$\cdots \to H_n(X) \xrightarrow{H_n(f)} H_n(Y) \xrightarrow{H_n(g)} H_n(Z) \xrightarrow{\partial_n} H_{n-1}(X) \to \cdots$$

is *exact*.

A chain complex over the opposite category $\boldsymbol{C}^0$ is called a *cochain complex* over $\boldsymbol{C}$: it is therefore a sequence X of objects and morphisms of $\boldsymbol{C}$

$$\cdots \to X_{n-1} \xrightarrow{d_n} X_n \xrightarrow{d_{n+1}} X_{n+1} \to \cdots$$

such that $d_{n+1}d_n = 0$ for all n. This time we have Im $d_n \subset$ Ker d_{n+1}, and the quotient object $H^n(X) = (\text{Ker } d_{n+1})/(\text{Im } d_n)$ is called the nth *cohomology object* of X. When the objects of $\boldsymbol{C}$ are sets, the elements of X_n are called *n-cochains*, those of Ker d_{n+1} are *n-cocycles*, those of Im d_n are *n-coboundaries*, and the elements of $H^n(X)$ are called *cohomology classes*; two n-cocycles are *cohomologous* if they are in the same cohomology class.

For example, if $\boldsymbol{C}$ is the category $\boldsymbol{Mod}_A$ of modules over a commutative ring A, each chain complex $X = (X_n, d_n)$ over $\boldsymbol{C}$ gives rise to a cochain complex $X^* = (X_n^*, {}^td_n)$, where X_n^* is the *dual* module $\text{Hom}_A(X_n, A)$ and ${}^td_n$ is the transpose of the homomorphism d_n.

Given an object A of $\boldsymbol{C}$, an *injective resolution* of A is a cochain complex $X = (X_n)_{n \geq 0}$ together with a morphism $A \xrightarrow{\varepsilon} X_0$ such that the sequence

(2) $$0 \to A \xrightarrow{\varepsilon} X_0 \to X_1 \to \cdots \to X_n \to X_{n+1} \to \cdots$$

is exact and the X_j are *injective* objects (**C** I) of $\boldsymbol{C}$. If B is another object of $\boldsymbol{C}$, and

$$0 \to B \xrightarrow{\varepsilon'} Y_0 \to Y_1 \to \cdots \to Y_n \to Y_{n+1} \to \cdots$$

is an injective resolution of B, then every morphism $f : A \to B$ can be extended to a morphism of complexes

$$\begin{array}{ccccccccccc} 0 \to & A & \xrightarrow{\varepsilon} & X_0 & \to \cdots \to & X_n & \to & X_{n+1} & \to \cdots \\ & f\downarrow & & f_0\downarrow & & f_n\downarrow & & f_{n+1}\downarrow & \\ 0 \to & B & \xrightarrow[\varepsilon']{} & Y_0 & \to \cdots \to & Y_n & \to & Y_{n+1} & \to \cdots \end{array}$$

and any two such extensions of f are homotopic.

If every object of $\boldsymbol{C}$ is a subobject of an injective object of $\boldsymbol{C}$ (in which case we say that $\boldsymbol{C}$ has "enough injectives"), every object of $\boldsymbol{C}$ admits an injective resolution. Suppose that this is the case, and let $T : \boldsymbol{C} \to \boldsymbol{C}'$ be a covariant additive functor from $\boldsymbol{C}$ to another abelian category $\boldsymbol{C}'$. For each object A of $\boldsymbol{C}$, consider an injective resolution (2) and the complex T(X) over $\boldsymbol{C}'$

$$0 \to T(X_0) \to T(X_1) \to \cdots \to T(X_n) \to \cdots.$$

The properties of injective resolutions imply that the cohomology objects $H^n(T(X))$ are *independent* of the injective resolution X, up to a canonical isomorphism. We write $H^n(T(X)) = R^nT(A)$, and the functor $R^nT : \boldsymbol{C} \to \boldsymbol{C}'$ is called the nth *right derived functor* of T. If T is left-exact, we have $R^0T = T$. If $0 \to A \xrightarrow{f} B \xrightarrow{g} C \to 0$ is an exact sequence in $\boldsymbol{C}$, we can construct injective resolutions X, Y, Z of A, B, C, respectively, and morphisms of complexes $0 \to X \xrightarrow{F} Y \xrightarrow{G} Z \to 0$ extending f and g and forming an exact sequence; this implies the existence of a cohomology exact sequence

$$\cdots \to R^nT(A) \xrightarrow{R^nT(f)} R^nT(B) \xrightarrow{R^nT(g)} R^nT(C) \xrightarrow{\partial_n} R^{n+1}T(A) \to \cdots.$$

We may think of the $R^nT(A)$, $R^nT(B)$, and $R^nT(C)$ for $n \geqslant 1$ as objects which evaluate the "defect from exactness" (or the "obstruction to exactness") of the sequence $0 \to T(A) \to T(B) \to T(C) \to 0$.

By considering the opposite category $\boldsymbol{C}^0$, we have the notion of a *projective resolution* of an object A of $\boldsymbol{C}$: this consists of a chain complex $(X_n)_{n \geqslant 0}$ and a morphism $X_0 \xrightarrow{\alpha} A$ such that

$$\cdots \to X_{n+1} \to X_n \to \cdots \to X_1 \to X_0 \xrightarrow{\alpha} A \to 0$$

is an exact sequence and the X_n are projective objects (**C** I) of $\boldsymbol{C}$. By reversing the arrows we obtain the construction of the *left derived functors* L_nT: $\boldsymbol{C} \to \boldsymbol{C}'$ of an additive functor $T : \boldsymbol{C} \to \boldsymbol{C}'$, provided that every object of $\boldsymbol{C}$ is a quotient of a projective object (in which case we say that $\boldsymbol{C}$ has "enough projectives"). If T is right-exact, we have $L_0T = T$. If $0 \to A \xrightarrow{f} B \xrightarrow{g} C \to 0$ is an exact sequence in $\boldsymbol{C}$, we obtain a homology exact sequence

$$\cdots \to L_{n+1}T(C) \xrightarrow{\partial_n} L_nT(A) \to L_nT(B) \to L_nT(C) \to \cdots.$$

One of the most powerful tools in homological algebra is the *spectral sequence* (J. Leray). This is concerned with (for example) cochain complexes $X = (X_n)$ in which each object X_n is endowed with a *filtration* $(F^p(X_n))_{p \geqslant 1}$, i.e., a decreasing sequence of subobjects of X_n; it is not assumed that $d_n(F^p(X_n))$ is contained in $F^p(X_{n+1})$. We can then in a certain sense "approximate" $H^{\bullet}(X)$ by a sequence of complexes E_r constructed with the help of the filtrations of the X_n, and such that $E_{r+1} = H^{\bullet}(E_r)$ ([28], [65]).

Spectral sequences are useful especially in the study of the cohomology of *bicomplexes*. A cochain bicomplex (for example) over $\boldsymbol{C}$ is a double sequence $(X_{mn})_{m \geqslant 0, n \geqslant 0}$ of objects of $\boldsymbol{C}$, endowed with morphisms

$$\begin{array}{ccccc}
 & \vdots & & \vdots & \\
 & \uparrow & & \uparrow & \\
\cdots \to & X_{m,n+1} & \xrightarrow{d^{(1)}_{m+1,n+1}} & X_{m+1,n+1} & \to \cdots \\
 & {\scriptstyle d^{(2)}_{m,n+1}}\uparrow & & \uparrow{\scriptstyle d^{(2)}_{m+1,n+1}} & \\
\cdots \to & X_{mn} & \xrightarrow[d^{(1)}_{m+1,n}]{} & X_{m+1,n} & \to \cdots \\
 & \uparrow & & \uparrow & \\
 & \vdots & & \vdots &
\end{array}$$

satisfying the conditions

$$d^{(1)}_{m+1,n}\, d^{(1)}_{mn} = 0, \qquad d^{(2)}_{m,n+1}\, d^{(2)}_{mn} = 0,$$

$$d^{(2)}_{m+1,n+1} d^{(1)}_{m+1,n} + d^{(1)}_{m+1,n+1} d^{(2)}_{m,n+1} = 0.$$

If we put $X_p = \bigoplus_{m+n=p} X_{mn}$ and if $d_{p+1} : X_p \to X_{p+1}$ is such that its restriction to X_{mn} is $d^{(1)}_{m+1,n} + d^{(2)}_{m,n+1}$, the above relations imply that $d_{p+1}d_p = 0$, i.e., that (X_p) is a cochain complex, the cohomology of which is called the *hypercohomology* of the bicomplex. The various natural filtrations of the bicomplex induce filtrations on the complex (X_p), to which the spectral sequence can be applied to provide information (sometimes very complete) on the hypercohomology. In the category of cochain complexes over $\boldsymbol{C}$, certain injective resolutions define bicomplexes, the hypercohomology of which is independent of the choice of injective resolution of this type: this is called the *hypercohomology* of the complex under consideration.

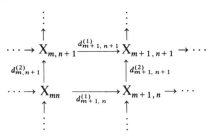

Derived functors can be defined in another way. To each abelian category $\boldsymbol{C}$, there is associated its *derived category* $D(\boldsymbol{C})$, in which the objects are cochain complexes over $\boldsymbol{C}$, but the morphisms are defined *differently* from above. The category $D(\boldsymbol{C})$ is no longer abelian, but under fairly wide conditions it is possible to define for an additive functor $T : \boldsymbol{C} \to \boldsymbol{C}'$ a right derived functor $RT : D(\boldsymbol{C}) \to D(\boldsymbol{C}')$ such that, for each object A of $\boldsymbol{C}$, if we identify A with the complex which is equal to A in degree 0 and is zero otherwise, the cohomology object $H^n(RT(A))$ is the $R^nT(A)$ defined earlier. The advantage of this method is that for two additive functors $T : \boldsymbol{C} \to \boldsymbol{C}'$ and $T' : \boldsymbol{C}' \to \boldsymbol{C}''$ we have $R(T' \circ T) = R(T') \circ R(T)$, whereas the calculation of $R^n(T' \circ T)(A)$ in terms of the derived functors of T and T′ requires the intervention of spectral sequences (B 300; LN 20).

Examples of derived functors. The category of left (resp. right) modules over a ring Λ has enough injectives and enough projectives. We can therefore define the nth right derived functor of the (left-exact) functor

$$B \mapsto \mathrm{Hom}_\Lambda(A, B)$$

from the category of left A-modules to the category of abelian groups; this derived functor is written $B \mapsto \mathrm{Ext}^n_\Lambda(A, B)$, and $A \mapsto \mathrm{Ext}^n_\Lambda(A, B)$ is also the nth right derived functor of the contravariant functor $A \to \mathrm{Hom}_\Lambda(A, B)$. The group $\mathrm{Ext}^1_\Lambda(A, B)$ can be identified with the set of isomorphism classes of extensions $0 \to B \to E \to A \to 0$ of B by A.† For a Λ-module A to be projective (resp. injective), it is necessary and sufficient that $\mathrm{Ext}^1_\Lambda(A, X) = 0$ (resp. $\mathrm{Ext}^1_\Lambda(X, A) = 0$) for every Λ-module X.

Likewise, for every left Λ-module B, we may define the nth left derived functor of the (right-exact) functor $A \mapsto A \otimes_\Lambda B$ from the category of right Λ-modules to the category of abelian groups; this derived functor is written $A \mapsto \mathrm{Tor}^\Lambda_n(A, B)$, and $B \mapsto \mathrm{Tor}^\Lambda_n(A, B)$ is also the nth left derived functor of the functor $B \mapsto A \otimes_\Lambda B$ from the category of left A-modules to the category of abelian groups. A right Λ-module A (resp. a left Λ-module B) is said to be *flat* if $\mathrm{Tor}^\Lambda_1(A, Y) = 0$ (resp. $\mathrm{Tor}^\Lambda_1(X, B) = 0$) for every left Λ-module Y (resp. every right Λ-module X). The functors Ext and Tor play a large part in commutative algebra (**C** II) (LN 11; [70]).

If $\mathscr{T}$ is a Grothendieck topology (**C** I), the category of sheaves of abelian groups on $\mathscr{T}$ (**C** I) has enough injectives (but not enough projectives, in general), and we may therefore define the right derived functors of any

† Two extensions E, E′ of B by A are isomorphic if there exists a bijective homomorphism $f : E \to E'$ of Λ-modules such that the diagram

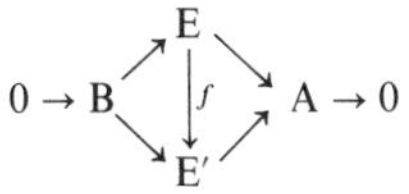

is commutative.

functor from this category of sheaves to an abelian category. A particularly important example is the functor $F \mapsto \Gamma_U(F)$, where, for a sheaf F and an object $U \in \operatorname{Cat} \mathscr{T}$, $\Gamma_U(F) = F(U)$; the nth derived functor $R^n\Gamma_U(F)$ is denoted by $H^n(\mathscr{T}, U; F)$ and is called the nth *cohomology group* of F on U with respect to the topology $\mathscr{T}$ (B 256; [7], [68]). These groups have a considerable importance in algebraic geometry (**A** IX).

When $\mathscr{T}$ is the usual topology of a topological space X, and the sheaves F are suitably chosen, the corresponding cohomology groups coincide with those defined in algebraic topology (**A** I).

2. Cohomology of groups

Let G be a group, **Z**[G] the algebra of G over the ring **Z**, and let A be a left **Z**[G]-module (or, as is also said, a left G-*module*). We put

$$\operatorname{Ext}^n_{\mathbf{Z}[G]}(\mathbf{Z}, A) = H^n(G, A),$$

$$\operatorname{Tor}_n^{\mathbf{Z}[G]}(\mathbf{Z}, A) = H_n(G, A),$$

Z being considered as a trivial G-module ($s \cdot n = n$ for all $s \in G$ and $n \in \mathbf{Z}$). $H^n(G, A)$ (resp. $H_n(G, A)$) is called the nth *cohomology group* (resp. nth *homology group*) of G with coefficients in A. These groups can be calculated by means of the "standard free resolution" of **Z** by free G-modules

$$\cdots \to L_j \to L_{j-1} \to \cdots \to L_0 \to \mathbf{Z} \to 0,$$

where L_j is the **Z**-module $\mathbf{Z}[G^{j+1}]$ having as a basis all sequences

$$(s_0, s_1, \ldots, s_j)$$

of $j + 1$ elements of G, and G acts on L_j by translation

$$s \cdot (s_0, s_1, \ldots, s_j) = (ss_0, ss_1, \ldots, ss_j);$$

the homomorphism $d : L_j \to L_{j-1}$ is defined by

$$d(s_0, s_1, \ldots, s_j) = \sum_{k=0}^{j} (-1)^k (s_0, \ldots, \hat{s}_k, \ldots, s_j) \tag{3}$$

with the usual convention that the symbol under the circumflex is to be omitted; finally the homomorphism $\varepsilon : L_0 \to \mathbf{Z}$ maps each $s_0 \in G$ to $1 \in \mathbf{Z}$. The elements of $K^j = \operatorname{Hom}_{\mathbf{Z}[G]}(L_j, A)$ may therefore be identified with functions $f : G^{j+1} \to A$ such that

$$f(ss_0, \ldots, ss_j) = s \cdot f(s_0, \ldots, s_j),$$

and such a function is determined uniquely by its restriction to sequences of the form $(1, s_1, s_1s_2, \ldots, s_1s_2 \cdots s_j)$. We may therefore interpret the elements of K^j as functions $g: G^j \to A$ ("cochains of degree j") with the "coboundary operator"

$$(4)\quad d_j g(s_1, \ldots, s_{j+1}) = s_1 \cdot g(s_2, \ldots, s_{j+1}) + \sum_{k=1}^{j} (-1)^k g(s_1, \ldots, s_{k-1}, s_k s_{k+1}, s_{k+2}, \ldots, s_{j+1}) + (-1)^{j+1} g(s_1, \ldots, s_j).$$

The $H^n(G, A)$ are then the cohomology groups of the cochain complex (K^j).

The group $H^0(G, A)$ may be identified with the subgroup A^G of elements of A fixed by G. If G acts trivially on A, we have $H^1(G, A) = \mathrm{Hom}(G, A)$. Also $H_0(G, A) = A/DA$, where DA is the subgroup of A generated by the elements $s \cdot a - a$ for $a \in A$ and $s \in G$. If $A = \mathbf{Z}$ considered as a trivial G-module, $H_1(G, \mathbf{Z})$ may be canonically identified with the quotient G/G' of G by its commutator subgroup.

The cohomological invariants of groups so obtained are of great importance in the situation of a group Γ acting on a topological space X, because they can be related to the cohomological invariants of X, and properties of either Γ or X can be deduced (B 90, 405; [28]). A particularly important case is that in which Γ is a discrete subgroup of a semisimple Lie group G, and Γ acts on a symmetric space $G/K = X$ (B 265, 399; LN 143; [28], [68]). Likewise, if Γ is a discrete subgroup of a p-adic or adelic simple group, it can be made to act on a Tits "building" (**B** III) or a product of such buildings, the cohomology of which is known (B 399, 437).

Variants. When G is a finite group, it is better to modify the definitions of $H^0(G, A)$ and $H_0(G, A)$. There is a canonical endomorphism $N: A \to A$ (the "norm") defined by $Na = \sum_{s \in G} s \cdot a$, and on passing to the quotient this induces a homomorphism $N^*: H_0(G, A) \to H^0(G, A)$. We now define $\hat{H}^0(G, A) = \mathrm{Coker}(N^*)$, $\hat{H}^{-1}(G, A) = \mathrm{Ker}(N^*)$, and for $n \geqslant 2$, $\hat{H}^{-n}(G, A) = H_{n-1}(G, A)$; if also we write $\hat{H}^n(G, A) = H^n(G, A)$ for $n \geqslant 1$, then for an exact sequence $0 \to A \to B \to C \to 0$ of G-modules we have a *doubly infinite* cohomology exact sequence

$$\cdots \to \hat{H}^i(G, A) \to \hat{H}^i(G, B) \to \hat{H}^i(G, C) \to \hat{H}^{i+1}(G, A) \to \cdots$$

with i varying from $-\infty$ to $+\infty$. These modified cohomology groups play an important role in class-field theory (**A** X); the finite groups G can be characterized for which the sequence $(\hat{H}^i(G, A))$ is periodic for every G-module A (B 77, 209; [155]).

Let G be a compact totally disconnected group, the inverse limit (**C** I) of the finite groups G/U, where U runs through the set of open normal subgroups of G. We consider only the G-modules A on which G acts continuously (A being given the discrete topology); this means that for each $a \in A$, the set of $s \in G$ such that $s \cdot a = a$ is an open subgroup of G. For such a G-module A, we put $H^i(G, A) = \varinjlim_{U} H^i(G/U, A^U)$ (**C** I), where U runs through the set of open normal subgroups of G, and A^U is the G/U-module consisting of the elements of A fixed by U. For these groups, there is again a cohomology exact sequence (B 189; [155]). The groups $H^i(G, A)$ can also be defined directly in terms of "cochains" as above, but now the cochains have to be *continuous* (with respect to the discrete topology on A).

If G is a separable, metrizable, locally compact group and A a separable, metrizable, locally compact abelian group on which G acts continuously, we can again modify the definition of the $H^i(G, A)$ by considering only cochains that are Borel functions. These groups $H^i(G, A)$ are involved in the definition of a notion of fundamental group $\pi_1(G)$, even when G is totally disconnected, and this notion is closely related to the congruence subgroup problem (**A** X) (see [127]).

Finally, we can define "cohomology sets" $H^0(G, A)$, $H^1(G, A)$ when A is a *nonabelian* group on which G acts by $(s, a) \mapsto s \cdot a$, in such a way that $s \cdot (ab) = (s \cdot a)(s \cdot b)$. We define $H^0(G, A)$ to be A^G, the subgroup of elements fixed by G; next we define 1-cocycles with values in A to be mappings $s \mapsto g(s)$ of G into A such that $g(st) = g(s)(s \cdot g(t))$, and two cocycles g_1, g_2 are said to be cohomologous if there exists $b \in A$ such that $g_2(s) = b^{-1} g_1(s)(s \cdot b)$ for all $s \in G$; this is an equivalence relation, and the quotient set is denoted by $H^1(G, A)$. It is no longer a group, but it has a "distinguished element," namely, the class of the mapping $s \mapsto e$ (where e is the identity element of A). For a subgroup B of A, stable under the action of G, we have an "exact sequence"

$$1 \to H^0(G, B) \to H^0(G, A) \to H^0(G, A/B)$$
$$\to H^1(G, B) \to H^1(G, A) \to H^1(G, A/B)$$

in the sense that the image of each mapping is equal to the inverse image of the distinguished element under the next mapping. If B is contained in the center of A, this exact sequence can be extended one more place $H^1(G, A/B) \to H^2(G, B)$. There is a variant of this exact sequence, in the situation that G and A are topological groups and the mapping $(s, x) \mapsto s \cdot x$ is continuous: to define $H^1(G, A)$, one must then use continuous cocycles (LN 5; [127]).

Galois cohomology. Let k be a field, K a (finite or infinite) Galois extension of k, and let $G = \mathrm{Gal}(K/k)$ be the Galois group. Galois cohomology is the study of the groups $H^i(G, A)$ for groups A on which G acts naturally. For example, G acts on the additive group K; if K/k is finite, we have $\hat{H}^n(G, K) = 0$ for all $n \in \mathbf{Z}$. G also acts on the multiplicative group $K^\times$, and we have $H^1(G, K^\times) = 0$. The group $H^2(G, K^\times)$ has an important interpretation in terms of the theory of *central simple algebras* over k, which are matrix algebras over division rings with center k. Two such algebras are said to be equivalent if they are matrix algebras (of different orders) over k-isomorphic division rings; on passing to the quotient, the operation of tensor product over k defines an abelian group structure on the set of equivalence classes, and the group so defined is called the *Brauer group* $\mathrm{Br}(k)$ of the field k. An extension field K of k is said to be *neutralizing* for a central simple k-algebra A if $A \otimes_k K$ is a matrix algebra *over* K; the equivalence classes of simple algebras for which a given Galois extension K of k is neutralizing form a subgroup of $\mathrm{Br}(k)$ isomorphic to the cohomology group $H^2(\mathrm{Gal}(K/k), K^\times)$ [155].

Let L be a linear algebraic group defined over the algebraic closure $\bar{k}$ of a field k; the Galois group $G = \mathrm{Gal}(\bar{k}/k)$ acts on L, and the cohomology set $H^1(G, L)$ plays an important role in the study of algebraic groups, especially over local and global fields (LN 5; [31]).

3. Cohomology of associative algebras

Let K be a field, Λ an associative K-algebra with identity element, and Λ^0 the opposite algebra; a Λ-bimodule A may then be considered as a left or right module over the tensor product algebra $\Lambda^e = \Lambda \otimes_K \Lambda^0$. By considering A as a right Λ^e-module, we define the groups $H_n(\Lambda, A) = \mathrm{Tor}_n^{\Lambda^e}(A, \Lambda)$, where Λ is considered as a left Λ^e-module by the rule $(\lambda \otimes \mu) \cdot \xi = \lambda\xi\mu$; and by considering A as a left Λ^e-module, we define the groups $H^n(\Lambda, A) = \mathrm{Ext}^n_{\Lambda^e}(\Lambda, A)$. The groups $H_n(\Lambda, A)$ (resp. $H^n(\Lambda, A)$) are called the *homology* (resp. *cohomology*) *groups* of Λ with coefficients in A. The $H^n(\Lambda, A)$ may also be calculated as the cohomology groups of a complex (K^j) of "cochains" that are K-multilinear mappings of Λ^j into A, with the "coboundary" (4), and there is an analogous method of calculation for the $H_n(\Lambda, A)$. These groups are related to questions of extensions of algebras and to properties of derivations in algebras.

A K-algebra Λ is said to be *semisimple* if it is the direct product of a finite number of matrix algebras over division rings containing K in their centers and of finite rank over K. A necessary and sufficient condition for an algebra Λ of finite rank over K to be such that, for each field extension $L \supset K$, the L-algebra $\Lambda \otimes_K L$ is semisimple is that $H^n(\Lambda, A) = 0$ for all $n \geqslant 1$ and all Λ-bimodules A [28].

4. Cohomology of Lie algebras

Let $\mathfrak{g}$ be a Lie algebra over a field K. There exists an associative K-algebra $U(\mathfrak{g})$, unique up to K-isomorphism, containing $\mathfrak{g}$ and generated by $\mathfrak{g}$ and the identity element, such that every K-linear mapping $f : \mathfrak{g} \to \Lambda$ of $\mathfrak{g}$ into an associative K-algebra that satisfies the relation

$$f([x, y]) = f(x)f(y) - f(y)f(x)$$

for all $x, y \in \mathfrak{g}$ extends to a homomorphism of associative algebras of $U(\mathfrak{g})$ into Λ. The algebra $U(\mathfrak{g})$ is called the *universal enveloping algebra* of $\mathfrak{g}$ (**B** II). For every right $U(\mathfrak{g})$-module A, we define $H_n(\mathfrak{g}, A) = \mathrm{Tor}_n^{U(\mathfrak{g})}(A, K)$, and for every left $U(\mathfrak{g})$-module A, we define $H^n(\mathfrak{g}, A) = \mathrm{Ext}^n_{U(\mathfrak{g})}(K, A)$ ($U(\mathfrak{g})$ is the direct sum of K and the two-sided ideal $\mathfrak{J}$ generated by $\mathfrak{g}$, hence we have a K-homomorphism $U(\mathfrak{g}) \to K$ which is zero on $\mathfrak{J}$ and equal to the identity on K; this gives K a canonical structure of left or right $U(\mathfrak{g})$-module, the product of an element of $\mathfrak{J}$ and an element of K being zero). The $H_n(\mathfrak{g}, A)$ (resp. $H^n(\mathfrak{g}, A)$) are called the *homology* (resp. *cohomology*) *groups* of $\mathfrak{g}$ with coefficients in A. The $H^n(\mathfrak{g}, A)$ can also be calculated as the cohomology groups of a complex (K^q), where now the "cochains" are alternating K-multilinear mappings of $\mathfrak{g}^q$ into A, with a "coboundary" defined by

$$(5)\quad d_q f(x_1, \ldots, x_{q+1}) = \sum_{i=1}^{q+1} (-1)^{i+1} x_i \cdot f(x_1, \ldots, \hat{x}_i, \ldots, x_{q+1}) + \sum_{1 \leqslant i < j \leqslant q+1} (-1)^{i+j} f([x_i, x_j], x_1, \ldots, \hat{x}_i, \ldots, \hat{x}_j, \ldots, x_{q+1}).$$

There is an analogous method of calculation of the $H_n(\mathfrak{g}, A)$ [28].

If K is a field of characteristic 0 and $\mathfrak{g}$ is a finite-dimensional semisimple Lie algebra, we have $H^1(\mathfrak{g}, A) = H^2(\mathfrak{g}, A) = 0$ for all $U(\mathfrak{g})$-modules A; these properties imply the complete reducibility of linear representations of $\mathfrak{g}$, and E. E. Levi's theorem on the decomposition of a finite-dimensional Lie algebra $\mathfrak{a}$ over K as the direct sum of its radical and a semisimple subalgebra [D, Chapter 21].

If $\mathfrak{g}$ is the Lie algebra of a compact connected Lie group G, the groups $H^n(\mathfrak{g}, \mathbf{R})$ are isomorphic to the cohomology groups of the manifold G with real coefficients (B 1, 8, 12). If $\mathfrak{g}$ is the Lie algebra of a compact p-adic analytic group G and M is a vector space over $\mathbf{Q}_p$ on which G acts continuously, the groups $H^n(\mathfrak{g}, M)$ can be identified with the cohomology groups $H^n_c(U, M)$ formed with continuous cochains, where U is a sufficiently small open subgroup of G (B 270).

There are variants of the cohomology groups for topological Lie algebras $\mathfrak{g}$ over a topological field k and topological k-vector spaces A on which $\mathfrak{g}$

acts continuously; the most important case is that of the Lie algebra of formal vector fields, the cohomology of which plays an important part in the theory of foliations (B 412, 421).

5. Simplicial structures

Historically, complexes first appeared in H. Poincaré's definition of the homology of a polyhedron. This definition was then generalized to that of the *singular homology* of an arbitrary topological space E (**A** I), which in turn led to the notion of a *simplicial object*. For each $n \geqslant 0$, consider the set X_n of continuous mappings $\Delta(n) \to E$, where $\Delta(n)$ is the "Euclidean simplex" consisting of the points $(\xi_0, \xi_1, \ldots, \xi_n) \in \mathbf{R}^{n+1}$ such that $\xi_j \geqslant 0$ for $0 \leqslant j \leqslant n$, and $\sum_{j=0}^{n} \xi_j = 1$. The "face" operators $F_i^n : X_n \to X_{n-1}$ $(n > 0)$ and the "degeneracy" operators $D_i^n : X_n \to X_{n+1}$ $(n \geqslant 0)$ are defined by the formulas

$$F_i^n f(\xi_0, \ldots, \xi_{n-1}) = f(\xi_0, \ldots, \xi_{i-1}, 0, \xi_i, \ldots, \xi_{n-1}),$$

$$D_i^n f(\xi_0, \ldots, \xi_{n+1}) = f(\xi_0, \ldots, \xi_{i-1}, \xi_i + \xi_{i+1}, \xi_{i+2}, \ldots, \xi_{n+1})$$

$(0 \leqslant i \leqslant n)$, and it is immediately verified that these operators satisfy the relations

$$(6) \qquad \begin{cases} D_i D_j = D_{j+1} D_i, \qquad F_i F_{j+1} = F_j F_i & (i \leqslant j), \\ F_i D_j = D_{j-1} F_i & (i < j), \\ F_j D_j = F_{j+1} D_j = 1, & \\ F_i D_j = D_j F_{i-1} & (i > j+1). \end{cases}$$

We now define generally, for *any* category $\boldsymbol{C}$, a *simplicial object* of $\boldsymbol{C}$ to be a sequence $(X_n)_{n \geqslant 0}$ of objects of $\boldsymbol{C}$ endowed with morphisms F_i^n, D_i^n which are only required to satisfy the relations (6). If $\boldsymbol{C}$ is an abelian category, we can then define morphisms $d_n = \sum_{i=0}^{n} (-1)^i F_i^n : X_n \to X_{n-1}$, and the relations (6) imply that $d_n d_{n+1} = 0$, so that we have a chain complex (X_n) over $\boldsymbol{C}$, with $X_n = 0$ for $n < 0$ (B 199).

We can go on to define "projective resolutions" as before, but now requiring that the elements form a simplicial object; this enables us to define the derived functors of nonadditive functors (B 170).

When $\boldsymbol{C}$ is the category of sets, a simplicial object $X = (X_n)$ of $\boldsymbol{C}$ is called a *simplicial set*, and the elements of X_n are the *n-simplexes* of X. We can associate canonically with X a topological space $|X|$ called the "*geometric realization*" of X, as follows. Each X_n is given the discrete topology, and we form the topological sum (i.e., disjoint union) Y of the spaces $X_n \times \Delta(n)$ $(n \geqslant 0)$; the space $|X|$ is the quotient of Y by the smallest equivalence relation containing the pairs

$$((F_i^n x, (\xi_0, \ldots, \xi_{n-1})), (x, (\xi_0, \ldots, \xi_{i-1}, 0, \xi_i, \ldots, \xi_{n-1})))$$

$$((D_i^n x, (\xi_0, \ldots, \xi_{n+1})), (x, (\xi_0, \ldots, \xi_{i-1}, \xi_i + \xi_{i+1}, \xi_{i+2}, \ldots, \xi_{n+1})))$$

belonging to $(X_{n-1} \times \Delta(n-1), X_n \times \Delta(n))$ and $(X_{n+1} \times \Delta(n+1), X_n \times \Delta(n))$, respectively. It can be shown that the space $|X|$ is a CW-complex [170]. If X is the simplicial set constructed as above from a topological space E, then $|X|$ and E have the same homotopy type.

To each category $\boldsymbol{C}$ is canonically associated a simplicial set $N\boldsymbol{C} = (X_n)$, where X_n is the set of all diagrams of $\boldsymbol{C}$-morphisms

$$Z_0 \to Z_1 \to \cdots \to Z_n. \tag{7}$$

The mapping F_i^n (resp. D_i^n) has the effect of replacing $Z_{i-1} \to Z_i \to Z_{i+1}$ in this diagram by the composite morphism $Z_{i-1} \to Z_{i+1}$ (resp. $Z_i \to Z_{i+1}$ by $Z_i \xrightarrow{\text{id}} Z_i \to Z_{i+1}$). The topological space $|N\boldsymbol{C}| = B\boldsymbol{C}$ is called the *classifying space* of $\boldsymbol{C}$, and leads to a family of homotopy groups $\pi_i(B\boldsymbol{C}, Z)$ for each $Z \in \boldsymbol{C}$ regarded as a point of $B\boldsymbol{C}$. In many cases these groups are trivial, for example, when $\boldsymbol{C}$ admits an initial object or a final object (B 438; LN 341 (Quillen)).

6. K-theory

If X is any topological space, let $\Phi(X)$ denote the set of isomorphism classes of complex vector bundles (**A** I) on X. This set is naturally endowed with a structure of a commutative monoid, defined by the addition of vector bundles (the sum of two bundles E, F being the vector bundle $E \oplus F$ whose fiber at each point $x \in X$ is the direct sum of the fibers E_x and F_x). This monoid has a neutral element (the class of the zero-dimensional bundle). There exists an abelian group K(X), unique up to isomorphism, such that every homomorphism of monoids $\Phi(X) \to G$, where G is an abelian group, factorizes uniquely into $\Phi(X) \to K(X) \to G$, the second arrow being a group homomorphism. The group K(X) is called the *Grothendieck group* of X, and $X \mapsto K(X)$ is a contravariant functor from the category of topological spaces into the category of abelian groups. If P is a space consisting of a single point, we have $K(P) \cong \mathbf{Z}$. For any space X, there corresponds to the unique continuous mapping $X \to P$ an injective homomorphism $\mathbf{Z} = K(P) \to K(X)$, the cokernel of which is denoted by $\tilde{K}(X)$. Now put $K^{-n}(X) = \tilde{K}(S^n X)$, where $S^n X$ is the nth suspension of X (**A** I); then it can be shown that the groups $K^{-n}(X)$ are the generalized cohomology groups arising from a spectrum of spaces (**A** I), provided that the space X is sufficiently "regular" (SAMS III (Atiyah–Hirzebruch); B 177, 223; LN 28).

For this type of space, the category of vector bundles on X is equivalent to the category $\mathscr{P}$(A) of finitely generated projective modules over the ring A = $\mathscr{C}$(X) of continuous real-valued functions on X. This fact leads to the idea of defining an abelian group $K_0(A)$ for *any* commutative ring A, by replacing Φ(X) in the definition above by the set of isomorphism classes of finitely generated projective A-modules (which is naturally endowed with a structure of a commutative monoid). But since the notion of suspension has no obvious analog in the theory of modules, the definition of the groups $K_n(A)$ for $n \geqslant 1$ (which should be the analogs of the groups $K^{-n}(X)$) posed serious problems. As to $K_1(A)$, a construction of vector bundles on S^1X led to a proposed definition of $K_1(A)$ as the quotient of the group $\mathbf{GL}_\infty(A)$, the direct limit (**C** I) of the groups $\mathbf{GL}_n(A)$ as $n \to \infty$,† by its commutator subgroup. This group does in fact have the expected properties; moreover, when A is the group-algebra $\mathbf{Z}[\pi]$ of an abelian group π over the ring $\mathbf{Z}$, the quotient $\mathrm{Wh}_1(\pi)$ of $K_1(\mathbf{Z}[\pi])$ by the subgroup generated by the images of π and -1 (called the *Whitehead group* of π) had already naturally arisen in the theory of simple homotopy type and in *h*-cobordism theory (**A** I) (B 392; LN 342; [10]; BAMS 72 (Milnor)).

Several different definitions of the $K_n(A)$ for $n \geqslant 2$ have been put forward, but it is only recently that a general theory has been developed which enables one to show that all these definitions are equivalent in the most important cases (B 337; Nice I (Swan); Nice C I (Quillen); LN 341). It is now possible to define the groups $K_n(\boldsymbol{M})$ for any abelian category $\boldsymbol{M}$ (or more generally for any full additive subcategory $\boldsymbol{M}$ of an abelian category $\boldsymbol{A}$ such that if $0 \to M' \to M \to M'' \to 0$ is an exact sequence in $\boldsymbol{A}$ in which M′ and M″ are in $\boldsymbol{M}$, then also M is in $\boldsymbol{M}$). From $\boldsymbol{M}$ we construct a category $Q\boldsymbol{M}$ in which the objects are those of $\boldsymbol{M}$, but the morphisms are isomorphisms of objects of $\boldsymbol{M}$ onto quotients of subobjects of $\boldsymbol{M}$; we then form the classifying space $BQ\boldsymbol{M}$ defined above, and we take $K_n(M) = \pi_{n+1}(BQ\boldsymbol{M},*)$ (B 438; Vancouver (Quillen); LN 341). When $\boldsymbol{M} = \mathscr{P}(A)$, it can be shown that the groups $K_n(\mathscr{P}(A))$ for $n = 0$ and $n = 1$ are isomorphic to the groups $K_0(A)$ and $K_1(A)$ defined above, and the general properties of the $K_n(A) = K_n(\mathscr{P}(A))$ are as one would expect.

K-theory has already found numerous applications (notably for the functors K_0, K_1, and K_2), not only in algebra and algebraic geometry,

† The homomorphisms $\varphi_{n+1,n}: \mathbf{GL}_n(A) \to \mathbf{GL}_{n+1}(A)$ that define the direct limit map an $n \times n$ matrix X to the $(n+1) \times (n+1)$ matrix $\begin{pmatrix} X & 0 \\ 0 & 1 \end{pmatrix}$.

but also in group theory, where it is related to representation theory, the theory of Tits "buildings" (**B** III) and the congruence subgroup problem, and in number theory, where K-theory intervenes in connection with reciprocity laws and the behavior of zeta-functions; also the Whitehead groups Wh_1 and Wh_2 (the latter defined by means of K_2) have recently been applied to questions of isotopy.

Finally, in the definition of $K_1(A)$ from $\mathbf{GL}_\infty(A)$, the latter group may be replaced by $\mathbf{U}_\infty(A)$, the direct limit of the unitary groups $\mathbf{U}_n(A)$, when the ring A carries an involution. In this way we obtain a "unitary (or Hermitian) K-theory" that is related to the groups L_n introduced by C. T. C. Wall as groups of "obstructions" to problems of "surgery" (B 397; LN 343).

7. Connections with the natural sciences

None at present.

8. The originators

The main ideas in homological algebra are due to the following mathematicians:

Homology, simplicial objects, homology groups. H. Poincaré (1854–1912), E. Noether (1882–1935), S. Eilenberg, D. Kan.

Resolutions, derived functors, applications. H. Hopf (1894–1971), S. Eilenberg, S. MacLane, H. Cartan, G. Hochschild, C. Chevalley, J. P. Serre, A. Grothendieck, J. Tate, I. Gelfand.

K-theory. A. Grothendieck, M. Atiyah, F. Hirzebruch, J. H. C. Whitehead (1904–1960), J. P. Serre, H. Bass, J. Milnor, D. Quillen, C. T. C. Wall.

The following have also contributed substantially to these theories: R. Alperin, D. Anderson, M. Artin, A. Bak, M. Barratt, I. Berstein, S. Bloch, A. Borel, K. Brown, E. Calabi, S. Cappell, W. Casselman, S. Chase, P. Cohn, K. Dennis, A. Dold, A. Dress, B. Eckmann, M. Eichler, R. Elman, F. Farrell, D. Fuks, H. Garland, S. Gersten, C. Godbillon, R. Godement, G. Harder, A. Hatcher, A. Heller, P. Hilton, W. C. Hsiang, Y. Ihara, J. Jouanolou, M. Karoubi, M. Kervaire, J. L. Koszul, T. Lam, M. Lazard, R. Lee, J. Loday, R. Lyndon, Ju. Manin, J. May, Y. Matsushima, C. Moore, J. Moore, M. Murthy, T. Nakayama (1912–1964), A. Nobile, S. Novikov, C. Pedrini, T. Petrie, S. Priddy, D. Puppe, A. Ranicki, L. Roberts, B. Rosenfeld, S.

Schneider, G. Segal, A. Selberg, J. Shaneson, R. Sharpe, G. Shimura, J. Stallings, J. Stasheff, M. Stein, J. Strooker, A. Suslin, R. Swan, R. Szczarba, B. Venkov, J. L. Verdier, J. Vey (1944–1980), O. Villamayor, I. Volodin, J. Wagoner, F. Waldhausen, L. Wasserstein, A. Weil, G. W. Whitehead, J. Zilber.

References

B: 1, 8, 12, 77, 90, 170, 177, 189, 199, 209, 223, 256, 265, 270, 300, 337, 392, 397, 399, 405, 412, 421, 437, 438.

LN: 5, 11, 20, 28, 143, 341, 342, 343, 496, 551, 575, 652, 674, 778.

BAMS: 72 (Milnor).

[7], [10], [28], [31], [65], [68], [70], [127], [155], [170].

B II

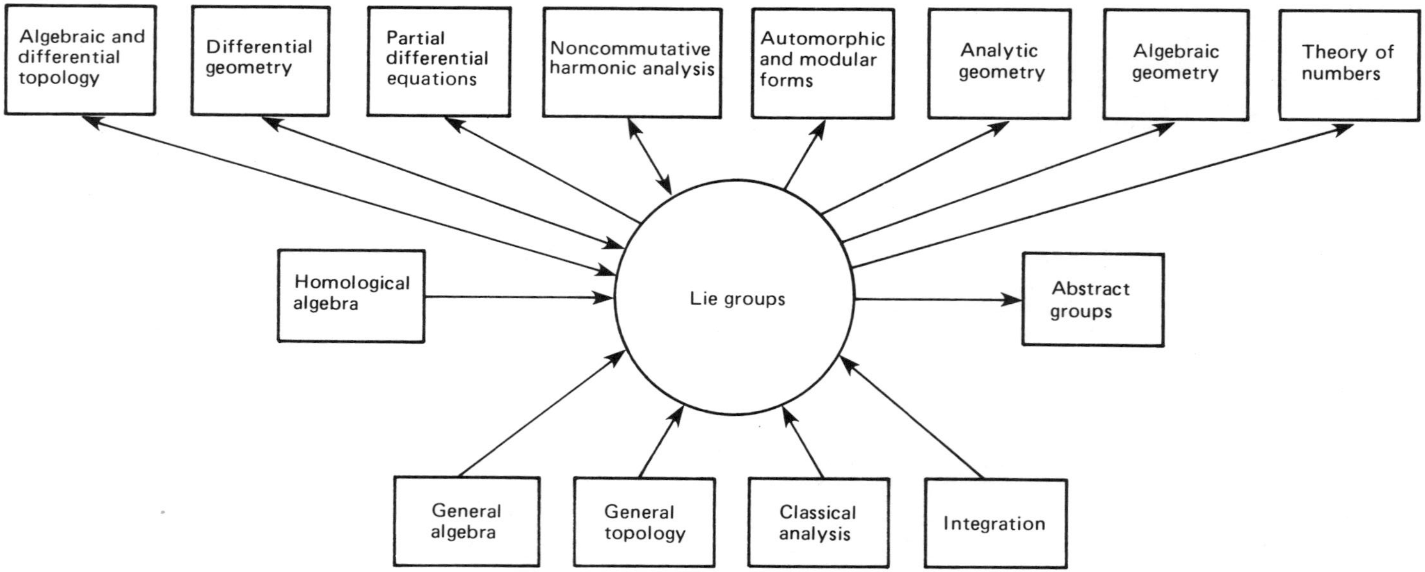

Algebraic and differential topology
Differential geometry
Partial differential equations
Noncommutative harmonic analysis
Automorphic and modular forms
Analytic geometry
Algebraic geometry
Theory of numbers
Homological algebra
Lie groups
Abstract groups
General algebra
General topology
Classical analysis
Integration

B II

Lie groups

A Lie group (resp. a complex Lie group) is a real (resp. complex) analytic manifold G endowed with a group structure such that the mapping $(x, y) \mapsto xy^{-1}$ from G × G to G is analytic. For a long time, it was an open question whether in this definition "real analytic manifold" and "analytic mapping" could be replaced by "topological manifold" and "continuous mapping" (Hilbert's fifth problem); this was answered in the affirmative by Gleason, Montgomery, and Zippin in 1951 (B 27, 29, 73).

The theory was founded by Lie in 1873 and, for a long time, developed in isolation from the mainstream of mathematics, having scarcely any contact with other branches except in connection with certain problems of integration of ordinary or partial differential equations. This situation changed rapidly from 1920 onward:

(a) Klein's conception of "geometries" as spaces that are acted on by transitive groups of transformations came to fruition in E. Cartan's theory of *symmetric spaces* (1927–1930), which embraces all the classical "geometries" as well as the theory of Riemannian manifolds of constant curvature [D, Chapter 20]; the fundamental discovery of E. Cartan is that this theory is substantially equivalent to the theory of semisimple Lie groups.

(b) Simultaneously, E. Cartan, by means of his theory of "moving frames," which was to develop into the theory of G-structures and connections (**A** II), showed that even when a connection has an automorphism group reduced to the identity, the group G of the structure nevertheless acts "infinitesimally," and the structure of its Lie algebra is essentially involved in calculating the invariants of the connection [D, Chapter 20]. Moreover, the automorphism group of a connection (on a connected manifold) is always naturally endowed with a Lie group structure (a theorem first proved by H. Cartan for a bounded open subset of $\mathbf{C}^n$, regarded as a complex manifold).

(c) The work of H. Weyl and E. Cartan on the global structure of Lie groups (1925–1930) showed that the classical theories of Fourier and of spherical harmonics should be attached to the general notion of a *linear representation* of a Lie group; this idea underwent considerable development from 1950 onward, into what is now known as *noncommutative harmonic analysis* (**A** VI), and includes the theory of most of the classical "special functions." At the same time, following the work of H. Weyl and E. Wigner, the representation theory of compact groups gradually became one of the essential tools of quantum physics.

(d) The study of the topology of compact groups, and in particular the determination (1935–1960) of their cohomology and homotopy groups, came to be of capital importance in topology by reason of their relations with characteristic classes and K-theory (**A** I and **B** I).

(e) It had been known for a long time that the compact connected Lie groups could be considered as *algebraic* subgroups of general linear groups $\mathbf{GL}(n, \mathbf{R})$ (i.e., defined by algebraic equations in the coefficients of the matrices). An unexpected discovery made between 1950 and 1960 is that it is possible to transfer the techniques of Lie groups to algebraic subgroups of $\mathbf{GL}(n, k)$, where k is any algebraically closed field, although these groups carry no topology (**A** IX). An analogous transference of the theory of Lie algebras gave rise to the theory of formal groups (**A** IX).

(f) The extension of the theory of Lie groups to the groups obtained by replacing the field $\mathbf{R}$ in their definition by a $\mathfrak{p}$-adic field (or more generally any local field) was much more natural. With the new formulation of algebraic number theory in terms of adèles and idèles, these groups and the "adelic" groups constructed from them acquired a central place in arithmetic (**A** VII and **A** X).

(g) An "abstract" group Γ that is isomorphic to a discrete subgroup of a Lie group G and sufficiently "close" to G in a certain sense enjoys special properties. Some of these groups, the so-called "arithmetic" groups, are the basis of the theory of automorphic functions and its connections with number theory (**A** VII and **A** X).

(h) The most surprising application of the theory of Lie algebras is Chevalley's discovery in 1955 that it is possible to associate canonically with each simple Lie algebra over $\mathbf{C}$ and each field K a simple group (in the sense of "abstract" group theory); in particular, if K is a finite field, the group so obtained is a finite simple group (**B** III).

(i) Quite recently, it has been found that the classical theory of semisimple Lie algebras is included in the study of the Kac–Moody Lie algebras, which are infinite dimensional and have relations with many apparently disconnected areas of mathematics (B 483, 577; LN 716; BAMS 3 (N.S.) (Kac–Peterson)).

1. Structure theorems

The left-invariant differential operators on a Lie group G form an associative algebra $\mathfrak{G}$ with respect to composition, called the *infinitesimal algebra* of G. The first-order operators form a real Lie algebra $\mathfrak{g}$ (with respect to the bracket $[X, Y] = XY - YX$) called the *Lie algebra* of the group G; as a vector space, it may be identified with the tangent space to G at the identity element. The associative algebra $\mathfrak{G}$ is generated by $\mathfrak{g}$, and is the *universal enveloping algebra* of $\mathfrak{g}$ (**B** I). Two simply connected Lie groups are isomorphic if and only if their Lie algebras are isomorphic, and for each finite-dimensional Lie algebra $\mathfrak{g}$ there is a simply connected Lie group having $\mathfrak{g}$ as its Lie algebra. The fundamental principle of the theory of Lie groups is to compile and use a "dictionary" enabling notions and properties of a Lie group to be translated into notions and properties of its Lie algebra. For example, to homomorphisms of Lie groups correspond homomorphisms of Lie algebras; to subalgebras (resp. ideals) of a Lie algebra $\mathfrak{g}$ correspond immersions of a Lie group into G (resp. immersions whose image is a normal subgroup), etc. ([D, Chapters 19 and 20], [76]; LN 7).

A simply connected Lie group G contains a largest connected closed solvable normal subgroup, called the *radical* of G. If the radical consists only of the identity element, G is said to be *semisimple*. In general, G is the semidirect product of its radical R (which is therefore simply connected) and a semisimple Lie group isomorphic to G/R (*Levi decomposition*).

A simply connected semisimple Lie group is a direct product of simply connected closed normal subgroups that are *almost simple*, i.e., contain no nontrivial closed normal subgroup of dimension >0. All these groups are explicitly known: they comprise four series of "classical" groups [D, Chapter 21] and five "exceptional" groups of dimensions 14, 52, 78, 133, and 248 (B 162; LN 40).

Every Lie group is locally isomorphic to a subgroup of $\mathbf{GL}(n, \mathbf{R})$ for some n (Ado). However, certain subgroups of Lie groups, in particular of semisimple groups, play an important part in various questions (**A** I, **A** II, **A** VII). In the first place, every connected Lie group contains maximal compact subgroups; every compact subgroup is contained in one of these, and two maximal compact subgroups are conjugate under an inner automorphism (E. Cartan). Moreover, if K is a maximal compact subgroup, G is diffeomorphic to $K \times \mathbf{R}^n$ (B 33). The maximal subalgebras and the semisimple subalgebras of a semisimple Lie algebra have been determined (B 119). Finally, the discrete subgroups Γ of a semisimple group G such that G/Γ has finite volume (in which case Γ is said to be a "lattice" in G) or, more particularly, is compact (in which case Γ is said to be *cocompact*) have important properties (B 265, 358, 468, 482; Nice C 3 (Mostow), C 5 (Raghunathan); BAMS 79 (L. Auslander)).

2. Lie groups and transformation groups

A topological group G acts continuously on a topological space X if the action $(s, x) \mapsto s \cdot x$ of G on X is a continuous mapping of G × X into X; the existence and nature of such actions are closely related to properties of G and X. One of the most important examples is that in which X is a finite-dimensional complex vector space and $\rho_s : x \mapsto s \cdot x$ is *linear* for each $s \in$ G; this amounts to the same thing as giving a continuous homomorphism $s \mapsto \rho_s$ of G into **GL**(X), i.e., a (continuous) *linear representation* of G in X. There exists a regular procedure for determining explicitly, in principle, all the *finite*-dimensional continuous linear representations of connected semisimple Lie groups ([D, Chapter 21], [76]; LN 40; see also B 191, 260) and fairly precise information on those of general Lie groups (B 159). For a connected semisimple Lie group G, every continuous linear representation of G in a complex vector space X of *finite* dimension is *completely reducible*; this means that X is the direct sum of vector subspaces X_j stable under the action of G, each of which is *irreducible*, i.e., contains no nontrivial G-stable vector subspace. For a given X, the problem of finding the X_j of dimension 1 is the generalization to all semisimple groups of the classical theory of *invariants* of the 19th century ([43], [54], [129]).

The general theory of continuous actions of groups is concerned mostly with the case in which G is compact (not necessarily a Lie group) and X is a compact space or a differential manifold. The main problems concern the classification of the possible actions for given G and X, relations between the dimensions of G and X and the orbits, etc. (B 163; Nice C 2 (W. C. Hsiáng); BAMS 58 (Samelson); LN 59, 298, 299). The case of actions of noncompact Lie groups is related to ergodic theory (**A** IV).

The particular case of group actions which has been studied most (along with the theory of linear representations, to which it is related) is the theory of *homogeneous spaces*, characterized by the fact that the action of the group G is *transitive*; this implies that X is isomorphic to G/H, the space of left cosets xH of a closed subgroup H of G, and G acts on G/H by $(s, x\text{H}) \mapsto sx\text{H}$. The algebraic, topological, and differential properties of G and H are reflected in G/H: this is the modern form of the current of ideas inaugurated by F. Klein's "Erlanger Programm." The most interesting cases are those in which G is a Lie group; from the algebraic point of view, this gives rise to a whole series of "geometries" that includes the classical geometries (B 112, 162; LN 10); and from the point of view of differential geometry, these spaces play an important role in the theory of connections (B 98, 101; [100], [193]).

A type of homogeneous space that has been intensively studied consists of those which can be endowed with an invariant complex-analytic structure, and in particular those which can be identified with bounded open sets in $\mathbf{C}^n$ (B 100; LN 241, 286; [32], [142]).

The most remarkable of the homogeneous spaces are the *Riemannian symmetric spaces*, which may be defined as Riemannian manifolds such that for each point x of the space, the symmetry with x as center (which reverses each geodesic through x) is an isometry of the manifold. Their structure was completely described by E. Cartan: they are products of Euclidean spaces and of two "irreducible" types of symmetric spaces, respectively noncompact and compact. The noncompact symmetric spaces are quotients of a (real) connected semisimple Lie group G with finite center by a maximal compact subgroup K. To each space of this type there is associated one of the other type, which is compact, and is obtained by considering in the complexification G_c of G the compact form G_u of G_c such that $G_u \cap G = K$, and forming the homogeneous space G_u/K [D, Chapter 21]. E. Cartan also determined all the noncompact symmetric spaces that are isomorphic to bounded open subsets of $\mathbf{C}^n$ (B 62; [76]).

It may be said that the symmetric spaces constitute one of the shrines of modern analysis, for they provide the natural context for many questions which traditionally were limited to $\mathbf{R}^n$.

In the first place, if Γ is a discrete subgroup of G, it acts by left multiplication on G and therefore also on G/K; if Γ is torsion-free, the orbit space (or space of double cosets) $\Gamma\backslash G/K$ is only a locally symmetric Riemannian space, but is not in general symmetric. Among these spaces are in particular the Riemannian manifolds of constant curvature. For those that arise from a symmetric space G/K isomorphic to a bounded open subset of $\mathbf{C}^n$, the holomorphic functions on $\Gamma\backslash G/K$ correspond to Γ-invariant holomorphic functions on G/K, which are called *automorphic functions* (**A** VII); the classical case is that in which $G = \mathbf{SL}(2, \mathbf{R})$, G/K is the upper half plane $\mathscr{I}z > 0$, and Γ is a Fuchsian group (B 132; C 1957–8; [17]). The general theory of automorphic functions is closely related to noncommutative harmonic analysis (**A** VI), algebraic geometry (**A** IX), and number theory (**A** X).

The fact that the upper half-plane is embedded in **C** and has the real axis as boundary, obvious though it is, is a particular example of a whole theory that associates with each noncompact symmetric space G/K a "boundary" that can be defined in several ways. It is this setting, which goes beyond the theory of Lie groups, that appears now to be the appropriate one for the classical theory of harmonic functions and its connections with probability theory, harmonic analysis (Poisson kernel), partial differential equations with constant coefficients, etc. (B 268, 370; SAMS IX, XXVI; Nice I (E. Stein),

Nice C 3 (Kobayashi), C 5 (Furstenberg); [32], [177]; BAMS 75 (J. Wolf); LN 148).

We should remark also that a good part of the theory of Lie groups generalizes to the situation in which the field **R** is replaced by a p-adic field (or more generally a local field of characteristic 0); but the theory becomes substantial only in the context of algebraic groups (**A** IX).

3. Topology of Lie groups and homogeneous spaces

The study of the topology of Lie groups and their homogeneous spaces was inaugurated by H. Weyl and E. Cartan in about 1925, and has been a subject of active research since then. For the semisimple groups and their homogeneous spaces, the general "philosophy" is that the topological invariants can be "read off" from the Lie algebra of the group and its associated combinatorial structures (weights, roots, Weyl chambers, Tits systems (**B** III), etc.). For solvable groups, the situation is quite different (B 142; BAMS 79 (L. Auslander)). The variety of techniques used to "extract" the required topological information from the Lie algebra of a semisimple group is quite remarkable: homological algebra (notably the Leray spectral sequence), differential geometry (the Weil algebra), Morse theory (R. Bott), and Hopf bigebras (**A** IX), which were discovered precisely in this context. The results are fairly complete as regards cohomology, the study of classifying spaces and loop spaces, much less so as regards homotopy (B 1, 8, 12, 45, 108, 172; C 1959–60; BAMS 58 (Samelson), 61 (A. Borel)).

4. Connections with the natural sciences

In his famous book "Group Theory and Quantum Mechanics," H. Weyl was the first to draw attention to the possible applications of the theory of Lie groups to quantum mechanics. He limited his attention essentially to the orthogonal group **SO**(3) and its irreducible linear representations. More recently, however, physicists have realized the possibility of applying to the theory of elementary particles the properties of linear representations of other compact groups, notably the unitary groups **SU**(n) for $n \leqslant 12$ (LN 52).

5. The originators

The principal ideas in the theory of Lie groups are due to the following mathematicians:

The notion of Lie group, structure theorems, and finite-dimensional representation theory. S. Lie (1842–1899), W. Killing (1847–1923), E. Cartan (1869–1951), A. Hurwitz (1859–1919), I. Schur (1875–1941), E. E. Levi

(1883–1917), H. Weyl (1885–1955), I. Ado, K. Iwasawa, C. Chevalley, Harish-Chandra, F. Bruhat, B. Kostant, A. Malcev (1909–1967), G. Mostow, L. Auslander, D. Kazhdan, G. Margulis, V. Kac, R. Moody.

Hilbert's fifth problem. A. Haar (1885–1933), J. von Neumann (1903–1957), A. Gleason, D. Montgomery, L. Zippin.

Homogeneous spaces and symmetric spaces. E. Cartan (1869–1951), C. L. Siegel (1896–1981), I. Piatetskii-Shapiro, H. Furstenberg, I. Satake.

Topology of Lie groups and homogeneous spaces. E. Cartan (1869–1951), H. Weyl (1885–1955), H. Hopf (1894–1971), L. Pontrjagin, J. Leray, A. Weil, H. Cartan, C. Chevalley, A. Borel, R. Bott.

The following have also contributed substantially to these theories: R. Azencott, W. Baily, M. Berger, G. Birkhoff, R. Brauer (1901–1977), E. Calabi, J. E. Campbell (1862–1924), H. Casimir, S. Chern, A. Coleman, H. S. M. Coxeter, P. Cartier, E. Dynkin, C. Ehresmann (1905–1979), S. Eilenberg, F. Engel (1861–1941), C. Fefferman, E. Floyd, H. Freudenthal, H. Garland, I. Gelfand, S. Gindikin, R. Godement, M. Gôto, J. Hano, F. Hausdorff (1868–1942), S. Helgason, R. Hermann, G. Hirsch, F. Hirzebruch, G. Hochschild, W. C. Hsiang, W. Y. Hsiang, L. K. Hua, G. Hunt, R. Jänich, F. Karpelevich, S. Kobayashi, M. Köcher, A. Koranyi, J. L. Koszul, T. Kudo, A. Lichnerowicz, Y. Matsushima, F. Mautner, C. Miller, C. Moore, S. Murakami, K. Nomizu, G. Paechter, R. Palais, H. Poincaré (1854–1912), M. Raghunathan, H. Samelson, F. Schur (1856–1932), A. Selberg, J. P. Serre, J. de Siebenthal, P. Smith (1900–1980), T. Springer, E. Stein, R. Steinberg, E. Stiefel (1909–1979), E. Study (1862–1930), A. Svarč, J. Tits, H. Toda, E. Vinberg, B. L. van der Waerden, H. C. Wang (1919–1978), G. W. Whitehead, J. H. C. Whitehead (1904–1960), N. Weiss, E. Witt, J. Wolf, H. Yamabe (1923–1960), C. Yang, Chih-Tah Yen, M. Adler, I. Frenkel, J. Lepowsky, I. G. Macdonald, P. van Moerbeke.

References

B: 1, 8, 12, 27, 29, 33, 45, 62, 73, 98, 100, 101, 108, 112, 119, 132, 142, 159, 162, 163, 172, 191, 260, 265, 268, 358, 370, 468, 482, 483, 577.

LN: 7, 10, 40, 52, 59, 158, 241, 286, 298, 299, 557, 562, 716.

BAMS: 58 (Samelson), 61 (A. Borel), 75 (J. Wolf), 79 (L. Auslander), 3 (N.S.) (Kac–Peterson).

SAMS: IX, XXVI.

[17], [32], [43], [54], [76], [100], [129], [142], [177], [193].

B III

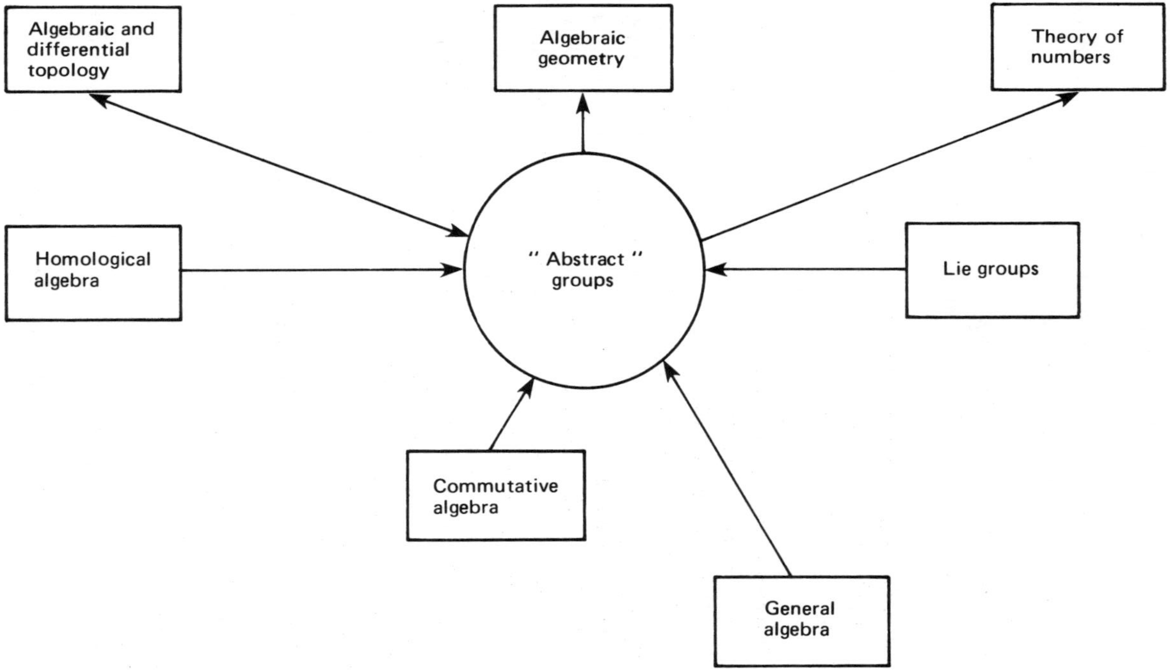
Algebraic and differential topology
Algebraic geometry
Theory of numbers
Homological algebra
" Abstract " groups
Lie groups
Commutative algebra
General algebra

B III

Abstract groups

1. Generators and relations

Groups defined "by generators and relations" have been studied continuously since the beginning of group theory. The *free group* F(X) generated by a set X (**C** I) is defined by the fact that every mapping $f : X \to G$ of X into any group G factorizes uniquely as $X \to F(X) \xrightarrow{g} G$, where g is a group homomorphism. If g is surjective, X (or $f(X)$) is called a *set of generators* of G; if N is the kernel of g, and (r_j) is a family of elements of F(X) such that N is the smallest normal subgroup of F(X) containing the r_j, the r_j are called the *relators* for the set of generators X of G. If $r_j = u_j^{-1}v_j$, with u_j and v_j in F(X), we say that G is generated by the elements of X subject to the relations $u_j = v_j$.

One of the most famous problems in this context is the Burnside problem. Suppose X finite and, for a given integer n, that N contains the nth powers of all elements of F(X); the problem is whether $G = F(X)/N$ is *finite*. The answer is affirmative for $n = 2$, 3, 4, and 6, but it is now known that the answer is negative for all sufficiently large odd integers n (Nice B 1 (Adjan)).

The minimum number $n(G)$ of generators of a group G and the minimum number $r(G)$ of relations between these generators are related to the cohomology of G (**B** I). In particular, there is a remarkable cohomological characterization of finitely generated free groups. The *cohomological dimension* of a group G is defined as the least upper bound cd(G) of integers q such that $H^q(G, A) \neq 0$ for some G-module A; for a finitely generated group, the condition $cd(G) \leqslant 1$ is equivalent to G being free (B 356; LN 245, 421).

2. Chevalley groups and Tits systems

If G is a complex connected Lie group and $\mathfrak{g}$ its Lie algebra, for each element $X \in \mathfrak{g}$, the mapping† $t \mapsto \exp(t \operatorname{ad} X) = \sum_{m=0}^{\infty} \frac{1}{m!} t^m (\operatorname{ad} X)^m$ of the

† We recall that ad(X) is the endomorphism $Y \mapsto [X, Y]$ of $\mathfrak{g}$.

additive group **C** into the linear group Aut($\mathfrak{g}$) $\subset$ **GL**($\mathfrak{g}$) is a homomorphism of the additive group **C** onto a one-parameter subgroup of Aut($\mathfrak{g}$). These subgroups generate a subgroup of Aut($\mathfrak{g}$) (called the *adjoint group* of G) isomorphic to G/Z, where Z is the center of G.

For an almost simple Lie group G (**B** II), Chevalley showed the existence of a basis of $\mathfrak{g}$ in which certain elements X_r have the property that the corresponding one-parameter subgroups $\mathfrak{X}_r : t \mapsto \sum_{m=0}^{\infty} \frac{1}{m!} t^m(\text{ad } X_r)^m$ generate the whole of the adjoint group, and in addition are such that (1) the matrix $(\text{ad}(X_r))^m$ is zero for sufficiently large m, so that $\sum_{m=0}^{\infty} \frac{1}{m!} t^m(\text{ad}(X_r))^m$ is a matrix whose elements are *polynomials* in t, and moreover (2) these polynomials have *integer* coefficients. We may therefore replace t in these polynomials by elements of an arbitrary *field* K, thereby obtaining a group $\mathfrak{X}_r(K)$ of matrices with coefficients in K, a subgroup of **GL**(n, K) (where $n = \dim \mathfrak{g}$). It can then be shown that, with four exceptions, the "abstract" group $G_K \subset$ **GL**(n, K) generated by the $\mathfrak{X}_r(K)$ is *simple* (B 194; LN 131). This group G_K is called a *split Chevalley group*. Some of these groups had been studied by Jordan and Dickson, and were known to be simple (B 169), but by *ad hoc* methods of proof depending on the type of group. Chevalley's method was independent of the type, and gave new results for the types F_4, E_7, and E_8, which had previously not been considered; in particular, by taking K to be a finite field, he obtained new series of *finite simple groups*. The group G_K is the commutator subgroup of the group of K-rational points of an algebraic group defined over K (**A** IX); in fact this algebraic group is itself obtained by base change from a group scheme (**A** IX) defined over **Z** (B 219; LN 153).

Since G_K can be considered as a group of automorphisms of the K-Lie algebra $\mathfrak{g} \otimes_{\mathbf{Z}} K$, for each automorphism σ of this algebra we may consider the subgroup G_K^σ of elements of G_K that commute with σ; in this way we obtain new simple groups, which are subgroups of finite index in G_K^σ (B 194). Another variation on this theme is possible when K has characteristic $p > 0$ and the Frobenius endomorphism $\xi \mapsto \xi^p$ of K admits a "square root"; when the type of G_K is B_2, G_2, or F_4 it is possible to define two endomorphisms α' and α'' of G_K and to consider the subgroup of elements of G_K on which α' and α'' are equal. In this way we again obtain simple groups, discovered by Ree and Suzuki (B 210; LN 10). By taking certain finite fields for K, we obtain three new series of finite simple groups.

The structure theory of semisimple algebraic groups over an algebraically closed field (**A** IX) shows that all these groups G possess pairs of subgroups (B, N) (where N corresponds to the normalizer of a maximal torus T, and B to a Borel subgroup T · U, where U is maximal among the unipotent subgroups normalized by T) having the following properties: G is generated by B ∪ N, and B ∩ N (which corresponds to T) is normal in N; also the group W = N/(B ∩ N) (which corresponds to the Weyl group) admits a particular system of generators S (corresponding to a basis of the root system associated with T). The characteristic properties of B, N, and S can be expressed in a form that does not involve the method of definition of G. The quadruples (G, B, N, S) satisfying these axioms are called *Tits systems*; the existence of a Tits system in a group G implies that the structure of G is very close to that of a semisimple algebraic group, and in particular that G has a "Bruhat decomposition" (**A** IX) ([25], [66]). In particular, the subgroups containing B (called "parabolic" subgroups) are in canonical one–one correspondence with the subsets X of S. By using the left cosets of certain of these subgroups it is possible to construct canonically a *simplicial set* (**B** I) called the *building* associated with the Tits system. In many respects, this simplicial set and its associated topological space (**B** I) are the analogs for G of the symmetric spaces attached to semisimple Lie groups (**B** II); it is even possible to develop, in a purely combinatorial way, an "analysis" which mimics the results of infinitesimal analysis (B 407, 437). These sets have recently been used with success in various questions concerning the linear representations of G (B 429, 441) and the cohomology of its subgroups (B 339, 437). Here again, the fundamental properties of buildings can be expressed in terms that do not involve the Tits systems from which they were built, and can be studied axiomatically (LN 386; Vancouver (Tits)).

The typical example of a building is that of the general linear group **GL**(n, K), which is the simplicial set whose simplexes are the flags in the projective space $\mathbf{P}_{n-1}(K)$.

3. Linear representations and characters

One of the fundamental tools of group theory is the notion of a *linear representation.* A linear representation of a group G in a vector space V over a field K is a homomorphism $\rho : G \to \mathbf{GL}(V)$ of G into the group **GL**(V) of automorphisms of V; the group G acts linearly via ρ on V by the rule $(s, x) \mapsto \rho(s) \cdot x$. If W is a vector subspace of V that is *stable* under this action, the mapping $s \mapsto \rho(s)|W$ of G into **GL**(W) is called a *subrepresentation* of ρ. The representation ρ is the *direct sum* of subrepresentations $\rho_j : G \to \mathbf{GL}(W_j)$ if V is the direct sum of the W_j. A representation ρ is said to be *irreducible* if the only G-stable subspaces of V are $\{0\}$ and V. Two representations $\rho : G \to \mathbf{GL}(V)$ and $\rho' : G \to \mathbf{GL}(V')$ are said to be *equivalent* if there exists an isomorphism θ of V onto V′ such that $\rho'(s) = \theta \circ \rho(s) \circ \theta^{-1}$ for all $s \in G$.

If $\rho : G \to \mathbf{GL}(V)$ is a linear representation of G, its *restriction* to a subgroup H of G is a linear representation of H; if ρ is irreducible, in general its restriction to H will not be irreducible. In the reverse direction, let $\sigma : \mathrm{H} \to \mathbf{GL}(\mathrm{W})$ be a linear representation of H, and let L be the vector space of mappings $g : \mathrm{G} \to \mathrm{W}$ such that $g(su) = \sigma(u^{-1}) \cdot g(s)$ for all $u \in \mathrm{H}$ and $s \in \mathrm{G}$. For each $s \in \mathrm{G}$, the function $\gamma(s) \cdot g : t \mapsto g(s^{-1}t)$ belongs to L if $g \in \mathrm{L}$, and $g \mapsto \gamma(s) \cdot g$ is a linear mapping of L into L; it is clear that $s \mapsto \gamma(s)$ is a linear representation of G in L, said to be *induced* by the representation σ of H.

If we now restrict our attention to *finite* groups G, the representations to be considered are in *finite*-dimensional vector spaces V. There are two branches of the theory: the classical theory, in which the field K is the field **C** of complex numbers (or an algebraically closed field of characteristic 0); and the "modular" theory, in which K is taken to be a finite field.

In both cases, the linear representations are closely related to the structure of the *group algebra* K[G] over K, which has as basis the elements of the group G with their law of multiplication; any linear representation of G extends to a K-homomorphism of the algebra K[G] into the algebra End(V).

The classical theory (Frobenius). The algebra **C**[G] is semisimple (**B** I); consequently every linear representation of G is a direct sum of irreducible representations, and it is sufficient to study the latter. If $\rho : \mathrm{G} \to \mathbf{GL}(\mathrm{V})$ is any linear representation, the mapping $s \mapsto \mathrm{Tr}(\rho(s))$ of G into **C** is called the *character* of the representation. Two representations of G are equivalent if and only if they have the same character; the determination of the representations of G therefore reduces to that of the characters, and every character is a sum of *irreducible* characters (i.e., characters of irreducible representations). The irreducible characters satisfy remarkable relations, discovered by Frobenius. The most important of these involves the scalar product, defined on the vector space generated by the characters of G by

$$(\chi_1 \mid \chi_2) = (\mathrm{Card}(\mathrm{G}))^{-1} \sum_{s \in \mathrm{G}} \chi_1(s)\overline{\chi_2(s)},$$

and is the fact that the irreducible characters form an *orthonormal basis* of this finite-dimensional Hilbert space (the "orthogonality relations"). Furthermore, the set of linear combinations of characters with (positive or negative) integer coefficients is a *ring* (BAMS 69 (R. Brauer), 75 (Suzuki); SAMS XXI).

One of the methods most often used to determine the characters of a finite group G consists of taking subgroups H of G whose representations are known and considering the representations of G *induced* by those of H. For finite groups G, a fundamental theorem of R. Brauer is that every character of G is a linear combination with *integer* coefficients of characters of representations induced from *elementary* subgroups of G (which by definition are direct products of a cyclic group and a p-group) (B 14, 92, 111; [156]). This result has important applications in the theory of finite groups and in the study of L-functions in number theory (**A** X).

The modular theory (R. Brauer). Here the algebra K[G] is no longer semisimple when the characteristic of K divides the order of G. The presence of the radical of this algebra has the effect of introducing relations between the various irreducible representations of G (whereas in the classical theory the orthogonality relations express a certain "independence" of the representations). These relations are brought out and developed in R. Brauer's theory of *blocks* (B 419; [156]; Nice B 3 (Brauer)). A general method of studying linear representations in a vector space over K is to consider K as the residue field of a field L of characteristic 0 endowed with a discrete valuation, and to "lift" when possible the representations over K to representations in vector spaces over L ([156]; B 441).

Characters of particular groups. The linear representations over **C** of the symmetric group $\mathfrak{S}_n$ and the alternating group $\mathfrak{A}_n$ have been known since Frobenius and are described in terms of "Young tableaux" [43]. The properties of these representations continue to be the subject of many investigations, in connection with various "combinatorial" problems (LN 240, 308, 495, 579, 638, 682).

The finite groups other than $\mathfrak{S}_n$ and $\mathfrak{A}_n$ whose representations have been studied most are the finite Chevalley groups and their variants; the aim is to obtain for the (classical or "modular") representations of these groups, an explicit formula for their characters, of the same type as H. Weyl's formula for compact connected Lie groups [D, Chapter 21]. But such a result is still far away. The general idea is that, due to the presence of Tits systems in such a group G, we may consider the representations of G induced by those of B or U or T or parabolic subgroups; for the representations induced from parabolic subgroups, a useful guide is the analogy with the theory of infinite-dimensional representations of semisimple groups (**A** VI) (B 429, 441; LN 131). Another recent method (B 487) is to construct from G an algebraic variety X, defined over the ground-field *k* of the Chevalley group, on which G acts; then G acts also on the étale cohomology spaces of X (**A** IX), and in this way "most" of the irreducible representations of G are obtained.

4. The search for finite simple groups

Since the beginnings of group theory, the determination of the finite simple nonabelian groups has been a fundamental problem. In 1960, the following infinite "series" of finite simple groups were known: the finite Chevalley groups and their variants; and the alternating groups $\mathfrak{A}_n$ ($n \geqslant 5$) ("groups of

Lie types"). In addition, five "exceptional" simple groups had been discovered in 1860 by E. Mathieu as multiply transitive permutation groups: two of these, subgroups of $\mathfrak{S}_{12}$ and $\mathfrak{S}_{24}$, respectively, are the only fivefold transitive groups known, apart from the symmetric and alternating groups. Since 1960 twenty-one other simple groups have been discovered, the smallest of which ("Janko's first group") is of order 175,560, and the largest is of order $> 8 \cdot 10^{53}$ (B 331, 375, 502; Nice I (Feit)). These so-called "sporadic" simple groups have been obtained by a variety of techniques and at present fit into no general theory.

After a tremendous amount of work on the systematic study of all simple groups, initiated about 1960, it seems now (1981) that the preceding list is the complete enumeration of *all* simple finite nonabelian groups (B 584). The fundamental result, which has made such a study feasible, is the Feit–Thompson theorem, confirming an old conjecture of Burnside: every finite nonabelian simple group has *even* order. The proof is by *reductio ad absurdum*, by examining the properties of a simple group of smallest possible odd order, so as to obtain a contradiction; it requires all the resources of group theory, and is one of the longest and most complex proofs in the whole of mathematics (more than 250 pages) (see a summary in [66]). Another result (which is as difficult) is J. Thompson's determination of all the *minimal* finite nonabelian simple groups, i.e., those in which every proper subgroup is solvable (BAMS 74 (Thompson)).

5. Connections with the natural sciences

Permutation groups and their linear representations occur in many questions of a combinatorial nature raised by various applications (LN 495).

6. The originators

The main ideas in the theory of "abstract" groups are due to the following mathematicians: A. Cauchy (1789–1857), E. Galois (1811–1832), C. Jordan (1838–1922), G. Frobenius (1849–1917), L. Sylow (1832–1918), W. Burnside (1852–1924), I. Schur (1875–1941), R. Brauer (1901–1977), P. Novikov (1901–1976), P. Hall, I. Shafarevich, M. Suzuki, C. Chevalley, O. Grün (1888–1973), R. Steinberg, R. Ree, J. Tits, W. Feit, J. Thompson, J. Stallings, Z. Janko.

The following have also contributed substantially to this theory: S. Adjan, J. Alperin, E. Artin (1898–1962), M. Aschbacher, R. Baer (1902–1979), H. Bender, N. Blackburn, H. Blichfeldt (1873–1945), A. Borel, A. Clifford, J. Conway, H. Coxeter, C. Curtis, E. Dade, R. Dedekind (1831–1916), P.

Deligne, L. Dickson (1874–1954), W. Dyck (1856–1943). B. Fischer, H. Fitting (1906–1938), P. Fong, K. Fowler, H. Freudenthal, P. Gallagher, W. Gaschütz, I. Gelfand, S. Gelfand, G. Glauberman, D. Goldschmidt, E. Golod, D. Gorenstein, M. Graev, J. Green, M. Hall, K. Harada, Harish-Chandra, D. Held, D. Higman, G. Higman, O. Hölder (1859–1937), D. Hughes, B. Huppert, N. Ito, N. Iwahori, O. Kegel, R. Kilmoyer, L. Kronecker (1823–1891), W. Krull (1899–1970), M. Lazard, K. Lusztig, R. Lyons, A. MacWilliams, J. McKay, J. McLaughlin, W. Magnus, E. Mathieu (1835–1890), V. Mazurov, B. Neumann, H. Neumann (1914–1971), J. Nielsen (1890–1959), M. O'Nan, D. Passman, I. Reiner, A. Rosenberg, A. Rudvalis, O. Schmidt (1891–1956), O. Schreier (1901–1929), J. de Séguier (1862–1935), J. P. Serre, C. Sims, R. Solomon, A. Speiser (1885–1970), T. Springer, B. Srinivasan, R. Swan, J. Tate, F. Timmesfeld B. L. van der Waerden, G. E. Wall, J. Walter, H. Wielandt, E. Witt, S. Wong, W. Wong, H. Zassenhaus, E. Bombieri, R. Griess, G. Seitz.

References

B: 14, 92, 111, 169, 194, 210, 219, 331, 356, 375, 399, 407, 419, 429, 437, 441, 487, 502, 584.

LN: 10, 131, 240, 245, 308, 386, 495, 513, 528, 579, 638, 674, 682, 744, 764, 806, 830.

BAMS: 69 (R. Brauer), 74 (J. Thompson), 75 (M. Suzuki), 83 (J. Alperin), 1 (New Series) (Gorenstein).

SAMS: XXI.

[25], [29], [43], [66], [156].

B IV

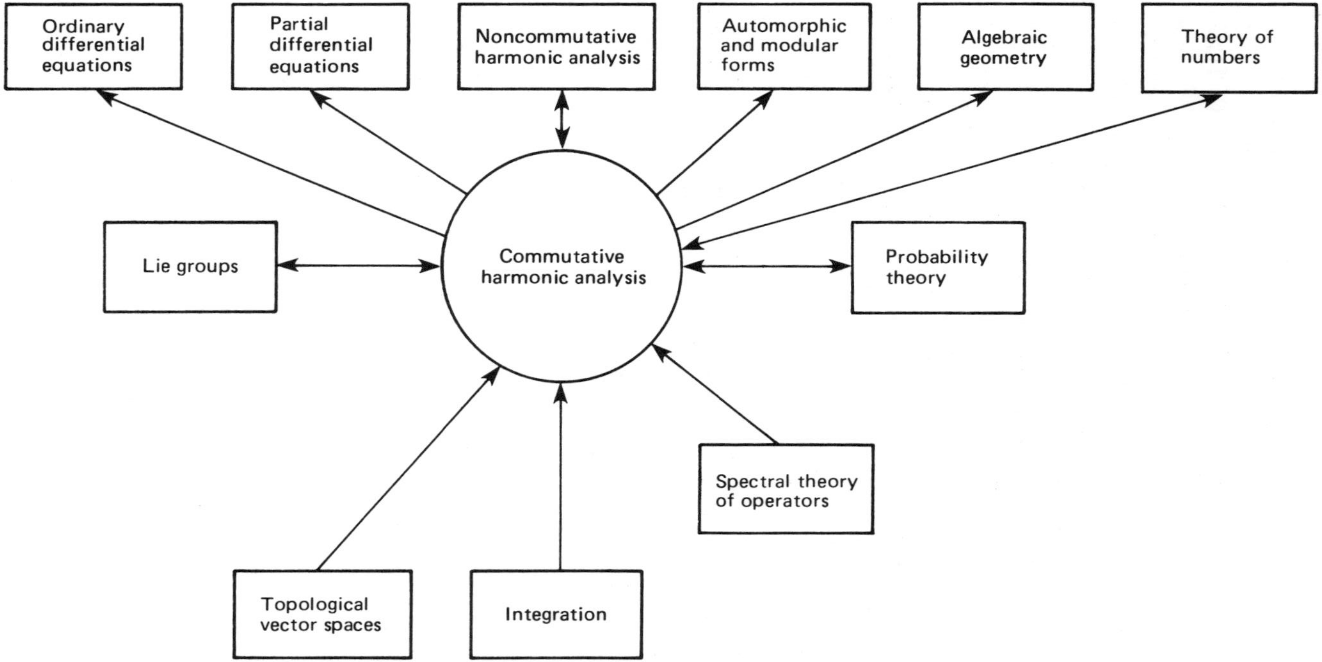

Ordinary differential equations
Partial differential equations
Noncommutative harmonic analysis
Automorphic and modular forms
Algebraic geometry
Theory of numbers
Lie groups
Commutative harmonic analysis
Probability theory
Spectral theory of operators
Topological vector spaces
Integration

B IV

Commutative harmonic analysis

Classical *Fourier analysis* is the study of trigonometric series

$$\sum_{n=0}^{\infty} (a_n \cos nx + b_n \sin nx).$$

When a "sum" $f(x)$ can be attached to this series, the function f is periodic with period 2π, and the coefficients a_n, b_n are given "formally" by the relations ("Fourier's formulas")

$$a_0 = \frac{1}{2\pi}\int_0^{2\pi} f(t)\,dt, \qquad a_n = \frac{1}{\pi}\int_0^{2\pi} f(t)\cos nt\,dt, \qquad b_n = \frac{1}{\pi}\int_0^{2\pi} f(t)\sin nt\,dt.$$

If we put $c_0 = a_0$, $c_n = \frac{1}{2}(a_n - ib_n)$, $c_{-n} = \frac{1}{2}(a_n + ib_n)$ for $n \geqslant 1$, these formulas take the simpler form

$$(1) \qquad c_n = \frac{1}{2\pi}\int_0^{2\pi} f(t)e^{-int}\,dt$$

for all $n \in \mathbf{Z}$. The question now arises of what meaning should be given to this correspondence between functions f with period 2π and sequences $(c_n)_{n\in\mathbf{Z}}$ of complex numbers.

Following the work of Fourier and Laplace, an analogous question naturally arises for integrals: if f is a function defined on $\mathbf{R}$, its "Fourier transform" is given by the formula

$$(2) \qquad \mathscr{F}f(x) = \int_{-\infty}^{+\infty} e^{-2\pi ixt} f(t)\,dt$$

and the question arises of what conditions must be imposed on f in order that this formula and the "inverse" formula

$$(3) \qquad f(t) = \int_{-\infty}^{+\infty} e^{2\pi ixt}\mathscr{F}f(x)\,dx$$

should make sense.

The work of H. Weyl and L. Pontrjagin showed that these two problems are particular cases of a general problem about *locally compact abelian groups* [D, Chapter 22]. If G is such a group, the *characters* of G are *continuous* homomorphisms $\hat{x} : \mathrm{G} \to \mathbf{U}$ of G into the group **U** of complex numbers of absolute value 1. These characters form an abelian group $\hat{\mathrm{G}}$ with respect to pointwise multiplication, and the topology of uniform convergence on compact subsets makes $\hat{\mathrm{G}}$ into a *locally compact* group, called the *dual* of G. The mapping $(x, \hat{x}) \mapsto \hat{x}(x)$ (also written $(x, \hat{x}) \mapsto \langle x, \hat{x} \rangle$) of $\mathrm{G} \times \hat{\mathrm{G}}$ into **U** is continuous, and for each $x \in \mathrm{G}$ the mapping

$$\eta(x) : \hat{x} \mapsto \langle x, \hat{x} \rangle$$

is a character of $\hat{\mathrm{G}}$. It can be shown that $x \mapsto \eta(x)$ is an *isomorphism* of the topological group G onto the topological group $\hat{\hat{\mathrm{G}}}$, the dual of $\hat{\mathrm{G}}$ (Pontrjagin duality), so that $\hat{\hat{\mathrm{G}}}$ may be canonically identified with G. If $\mathrm{G} = \mathbf{R}$, every character of **R** is uniquely expressible as $t \mapsto e^{2\pi ixt}$ for some $x \in \mathbf{R}$, and hence **R** may be identified with its dual. When $\mathrm{G} = \mathbf{Z}$, every character of **Z** is of the form $n \mapsto e^{2\pi inx}$ for some $x \in \mathbf{R}$; but if $x' - x \in \mathbf{Z}$, the two characters corresponding to x and x' are the same, and the dual group of **Z** may be identified with the "torus" $\mathbf{T} = \mathbf{R}/\mathbf{Z}$.

The formulas (1) and (2) thus appear as particular cases of a general definition. If f is a function defined on a locally compact abelian group G, its *Fourier transform* is the function *on* $\hat{\mathrm{G}}$ defined by

$$\mathscr{F}f(\hat{x}) = \int_{\mathrm{G}} f(x)\overline{\langle x, \hat{x} \rangle}\, dx, \tag{4}$$

where dx is a Haar measure on G [D, Chapter 14]. The question is to know when this formula makes sense and when the "reciprocity formula"

$$f(x) = \int_{\hat{\mathrm{G}}} \mathscr{F}f(\hat{x})\langle x, \hat{x} \rangle\, d\hat{x} \tag{5}$$

is true, for a suitable choice of Haar measure on $\hat{\mathrm{G}}$. The most important result is Plancherel's theorem: if $f \in \mathrm{L}^2(\mathrm{G})$, the integral on the right-hand side of (4) is not in general defined as a Lebesgue integral, but can be given a meaning by use of a limiting process; it is then the case that $\mathscr{F}f \in \mathrm{L}^2(\hat{\mathrm{G}})$, and the formula (5) is valid with an analogous interpretation of the integral. Moreover, the mapping $f \mapsto \mathscr{F}f$ of $\mathrm{L}^2(\mathrm{G})$ into $\mathrm{L}^2(\hat{\mathrm{G}})$ is an *isometry* of the first of these Hilbert spaces onto the second; in other words, we have

$$\int_{\hat{\mathrm{G}}} |\mathscr{F}f(\hat{x})|^2\, d\hat{x} = \int_{\mathrm{G}} |f(x)|^2\, dx. \tag{6}$$

This theory, called *commutative harmonic analysis*, is subordinate to the spectral theory of Hilbert–Gelfand (**C** III): we apply the latter theory to the commutative Banach algebra $L^1(G)$, in which the elements are the classes of complex-valued integrable functions on G with respect to a Haar measure, and the multiplication is the *convolution product*

$$(f * g)(x) = \int_G f(x - t)g(t)\,dt. \tag{7}$$

The characters of this algebra, in Gelfand's sense, may be identified with the linear forms $f \mapsto \mathscr{F}f(\hat{x})$ on $L^1(G)$, so that $\hat{G}$ is identified with the *spectrum* of the algebra $L^1(G)$, and the fundamental multiplicative property of characters takes the form

$$\mathscr{F}(f * g) = \mathscr{F}f \cdot \mathscr{F}g, \tag{8}$$

the product on the right being the ordinary product of functions.

Let H be a closed subgroup of G. The set of all $\hat{x} \in \hat{G}$ such that $\langle x, \hat{x} \rangle = 1$ for all $x \in H$ is a closed subgroup $H^\perp$ of $\hat{G}$, called the *annihilator* of H, and we have $(H^\perp)^\perp = H$; moreover, the *Poisson formula* asserts that

$$\int_H f(t)\,dt = \int_{H^\perp} \mathscr{F}f(\hat{s})\,d\hat{s} \tag{9}$$

for suitable choices of Haar measures on H and $H^\perp$, provided that f satisfies certain "regularity" conditions (for example, if $G = \mathbf{R}^n$, it is sufficient that f should be a declining function (see below)).

For the groups $G = \mathbf{R}^n$ of the classical theory, the notion of the Fourier transform of *functions* can be extended to certain *distributions*. A complex-valued function defined on $\mathbf{R}^n$ is said to be *declining* if it is of class C^∞ and if, for each polynomial p and multi-index α, the product $p \cdot D^\alpha f$ tends to 0 at infinity. The vector space $\mathscr{S}(\mathbf{R}^n)$ of these functions carries the seminorms $q_m(f) = \sup_{x \in \mathbf{R}^n, |\alpha| \leqslant m} |r^m(x) D^\alpha f(x)|$, where $r(x) = (x_1^2 + \cdots + x_n^2)^{1/2}$, and the topology they define makes $\mathscr{S}(\mathbf{R}^n)$ into a separable Fréchet space. It can be shown that the Fourier transformation $f \mapsto \mathscr{F}f$ is a *topological isomorphism* of $\mathscr{S}(\mathbf{R}^n)$ onto itself. A continuous linear form on $\mathscr{S}(\mathbf{R}^n)$ is called a *tempered distribution*. Bounded measures and locally integrable functions that do not increase more rapidly than polynomials are tempered distributions. For a tempered distribution T, its Fourier transform $\mathscr{F}T$ is defined to be the tempered distribution such that

$$\langle \mathscr{F}T, f \rangle = \langle T, \mathscr{F}f \rangle \tag{10}$$

for all functions $f \in \mathscr{S}(\mathbf{R}^n)$. For an arbitrary locally compact abelian group G, this definition is valid for bounded measures on G [D, Chapter 22].

1. Convergence problems

It has been known since Dirichlet that the Fourier series of a piecewise-differentiable continuous function converges at each point to the value of the function at that point. In 1873 P. du Bois-Reymond gave the first example of a continuous function whose Fourier series diverges at one point at least. Since then, the problem of convergence of Fourier series has been the subject of many investigations, not only for continuous functions but also for functions belonging to $L^p(0, 2\pi)$, where $1 \leqslant p \leqslant +\infty$. In 1926 Kolmogoroff gave an example of an L^1-function whose Fourier series diverges *everywhere*. But it was only in 1966 that L. Carleson proved that the Fourier series of every L^2-function *converges almost everywhere*, and this result was extended by R. Hunt to L^p-functions for $1 < p \leqslant +\infty$. This result is the best possible, because, for any given set E of measure zero, it is possible to define a continuous function f whose Fourier series diverges at all points of E (B 310; LN 199; Nice D 9 (Hunt)).

2. Normed algebras in harmonic analysis

Many problems, both classical and modern, of Fourier analysis may be expressed in a simple and general form by using the notion of a normed algebra and the theory of these algebras (especially their ideals and their homomorphisms) (Stockholm (Kahane)). In the first place, for any locally compact abelian group G, there is the Banach algebra $M^1_{\mathbf{C}}(G)$ of (complex) bounded measures on G, in which the product is "convolution" of measures (**C** III); next, the most important of its subalgebras, $L^1(G)$, consisting of the classes of integrable functions, which is also complete; and the (nonclosed) subalgebra $\mathscr{K}(G)$ of continuous functions with compact support. If G is compact, the $L^p(G)$ for $p \geqslant 2$ are subalgebras of $L^1(G)$; in general $L^\infty(G)$ is an algebra with respect to the usual product of functions, and so is the set $\mathscr{C}_b(G)$ of bounded continuous functions on G; $\mathscr{K}(G) \subset \mathscr{C}_b(G)$ is also an algebra with respect to this product, and so is its closure $\mathscr{C}_0(G)$, consisting of the continuous functions that tend to 0 at infinity.

Next come the *Fourier transforms* of these algebras: the most important of these is $A(\hat{G}) = \mathscr{F}L^1(G)$, a subalgebra of $\mathscr{C}_0(\hat{G})$ with respect to the usual product. When $G = \mathbf{R}^n$ or $G = \mathbf{Z}^n$, we can define $PM(\hat{G}) = \mathscr{F}L^\infty(G)$, the elements of which are called *pseudomeasures* on $\hat{G}$ (= $\mathbf{R}^n$ or $\mathbf{T}^n$). They are distributions, and $M^1_{\mathbf{C}}(\hat{G})$ is a subalgebra of $PM(\hat{G})$. When $G = \mathbf{Z}$, $A(\mathbf{T})$ is the algebra of *absolutely convergent Fourier series*, endowed with the norm obtained by transporting by $\mathscr{F}$ the norm on $L^1(\mathbf{Z}) = l^1$ (so that for $f(t) = \sum_n c_n e^{2\pi i n t}$ we have $\|f\| = \sum_n \|c_n\|$); $PM(\mathbf{T})$, as a Banach space (the

Fourier transform of l^∞), is the dual of A(T), and A(T) is the dual of PF(T), the Fourier transform of $c_0 = \mathscr{C}_0(\mathbf{Z})$, the elements of which are called *pseudofunctions*: they are pseudomeasures whose Fourier coefficients tend to 0, which in the classical terminology corresponds to trigonometric series which are not Fourier series of functions, although they may be everywhere convergent (they are of course Fourier series of pseudofunctions). In the same way we define PF(G), for any locally compact abelian group G, to be the Fourier transform of $\mathscr{C}_0(\hat{G})$. Finally, we remark that the algebra A(G) appears as a particular case (corresponding to $p = 2$) of algebras $A_p(G)$ defined for any locally compact group G (not necessarily abelian) (see **C** III); when G is abelian, these algebras are related to the question of "Fourier multipliers" (B 367).

Homomorphisms and idempotent measures. If G and H are two locally compact abelian groups, a problem is to determine all the homomorphisms of $L^1(G)$ into $M^1_{\mathbf{C}}(H)$. This problem can be reduced to the following: for a locally compact abelian group G, to find all measures $\mu \in M^1_{\mathbf{C}}(G)$ such that $\mu * \mu = \mu$. The complete solution has been obtained by P. Cohen (B 231).

Sets of uniqueness and pseudofunctions. A problem that goes back to Cantor is the study of *sets of uniqueness*, i.e., sets $E \subset \mathbf{T}$ such that a convergent trigonometric series whose sum is zero outside E has all its coefficients zero. It is known that every countable set is a set of uniqueness, and that a set of positive measure is never one; perfect sets of measure zero may or may not be sets of uniqueness, depending on their arithmetic properties (see below).

To say that a closed set E is a set of uniqueness also means that there exists no pseudofunction $\mu \neq 0$ with support contained in E. This definition makes sense for any locally compact abelian group, and leads to the study of the algebra $PF(G) \cap M^1_{\mathbf{C}}(G)$ of bounded measures that are pseudofunctions, and their supports. This algebra (which is a self-adjoint closed ideal in $M^1_{\mathbf{C}}(G)$) has rather surprising properties for nondiscrete groups G (B 282); for example, there exist measures $\mu \neq 0$ in this algebra with compact support, which generate a subgroup of G of zero Haar measure.

The algebras A(E) *and harmonic synthesis.* Let G be a locally compact abelian group and E a closed subset of G. We denote by A(E) the algebra of restrictions to E of functions belonging to A(G); it is isomorphic to $A(G)/I_E$, where I_E is the closed ideal in A(G) formed by the functions that vanish on E. There are a large number of questions concerning the algebras A(E) and their isomorphisms (LN 202; [95]); a recent technique (Varopoulos) for solving them consists of embedding A(E) in algebras of the form $\mathscr{C}(K_1) \hat{\otimes} \mathscr{C}(K_2)$ (**C** III), where K_1 and K_2 are compact spaces (B 291).

The general problem of "spectral synthesis" [200] presents itself here in the following form: a function $f \in A(G)$ satisfies harmonic synthesis if it is the limit in A(G) of a sequence of functions each vanishing in a neighborhood of the set $N(f)$ of zeros of f. A subset E of G is a *set of spectral synthesis* if the ideal I_E is equal to the closed ideal J_E generated by the functions which vanish in some neighborhood of E. If $N(f)$ is a set of spectral synthesis, f satisfies synthesis. A *set of spectral resolution* is a closed set all of whose closed subsets are sets of spectral synthesis. It can be shown that a set of spectral resolution is a set of uniqueness, but not conversely. For each nondiscrete group G, there exist nonempty subsets of G that are not sets of spectral synthesis (Malliavin) (B 291; LN 202; [95]).

Functions acting on algebras. A famous theorem of Wiener and P. Lévy is that if $f \in A(G)$, the composite function $F \circ f$ also belongs to A(G) if F is analytic in a neighborhood of $f(G)$. A function F, defined say on an interval $I \subset \mathbf{R}$, is said to *act* on A(G) if, for each function $f \in A(G)$ such that $f(G) \subset I$, the function $F \circ f$ belongs to A(G); it can be shown (Katznelson) that the only functions F with this property are those that are analytic in a neighborhood of I. The same problem can be posed for other algebras (B 282), and in particular for the algebras A(E) where $E \subset G$. The sets E for which the analog of Katznelson's theorem is true are called *sets of analyticity*. Subsets $E \subset \mathbf{T}$ of positive measure are sets of analyticity. At the other extreme are subsets $E \subset G$ such that all continuous functions act on A(E), i.e., such that $A(E) = \mathscr{C}(E)$; these are called *Helson sets* and play an important role in various questions (LN 202, 266; Nice D 4 (Varopoulos); [95], [150]).

For a fixed function $f \in A(G)$, another problem is to find all functions F defined on $f(G)$ and such that $F \circ f \in A(G)$ ("individual symbolic calculus" (B 197; [95])).

3. Symmetric perfect sets in harmonic analysis: connections with number theory

In order to find subsets E of **R** that are "thin" sets in the sense of harmonic analysis on **R**, some types of which we have described above (see [95]), a method frequently used is the generalization of Cantor's perfect set. Consider a sequence (ξ_k) of real numbers such that $0 < \xi_k < \frac{1}{2}$, and the perfect set E of real numbers of the form $\sum_k \varepsilon_k \xi_1 \xi_2 \cdots \xi_{k-1}(1 - \xi_k)$, where each ε_k is 0 or 1. For example (B 341), if $\sum_k \xi_k^2 < \infty$, E is a set of uniqueness and a set of synthesis.

Analogous sets may be obtained by considering a number $\theta > 1$ and the set E_θ of numbers of the form $\sum_k \varepsilon_k \theta^{-k}$, which is perfect and totally disconnected. Here the arithmetical nature of the number θ is decisive; E_θ is a uniqueness set if and only if θ is a *Pisot number*, i.e., an algebraic integer all of whose conjugates (other than itself) have absolute value <1; moreover, in this case E_θ is a set of synthesis (B 379; LN 117; Nice D 9 (Y. Meyer); [122]).

4. Almost-periodic functions and mean-periodic functions

On a locally compact abelian group G, the *almost-periodic functions* are the *uniform* limits of linear combinations of characters of G. If G is compact, they comprise all the continuous functions; in the general case, G can be embedded as a dense subgroup in a compact group H (the topology induced by that of H being strictly coarser than the original topology on G), and the almost-periodic functions are the restrictions to G of continuous functions on H. They may also be characterized by the fact that the translates $t \mapsto f(s-t)$ of such a function f form a relatively compact set for the topology of uniform convergence.

Another generalization of periodic functions on G is the notion of *mean-periodic functions*; these are locally integrable functions f such that there exists a compactly supported measure $\mu \neq 0$ on G for which $\mu * f = 0$. By taking μ to be the difference of two Dirac measures, we retrieve the notion of periodic function. The function e^x is mean-periodic on **R**, because we have $f * (\varepsilon_a - e^{-a}\varepsilon_0) = 0$ for all $a \neq 0$.

On the real line **R**, an almost-periodic function is the uniform limit of finite linear combinations $\sum_j c_{jn} e^{i\lambda_j x}$, where the λ_j (real) and the $c_{jn} \neq 0$ are well determined. A mean-periodic function f on **R** is likewise the uniform limit on each compact set of a linear combination of *exponential monomials* $x^k e^{i\lambda x}$, where the exponents λ (complex) are determined by f (B 97) (they form what is called the *spectrum* of f); if in addition f is bounded on **R**, it is the second derivative (in the distributional sense) of an almost-periodic function. The spectra of mean-periodic functions on **R** can be characterized by density properties (B 225).

5. Applications of commutative harmonic analysis

The most important application of Fourier analysis on $\mathbf{R}^n$ is to the integration of partial differential equations and their generalizations (**A** V) (B 560; Vancouver (Fefferman)).

Harmonic analysis on $\mathbf{R}^n$ and $\mathbf{T}^n$ has many points of contact with the theory of holomorphic functions on polydisks and the theory of Newtonian potential (LN 336, 404; Nice D 4 (Rudin); [95], [151]); it also intervenes in the generalizations of potential theory on locally compact abelian groups (B 315). The theory of theta functions [88] and of abelian varieties (**A** IX) and the theory of modular functions (**A** VII) both make essential use of Fourier analysis on $\mathbf{R}^n$ and $\mathbf{T}^n$. In probability theory, the Fourier transform of bounded measures on $\mathbf{R}$ has become since 1925 a fundamental tool; representations of locally compact abelian groups in Hilbert spaces feature also in statistical prediction theory (B 218); and in the reverse direction, probability theory can be used to prove results valid for "almost all" Fourier series, in the sense of the theory of random Fourier series (**B** VII) (B 200; [94]). Finally, the most unexpected application of harmonic analysis concerns the adèle and idèle groups of number theory (B 103), where Fourier theory unifies and simplifies a number of concepts and proofs (**A** X).

6. Connections with the natural sciences

The mathematical study of periodic phenomena was the origin of the theory of Fourier series, which is still the main instrument for this purpose; even the words "harmonic analysis" originate from the study of periodicities in variations of physical quantities [197]. Moreover, the Fourier transform plays a large part in quantum mechanics. However, the mathematical questions mentioned in the preceding sections, which are the subject of much research in modern harmonic analysis, are oriented in directions different from those of interest to the physicists.

7. The originators

The principal ideas in commutative harmonic analysis are due to the following mathematicians:

The classical theory. J. Fourier (1768–1830), P. Laplace (1749–1827), D. Poisson (1781–1840), A. Cauchy (1789–1857), P. G. Lejeune-Dirichlet (1805–1859), B. Riemann (1826–1866), G. Cantor (1845–1918), P. du Bois-Reymond (1831–1889), H. Lebesgue (1875–1941), L. Féjer (1880–1959), N. Wiener (1894–1964), A. Zygmund, L. Carleson.

Fourier analysis of distributions, almost-periodic functions, mean-periodic functions: H. Bohr (1887–1951), J. Delsarte (1903–1968), S. Bochner, L. Schwartz.

Harmonic analysis on locally compact abelian groups: H. Weyl (1885–1955), L. Pontrjagin, A. Weil, I. Gelfand, A. Beurling, J. P. Kahane, P. Malliavin, H. Helson, W. Rudin, Y. Katznelson, P. Cohen, N. Varopoulos.

Arithmetic properties of perfect sets: R. Salem (1898–1963), Y. Meyer.

The following have also made substantial contributions to the theory: J. Alexander (1888–1971), N. Bary (1901–1961), S. Banach (1892–1945), S. Bernstein (1880–1968), A. Besicovich (1891–1970), R. Boas, P. Bohl (1865–1921), J. Braconnier, T. Carleman (1892–1949), H. Cartan, P. Daniell (1889–1946), K. De Leeuw (1930–1978), A. Denjoy (1884–1974), S. Drury, C. Dunkl, E. Esclangon (1876–1954). C. Fefferman, A. Figa-Talamanca, I. Glicksberg, R. Godement, G. H. Hardy (1877–1947), C. Herz, R. Hunt, C. Jordan (1838–1922), R. Kaufman, A. Kolmogoroff, P. Koosis, P. Lévy (1886–1971), J. Littlewood (1885–1977), N. Lusin (1883–1950), W. Maak, S. Mandelbrojt, O. McGehee, R. Mathias, J. Marcinkiewicz (1910–1940), J. Méla, D. Menchoff, B. Mitjagin, R. Paley (1907–1933), H. Pitt, M. Plancherel (1885–1967), H. Pollard, D. Raikov, D. Ramirez, H. Reiter, D. Rider, F. Riesz (1880–1956), M. Riesz (1886–1969), H. Rosenthal, R. Schneider, I. Segal, S. Sidon (1892–1941), P. Sjölin, S. Stechkin, E. Stein, M. Stone, P. Uljanov, E. Titchmarsh (1899–1963), E. van Kampen (1908–1942), J. von Neumann (1903–1957), I. Wik, J. Williamson, A. Wintner (1903–1958), W. Young (1863–1942).

References

B: 97, 103, 197, 200, 202, 218, 225, 231, 282, 291, 310, 315, 336, 341, 379, 528, 560.
LN: 117, 199, 202, 266, 404, 779, 781.
Astérisque: 1, 5.
[88], [94], [95], [122], [150], [151], [197], [200], [218].

B V

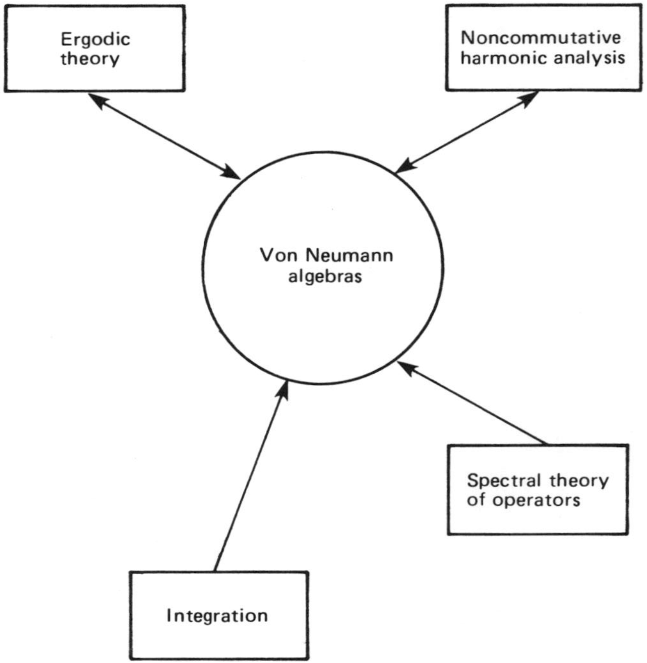
Ergodic theory
Noncommutative harmonic analysis
Von Neumann algebras
Spectral theory of operators
Integration

B V

Von Neumann algebras

Von Neumann algebras are a particular type of C*-algebras (**C** III), which are defined not abstractly but as subalgebras of the algebra $\mathscr{L}(H)$ of continuous endomorphisms of a complex Hilbert space H. One definition is that $\mathscr{A} \subset \mathscr{L}(H)$ is a von Neumann algebra if it contains the identity, is stable under the involution on $\mathscr{L}(H)$ and is closed in the *weak* topology (**C** III) of $\mathscr{L}(H)$. An equivalent definition is based on the notion of *commuting algebra*: the commuting subalgebra of a subset M of $\mathscr{L}(H)$ is the set M′ of elements of $\mathscr{L}(H)$ that commute with every element of M, and $\mathscr{A}$ is a von Neumann algebra if it is stable under the involution on $\mathscr{L}(H)$ and satisfies $\mathscr{A} = (\mathscr{A}')'$. Then $\mathscr{A}'$ is also a von Neumann algebra, and $\mathscr{Z} = \mathscr{A} \cap \mathscr{A}'$ is a commutative von Neumann algebra, the common center of $\mathscr{A}$ and $\mathscr{A}'$ [45].

The structure of commutative von Neumann algebras is very simple: for such an algebra $\mathscr{Z}$, there exists a locally compact topological space Z, a positive measure ν with support Z and an isometric isomorphism of algebras with involution (**C** III) of $L^\infty_{\mathbf{C}}(Z, \nu)$ onto $\mathscr{Z}$ [45].

A von Neumann algebra with center **C** is called a *factor*. The most important von Neumann algebras correspond to the case where the Hilbert space H is separable; they may be obtained from factors by a process of "continuous summation" or "direct integration" over the space Z attached to the center $\mathscr{Z} = L^\infty_{\mathbf{C}}(Z, \nu)$ of the algebra in question (B 19, 25; [45]). Many problems about von Neumann algebras can be reduced in this way to the same problems about factors.

The factors have been classified by Murray and von Neumann into five *types*. This classification is based on the notion of a *weight*, which generalizes that of a positive linear form (**C** III). A weight on a von Neumann algebra $\mathscr{A}$ is a mapping φ of $\mathscr{A}^+$ (the set of *positive self-adjoint* operators in $\mathscr{A}$) into $[0, +\infty]$ such that $\varphi(x + y) = \varphi(x) + \varphi(y)$ and $\varphi(\lambda x) = \lambda\varphi(x)$ for $\lambda \in \mathbf{R}_+$ (with the convention that $0 \cdot (+\infty) = 0$). A weight φ is a *trace* if it satisfies $\varphi(xx^*) = \varphi(x^*x)$ for all $x \in \mathscr{A}$. A weight φ is said to be *finite* if it takes only finite values on $\mathscr{A}^+$ (in which case it can be extended to a positive linear form on $\mathscr{A}$), and *semifinite* if for each $x \in \mathscr{A}^+$, $\varphi(x)$ is the least upper bound of the $\varphi(y)$ for $y \in \mathscr{A}^+$ such that $y \leqslant x$ and $\varphi(y) < +\infty$. A von Neumann algebra $\mathscr{A}$ is said to be *finite* (resp. *semifinite*) if for each nonzero $x \in \mathscr{A}^+$, there exists a finite (resp. semifinite) *trace* φ such that $\varphi(x) \neq 0$.

Among the *finite* factors are the matrix algebras $\mathbf{M}_n(\mathbf{C})$, said to be of *type* I_n; the others are said to be of *type* II_1. For a factor $\mathscr{A}$ of type II_1, there is a canonical trace on $\mathscr{A}^+$, the values of which on the orthogonal projections belonging to $\mathscr{A}^+$ are *all real numbers* in the interval [0, 1]. Among the nonfinite semifinite factors are the endomorphism algebras $\mathscr{L}(\mathrm{H})$ of infinite-dimensional Hilbert spaces, which are said to be of *type* I_∞; the others are said to be of *type* II_∞. Finally, the factors which are not semifinite are said to be of *type* III.

If $\mathscr{A} \subset \mathscr{L}(\mathrm{H})$ is a factor, we associate with $\mathscr{A}$ the set $\mathfrak{B}$ of closed vector subspaces $\mathrm{M} \subset \mathrm{H}$ such that the orthogonal projection P_M of H onto M belongs to $\mathscr{A}^+$. We define a preordering on $\mathfrak{B}$ as follows: $\mathrm{M} \prec \mathrm{N}$ means that there exists an operator $u \in \mathscr{A}$ that is zero on the orthogonal supplement of M and is an isometry of M onto a subspace of N. For semifinite factors, there exists a "dimension" function $\mathrm{M} \mapsto \mathrm{D}(\mathrm{M})$ on $\mathfrak{B}$ such that (1) $0 \leqslant \mathrm{D}(\mathrm{M}) \leqslant +\infty$, and $\mathrm{D}(\mathrm{M}) = 0$ if and only if $\mathrm{M} = 0$; (2) the relation $\mathrm{M} \prec \mathrm{N}$ implies $\mathrm{D}(\mathrm{M}) \leqslant \mathrm{D}(\mathrm{N})$; (3) if $\mathrm{M}, \mathrm{N} \in \mathfrak{B}$ are orthogonal, then $\mathrm{D}(\mathrm{M} \oplus \mathrm{N}) = \mathrm{D}(\mathrm{M}) + \mathrm{D}(\mathrm{N})$. For the factors of type I_n (resp. I_∞), D takes the values $0, 1, \ldots, n$ (resp. $0, 1, 2, \ldots, +\infty$). For factors of type II_1 (resp. II_∞), D takes all real values in [0, 1] (resp. $[0, +\infty]$), and for factors of type II_1, D(M) may be defined as the value of the canonical trace on P_M (B 30; [45]).

A general method of constructing factors of types II_1, II_∞, and III is as follows: Let G be a discrete group acting (on the left) on a separable, metrizable, locally compact space X. Suppose that X carries a positive measure μ and that for each $s \in \mathrm{G}$ the measure $s \cdot \mu$ (the transform of μ by the homeomorphism $x \mapsto s \cdot x$) is equivalent to μ; this signifies that there exists a strictly positive, finite, locally μ-integrable function $x \mapsto r_s(x)$ on X such that $s \cdot \mu = r_s \cdot \mu$ (the measure with base μ and density r_s). Now consider the Hilbert space $\mathrm{H} = \mathrm{L}^2(\mathrm{G} \times \mathrm{X})$, where $\mathrm{G} \times \mathrm{X}$ is endowed with the product of the discrete measure on G, for which each point has measure 1, and the measure μ on X. In $\mathscr{L}(\mathrm{H})$ there are on the one hand the multiplication operators T_f for $f \in \mathrm{L}^\infty_\mathbf{C}(\mathrm{X}, \mu)$, which take $u \in \mathrm{L}^2(\mathrm{G} \times \mathrm{X})$ to the function $(s, x) \mapsto f(x)u(s, x)$, and on the other hand, for each $s \in \mathrm{G}$, the operator $U(s)$ which takes u to the function $(t, x) \mapsto r_{s^{-1}}(x)^{1/2}u(s^{-1}t, s^{-1} \cdot x)$, and which is a unitary operator; for suitable conditions on μ and the action of G on X, the von Neumann algebra $\mathscr{A}$ generated by the T_f and the $U(s)$ is a factor of type II_1, II_∞, or III. For example, if $\mathrm{X} = \mathbf{R}$ and μ is Lebesgue measure, and G is the group of matrices $\begin{pmatrix} a & b \\ 0 & 1 \end{pmatrix}$ with a, b rational and $a > 0$, acting on $\mathbf{R}$ by the rule $\left(\begin{pmatrix} a & b \\ 0 & 1 \end{pmatrix}, x\right) \mapsto ax + b$, then $\mathscr{A}$ is a factor of type III [45].

1. Tomita theory and the Connes invariants

Among the subalgebras with involution of the algebras $\mathscr{L}(\mathrm{H})$, the *Hilbert algebras* (**C** III) occupy a distinguished place; the prototype of these is the algebra $\mathscr{K}(\mathrm{G})$ of continuous functions with compact support on a *unimodular* locally compact group G, the multiplication being convolution $(f, g) \mapsto f * g$, and the involution that which takes f to the function $s \mapsto \overline{f(s^{-1})}$. A Hilbert algebra $\mathfrak{A}$ is by definition (**C** III) endowed with a scalar product, with respect to which $\mathfrak{A}$ is a Hausdorff pre-Hilbert space, and therefore a dense subspace of a Hilbert space H. The properties of $\mathfrak{A}$ imply that the mapping $T_x : y \mapsto xy$ of $\mathfrak{A}$ into itself extends to a continuous endomorphism (also denoted by T_x) of H, and we may therefore consider the von Neumann algebra $\mathscr{A}$ generated by these operators T_x in $\mathscr{L}(\mathrm{H})$; the study of the von Neumann algebras constructed in this way is greatly facilitated by the properties of the Hilbert algebra $\mathfrak{A}$. Unfortunately, we obtain in this way only semifinite von Neumann algebras. M. Tomita discovered that *all* von Neumann algebras can be obtained in an analogous way by replacing the notion of a Hilbert algebra by the more general notion of a *left Hilbert algebra*. To define these, we retain the first three axioms of a Hilbert algebra (**C** III), but weaken the last axiom by requiring only that the graph of the involution $x \mapsto x^*$ on $\mathfrak{A}$ should have as closure in $\mathrm{H} \times \mathrm{H}$ the graph of some linear mapping of a dense subspace of H into H.

The prototype of these algebras is the algebra $\mathscr{K}(\mathrm{G})$ for an *arbitrary* locally compact group G; if Δ is the modulus function on G, the involution on $\mathscr{K}(\mathrm{G})$ now takes a function f to the function $s \mapsto \Delta(s^{-1})\overline{f(s^{-1})}$.

In this example, there is a complex one-parameter group of *automorphisms* of $\mathscr{K}(\mathrm{G})$, consisting of the mappings $\Delta(\alpha)$ for $\alpha \in \mathbf{C}$, which map f to the function $s \mapsto \Delta(s)^{\alpha} f(s)$. Tomita discovered that the existence of such a group of automorphisms is a property of a very general class of left Hilbert algebras (called *modular* left Hilbert algebras). Furthermore, if $\mathscr{A}$ is a von Neumann algebra contained in $\mathscr{L}(\mathrm{H})$ such that there exists a vector $\xi_0 \in \mathrm{H}$ for which the mapping $x \mapsto x \cdot \xi_0$ of $\mathscr{A}$ into H is injective with dense image, then by transporting to $\mathfrak{A} = \mathscr{A} \cdot \xi_0$ the algebra structure of $\mathfrak{A}$, we obtain a left Hilbert algebra having ξ_0 as identity element. By subtle arguments from spectral theory, Tomita showed that one can associate canonically with $\mathfrak{A}$ a *modular* left Hilbert algebra $\mathfrak{B}$ having the same closure H as $\mathfrak{A}$, and that

$\mathscr{A}$ is isomorphic to the von Neumann algebra of extensions to H of left multiplications in $\mathfrak{B}$ (B 371; LN 128; Nice D 2 (Takesaki)).

Tomita's theory has enabled considerable progress to be made in the study of factors, especially those of type III. If $\mathscr{A}$ is a factor, let P($\mathscr{A}$) denote the set of semifinite weights that are lower semicontinuous on $\mathscr{A}^+$ and faithful, i.e., vanishing only at the origin of $\mathscr{A}^+$. For such a weight φ, consider the set $\mathfrak{N}_\varphi$ of $x \in \mathscr{A}$ such that $\varphi(x^*x) < +\infty$, and the intersection $\mathfrak{A}_\varphi = \mathfrak{N}_\varphi \cap \mathfrak{N}_\varphi^*$; this is a left Hilbert algebra having $\mathscr{A}$ as algebra of left multiplications. There corresponds therefore to φ a one-parameter group σ^φ: $t \mapsto \Delta_\varphi^{it}$ (for $t \in \mathbf{R}$), where Δ_φ is a positive self-adjoint operator on the closure H of $\mathfrak{A}_\varphi$. This being so, A. Connes associates with $\mathscr{A}$ two invariants: S($\mathscr{A}$), which is the intersection of the spectra of the Δ_φ for $\varphi \in$ P($\mathscr{A}$); and T($\mathscr{A}$), which is the union of the kernels of the homomorphisms σ^φ. T($\mathscr{A}$) is a subgroup of the additive group $\mathbf{R}$, and S($\mathscr{A}$) $\cap\, \mathbf{R}_+^*$ a subgroup of the multiplicative group $\mathbf{R}_+^*$ if $\mathscr{A}$ is a factor. He obtains in this way for factors of type III a finer classification into types III_0, III_1, and III_λ with $0 < \lambda < 1$, according as S($\mathscr{A}$) is $\{0, 1\}$, the interval $[0, +\infty] = \mathbf{R}_+$ or the group of powers λ^n, $n \in \mathbf{Z}$. In the last two cases, T($\mathscr{A}$) is the annihilator of S($\mathscr{A}$) $\cap\, \mathbf{R}_+^*$ in the sense of Pontrjagin duality, but in the first case T($\mathscr{A}$) can be any countable subgroup of $\mathbf{R}$. Moreover, the factors of type III can be generated from a factor of type II_∞ by forming a "crossed product" of the latter with one of its automorphisms, or with a one-parameter group of such automorphisms (B 333, 461; Vancouver (A. Connes)).

2. Applications to C*-algebras

A C*-algebra is always isomorphic to a closed subalgebra (with respect to the norm topology) $\mathfrak{A}$ of an algebra $\mathscr{L}$(H) for some Hilbert space H. The closure of $\mathfrak{A}$ in the weak topology is a von Neumann algebra. This association enables the theory of von Neumann algebras to be applied to various problems about isomorphisms or derivations of C*-algebras: for example, every derivation of $\mathfrak{A}$ can be extended to an inner derivation of its weak closure in $\mathscr{L}$(H) (B 140, 207, 324; [46]).

Recently, A. Connes has developed remarkable relations between foliations (**A** V) and C*-algebras (B 551, LN 725), the "bad" topology of the spaces of leaves of a foliation being replaced by the consideration of suitable (in general, noncommutative) C*-algebras. This generalizes the fact that, for "good" locally compact spaces, the Gelfand–Naimark theorem (**C** III) establishes a one–one correspondence between these spaces and commutative C*-algebras. That theory enables one to extend many topological notions and theorems (Betti numbers, K-theory, Atiyah–Singer theorem) to spaces of leaves of a foliation.

3. Connections with the natural sciences

In quantum field theory, mathematicians and physicists have been led to introduce concepts related to C*-algebras (Nice D 2 (I. Segal)).

4. The originators

The principal ideas in the theory of von Neumann algebras are due to the following mathematicians: J. von Neumann (1903–1957), M. Tomita, A. Connes.

The following have also contributed substantially to this theory: H. Araki, M. Atiyah, M. Breuer, L. Coburn, F. Combes, J. Dixmier, H. Dye, E. Effros, J. Fell, B. Fuglede, J. Glimm, R. Godement, A. Guichardet, M. Herman, B. Johnson, R. Kadison, I. Kaplansky, M. Kondo, W. Krieger, F. Murray, M. Nakamura, E. Nelson, R. Pallu de la Barrière, R. Powers, L. Pukanszky, J. Ringrose, S. Sakai, J. Schwartz, I. Segal, I. Singer, W. Stinespring, E. Størmer, H. Sunouchi, Z. Takeda, O. Takenouchi, M. Takesaki, T. Turumaru, H. Ugesaki, E. Woods, G. Zeller-Meier.

References

B: 19, 25, 30, 140, 207, 324, 333, 371, 461, 551.
LN: 128, 575, 725, 731.
Astérisque: 32–33 (Atiyah).
[45], [46], [225], [226].

B VI

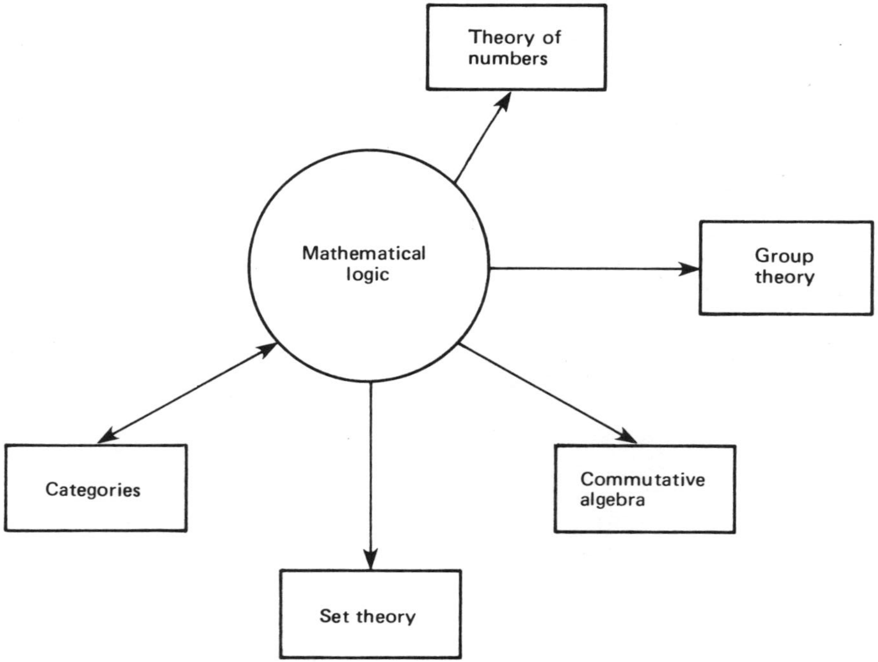

Theory of numbers
Mathematical logic
Group theory
Categories
Commutative algebra
Set theory

B VI

Mathematical logic

For a long time, "mathematical objects" were considered to be "idealizations" of objects of sensory experience, subjected like the latter to the rules of Aristotelian logic. The introduction in the 19th century of ever more abstract mathematical concepts, and in particular the theory of sets, cast doubt on this correspondence between mathematical notions and notions drawn from sensory experience, especially after the appearance around 1900 of the "paradoxes" of set theory (LN 255 (Moss)). Some mathematicians ("intuitionists," "constructivists"), wishing to preserve this correspondence, imposed restrictions on the type of mathematical objects that could in their view legitimately be considered, and on the logical arguments to be used on these objects (LN 95, 274 (Goodman and Myhill)). The majority of contemporary mathematicians have preferred to follow another path, which leaves classical logic intact but abstains from any rigid attachment of mathematical notions and objects to physical reality: everyone is free to think what he will on this subject, provided that his arguments are *formalizable*, that is to say, capable of translation into a "formal language," a manipulation of symbols fixed once and for all, according to exact and completely codified rules; but the symbols are no longer supposed to represent anything but themselves. The rules to which they are subject are on the one hand the logical rules, which constitute a formalization of classical logic, and on the other hand the "axioms" of set theory which govern the use of the symbols $=$ and $\in$ ("belonging"); the most popular of these systems of axioms is the Zermelo–Fraenkel system, denoted by ZF. (For convenience of exposition, we shall omit from this system the axiom of choice, although it featured in Zermelo's original formulation) ([98], [149]). The theory of sets, so conceived, embraces all mathematical theories, each of which is defined by the assignment of a certain number of letters (the "constants" of the theory) and relations which involve these letters (the "axioms" of the theory): for example, the theory of groups contains two constants, G and m (representing respectively the set on which the group is defined, and the law of composition), and the relations express first that m is a mapping from G × G to G, and second the classical properties of the law of composition (see [23]).

With the appearance in the 19th century of mathematical theories having no relationship with sensory reality (the first of these, historically, being non-Euclidean geometry), the problem naturally arose of whether the axioms of such a theory might not lead to a contradiction. Hilbert proposed a general method for examining whether a given theorem is or is not provable in a given theory (which includes the question of noncontradiction, by taking as theorem "A and (not A)" where A is a relation in the theory); this is what is called *metamathematics* or *proof theory*. It consists in analyzing the structure of the sequence of assemblies of symbols that, in a formal language, should constitute a proof of the theorem under consideration; without attributing any meaning to the symbols used, the question is simply to determine whether such a sequence of assemblies can exist in conformity with the rules of the formal language. The problem is a combinatorial one, which is examined by making use of mathematical arguments such as the principle of mathematical induction, but handled in such a way as to give conviction that each step describes a process that could be effectively realized.

This study of formal languages and their possibilities has been greatly developed since the time of Hilbert, and constitutes what is now called *mathematical logic*; it has largely transcended its original purposes as envisaged by Hilbert, and although many questions that it treats appear not to excite the interest of many mathematicians at present (see B 153, 266), yet by contrast it has produced a whole series of spectacular results on numerous problems that had obstinately resisted the methods of traditional mathematics.

1. Noncontradiction and undecidability

Hilbert's original hope of proving by metamathematical methods the noncontradiction of ZF (or of parts of this system) vanished in 1931 when Gödel showed that such a proof is impossible in any formal system from which Peano's axioms for arithmetic can be deduced (B 266; [97]). Since then the noncontradiction of ZF has generally been postulated, and the problems studied have been of the following type: is a relation A provable in ZF? Most effort has been concentrated on two central statements of Cantor's theory, the axiom of choice AC and the generalized continuum hypothesis CH, which asserts that for each infinite cardinal $\mathfrak{m}$, there exists no cardinal between $\mathfrak{m}$ and $2^{\mathfrak{m}}$ and distinct from these two. The first fundamental result was obtained by Gödel in 1940: the negations of AC and of

CH are not provable in ZF. Then, in 1963, P. Cohen established that AC and CH are themselves not provable in ZF; they are therefore *undecidable* propositions in ZF.

The technique used in these metamathematical proofs is that of *models*, which transposes into this domain the mathematical proofs of "relative noncontradiction," which were elaborated in the 19th century, notably for non-Euclidean geometry, and which consisted in "translating" the axioms of a theory whose noncontradiction was to be proved into propositions of another theory assumed to be noncontradictory. In broad terms, the general method consists in establishing an explicit correspondence that associates with each assembly R of symbols in ZF another assembly R′ in such a way that R′ is a relation if R is, and that logical operations (negation, conjunction, etc.) on relations R, S, ... give relations to which correspond the relations obtained by the same operations on R′, S′, ... Suppose that the relations R′ corresponding to the axioms R of ZF are theorems in ZF, and let A be a relation whose corresponding relation A′ is a logical consequence of the relations R′; then (not A) is not provable in ZF, since otherwise (not A′) would also be a consequence of the relations R′, which is impossible if ZF is noncontradictory. The "translation" devised by Gödel consists essentially in working only with certain particular sets, called "constructible" (LN 37, 345, 617). Cohen's method (called "forcing") is based on more subtle constructions (B 357; LN 37, 217, 450); other more elementary methods have since been put forward (B 317; LN 274; [175]).

A consequence of these theorems of undecidability is that it is possible to develop an *infinity* of different set theories by adjoining to ZF one or other supplementary axiom whose negation is known to be unprovable within ZF; for example, it follows from the work of P. Cohen that any one of the axioms $2^{\aleph_0} = \aleph_k$ may be adjoined, for any integer $k \geqslant 1$. But there are many other possibilities. Many theorems of classical analysis require only a weak form of the axiom of choice, namely, the statement ACD that a *denumerable* product of nonempty sets is nonempty. On the contrary, hardly any of the theories described in this volume requires the strong form AC, nor a fortiori CH. However, it is not excluded that other axioms adjoined to ZF + ACD will not in the end be assumed by analysts, for reasons of convenience. A remarkable example is due to Solovay (B 357): in analysis it is often necessary to show that a subset of $\mathbf{R}^n$ is measurable (in Lebesgue's sense), because ZF + AC implies the existence of *nonmeasurable* sets. Now Solovay has shown that if we renounce AC but instead adjoin to ZF + ACD the axiom that *every* subset of $\mathbf{R}^n$ is measurable, there is no risk of contradiction, provided that the theory obtained by adjoining to ZF + AC an axiom guaranteeing the existence of "inaccessible" cardinals is itself noncontradictory (see also (B 494) on "singular" cardinals).

2. Uniform effective procedures and recursive relations

Hilbert posed the problem of determining not only the "decidable" statements in a theory (i.e., those for which there is certainty that either the statement or its negation is provable within the theory) but also those that are decidable by a "uniform effective" or "mechanical" procedure, without making precise exactly what he meant by that phrase. Subsequent work of mathematical logicians has elucidated this point by means of the theory of "recursive functions" or the equivalent theory of "Turing machines" (B 55, 61, 266; [97], [120]). Briefly, we may say that a subset of $\mathbf{N}^p$ (or the relation between $x_1, \ldots, x_p$ that it defines) is *recursively enumerable* if it is obtained from the graphs of addition and multiplication in $\mathbf{N}$ by a finite number of operations of conjunctions, disjunctions, existential quantifications, bounded universal quantifications, and changes of variables, performed in any order. A subset of $\mathbf{N}^p$ is said to be *recursive* if both it and its complement are recursively enumerable. The fundamental result of the theory is that there exists a recursively enumerable subset of $\mathbf{N}$ *that is not recursive.*

Hilbert's 10th problem was to devise a "mechanical" procedure for determining whether an arbitrary Diophantine equation has a solution or not. This may be made precise by first defining a *Diophantine relation* $\mathrm{R}(x_1, \ldots, x_p)$ between variables taking their values in the set $\mathbf{N}^+$ of positive integers: this signifies that there exists an integer $n \geqslant 0$ and a polynomial $\mathrm{P}(x_1, \ldots, x_p, y_1, \ldots, y_n)$ with coefficients in $\mathbf{Z}$ such that the $(x_1, \ldots, x_p) \in (\mathbf{N}^+)^p$ that satisfy $\mathrm{R}(x_1, \ldots, x_p)$ are precisely those for which there exist $y_1, \ldots, y_n$ in $\mathbf{Z}$ such that $\mathrm{P}(x_1, \ldots, x_p, y_1, \ldots, y_n) = 0$. It is easy to see that a Diophantine relation is recursively enumerable, but it was only in 1970, after many efforts, that it was proved that, conversely, every recursively enumerable relation in $(\mathbf{N}^+)^p$ is Diophantine (B 383). The crucial point in this proof is to show that the equation $x = y^z$ in three variables is Diophantine. Since there exist recursively enumerable relations that are not recursive, the answer to Hilbert's problem is negative.

Analogous problems arise in algebra, and particularly in group theory. In a group G generated by a finite number of elements $a_1, \ldots, a_n$, these elements are in general connected by certain relations: for example, the alternating group $\mathfrak{A}_4$ is generated by two elements a, b connected by the relations $a^3 = b^2 = (ab)^3 = e$. Every element of G can be written as a "word" obtained by taking a product $x_1 x_2 \cdots x_m$ of arbitrary length, where each x_j is either an a_i or an a_i^{-1}. The "word problem" (A. Thue, 1907) consists of giving a "uniform effective procedure" for deciding whether two "words" represent the same element of G, having regard to the relations between the a_i. This may be made precise as follows: the notions of recursively enumerable set and recursive set can be defined not only in $\mathbf{N}^p$ but in any denumerable set. A group G generated by $a_1, \ldots, a_n$ is the quotient of the free group F generated by $a_1, \ldots, a_n$ by a normal subgroup R (defined by the relations connecting the a_i in G), and the word problem reduces to the question whether R is recursive. The answer is negative in general (B 266); however, the word problem is in fact solvable for certain groups, which can now be completely characterized (B 457).

3. The technique of ultraproducts

Let I be an infinite set, $\mathfrak{U}$ a nontrivial ultrafilter† on I, and let $(A_i)_{i \in I}$ be a family of sets indexed by I. On the product set $A = \prod_{i \in I} A_i$, let $R_{\mathfrak{U}}$ denote the following relation between $x = (x_i)$ and $y = (y_i)$: "the set of $i \in I$ such that $x_i = y_i$ belongs to $\mathfrak{U}$." The quotient $A_{\mathfrak{U}} = A/R_{\mathfrak{U}}$ is called the *ultraproduct* of the A_i with respect to the ultrafilter $\mathfrak{U}$. If the A_i are fields, so also is $A_{\mathfrak{U}}$; there are analogous results for other types of algebraic structures.

The technique of ultraproducts has interesting applications in algebra and in mathematical logic. For example, in field theory, the notion of an "elementary property" is defined by an inductive procedure similar to the definition of recursively enumerable properties: starting from a certain number of "atomic formulas," operations of negation, disjunction, and existential quantification are applied in some order, and the result is an elementary property if it contains no letter other than the constants of the theory. With this notion, there is the following fundamental principle: if $A_{\mathfrak{U}}$ is an ultraproduct of fields A_i and if P is an elementary property, then P is true for $A_{\mathfrak{U}}$ if and only if the set of $i \in I$ such that P is true for A_i belongs to the ultrafilter $\mathfrak{U}$ (Nice I (Keisler)).

By an ingenious application of this principle, Ax and Kochen obtained in particular the following result on p-adic fields: for each integer $d > 0$, there exists a finite set $E(d)$ of prime numbers such that if p is a prime number *not in* $E(d)$, every homogeneous polynomial $f \in \mathbf{Q}_p(X_1, \ldots, X_n]$ of degree d, *where the number of indeterminates is* $n > d^2$, has a nontrivial zero in $\mathbf{Q}_p^n$. E. Artin had conjectured this result with $E(d) = \varnothing$ (**C** II), but counter-examples show that these "exceptional" prime numbers cannot be avoided (B 299).

† We recall that an ultrafilter on an infinite set I is a set $\mathfrak{U}$ of subsets of I such that (1) the empty subset of I does not belong to $\mathfrak{U}$; (2) the relations $A \in \mathfrak{U}$ and $B \in \mathfrak{U}$ imply $A \cap B \in \mathfrak{U}$; (3) for each partition of I into two sets A, B, either A or B belongs to $\mathfrak{U}$. If $i \in I$, the set of subsets of I that contain i is an ultrafilter; such ultrafilters are called *trivial*. The existence of nontrivial ultrafilters is a consequence of the axiom of choice.

If all the fields A_i are equal to the same field K, an ultraproduct is an overfield *K of K. If, for example, we take $K = \mathbf{R}$, the field $^*\mathbf{R}$ is a nonarchimedean ordered field containing "infinitely small" elements (i.e., elements $x > 0$ such that $x < r$ for all $r \in \mathbf{R}_+^*$). By using the field $^*\mathbf{R}$, theorems of analysis can be translated into statements involving "infinitesimals" in the style of Leibniz, and for some problems the proofs are easier and more comprehensible in this language of "nonstandard analysis" (B 580; BAMS 73 (A. Robinson); [147]).

4. Connections with the natural sciences

The idea of solving mathematical problems by a "logical machine" has certainly influenced the development and the theory of computers. This theory has by now evolved into a general theory of "automata," which partakes of both algebra and mathematical logic (Stockholm (A. Church)).

5. The originators

The principal ideas in mathematical logic are due to the following mathematicians:

Proof theory. D. Hilbert (1862–1943), K. Gödel (1906–1978), P. Cohen, R. Solovay.

Recursive relations and word problems. A. Turing (1912–1954), E. Post, A. Tarski, P. Novikov (1901–1976), J. Robinson, I. Matiasevich.

Ultraproducts. T. Skolem (1887–1963), A. Robinson (1919–1974), J. Ax, S. Kochen.

The following have also contributed substantially to these theories: W. Ackermann (1896–1962), P. Bernays (1888–1977), W. Boone, A. Church, M. Davis, A. Ehrenfeucht, G. Gentzen (1909–1945), A. Grzegorczyk, M. Hall, J. Herbrand (1908–1931), G. Higman, R. Jensen, S. Kleene, M. Kondo, F. Lawvere, A. Macintyre, A. Malcev (1909–1967), A. Mostowski (1913–1975), B. Neumann, R. Peter, H. Putnam, M. Rabin, B. Rosser, G. Sacks, D. Scott, J. Silver, J. Stallings, S. Tannenbaum, M. Tierney, J. von Neumann (1903–1957).

References

B: 55, 61, 153, 256, 266, 299, 317, 357, 383, 457, 478, 494, 513, 580.
LN: 37, 95, 217, 255, 274, 354, 445, 450, 617, 619, 669, 759, 881.
BAMS: 73 (A. Robinson), 83 (E. Nelson).
[23], [97], [98], [120], [147], [149], [175], [209], [213], [216], [219].

B VII

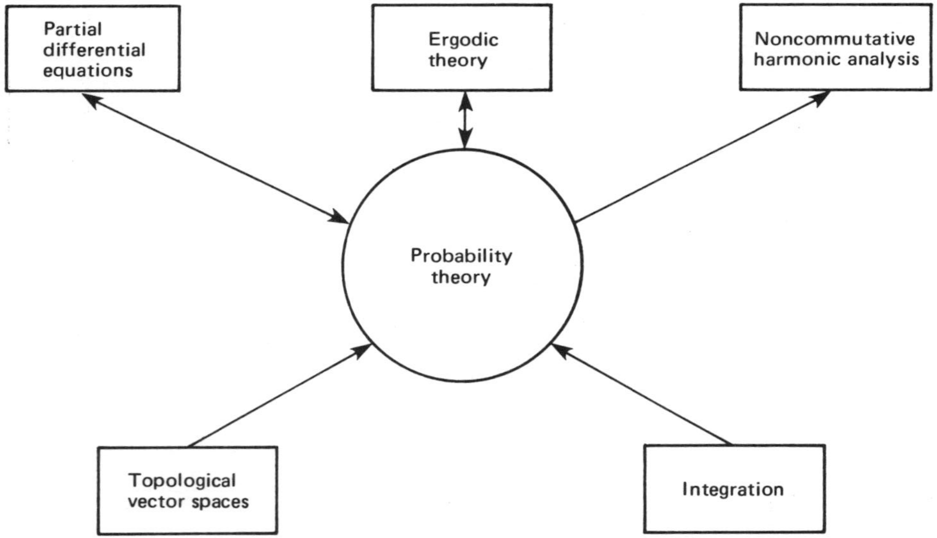

Partial differential equations
Ergodic theory
Noncommutative harmonic analysis
Probability theory
Topological vector spaces
Integration

B VII

Probability theory

Probability theory, as a mathematical discipline, can be said to date from 1933, as a part of the modern theory of integration; but it has inherited its own problems and even its own language from the preceding three centuries in which the calculus of probabilities was a mixture of arguments of a mathematical nature and more or less intuitive considerations on the role and the evaluation of chance in human behavior and natural phenomena.

The basic notions are those of a *probability space* $(\Omega, \mathscr{A}, P)$ and a *random variable*; here Ω is a set, $\mathscr{A}$ is a *σ-algebra* of subsets of Ω (called *events*), i.e., a set of subsets that contains Ω and is stable under countable unions and complementation, and P is a *probability* on $\mathscr{A}$, that is to say a real-valued function defined on $\mathscr{A}$ with values in $[0, 1]$, such that $P(\Omega) = 1$ and $P\left(\bigcup_n B_n\right) = \sum_n P(B_n)$ for a finite or infinite *sequence* (B_n) of pairwise-disjoint subsets belonging to $\mathscr{A}$. A property depending on $\omega \in \Omega$ is said to be *almost certain* if the set N of $\omega \in \Omega$ for which it is not true is such that $P(N) = 0$.

A random variable X is a mapping of Ω into $\mathbf{R}^k$ (for some $k \geqslant 1$) that is *$\mathscr{A}$-measurable*, i.e., such that $X^{-1}(S) \in \mathscr{A}$ for all Borel subsets S of $\mathbf{R}^k$. If X is P-integrable, we write $E(X) = \int_\Omega X\, dP$.

The (probability) *distribution* of X is the probability on the σ-algebra $\mathscr{S}$ of Borel subsets of $\mathbf{R}^k$ defined by $P_X(S) = P(X^{-1}(S))$ for $S \in \mathscr{S}$. Probability theory is concerned with sequences, or more generally families (called *processes*) $(X_t)_{t\in T}$ of random variables defined on Ω. A family $(X_t)_{t\in T}$ is said to be *independent* if for all $t_1, \ldots, t_n \in T$ we have

$$(1)\quad P(X_{t_1}^{-1}(S_1) \cap X_{t_2}^{-1}(S_2) \cap \cdots \cap X_{t_n}^{-1}(S_n)) = P(X_{t_1}^{-1}(S_1)) \cdot \cdots \cdot P(X_{t_n}^{-1}(S_n))$$

for all choices of Borel sets $S_1, \ldots, S_n$.

The typical problem dealt with by probability theory is to determine the distribution of a random variable Y defined in terms of a family (X_t) of random variables whose distributions are assumed known. The classical example is the "law of large numbers": for a sequence $X_1, \ldots, X_n, \ldots$ of independent random variables, one considers the distribution of

$$\frac{1}{n}(S_n - E(S_n)),$$

where $S_n = X_1 + \cdots + X_n$, and its "limit" in various senses as $n \to +\infty$. These researches have been enormously developed and diversified in the course of the past 20 years. Apart from the classical works [15], [47], [49], [53], [110], [114], the publications of lectures given at the Séminaire de Strasbourg (LN 39, 51, 88, 124, 191, 258, 321, 381, 465, 649, 721, 784), and at the École d'été de Saint-Flour (LN 307, 390, 480, 539, 678, 774), together with (LN 26, 77, 190, 284, 440, 656, 672, 675, 695, 706, 709, 828), will enable the reader to inform himself of these developments. The lectures in the Séminarie Bourbaki provide only a few samples.

1. Fluctuations in sequences of independent random variables

Let $(X_n)_{n \geqslant 1}$ be a sequence of independent real-valued random variables, all having the same distribution, and let $S_n = X_1 + \cdots + X_n$. One can associate various random functions with S_n: for example, N_n is the number of indices i between 1 and n such that $S_i \geqslant 0$; or again, if $M_n = \sup(S_1, \ldots, S_n)$, we define L_n to be the largest index i such that $M_n = S_i$. The distributions of N_n and L_n can be derived by ingenious combinatorial calculations (B 241; LN 88). As an example of the application of these results, we give a result of P. Lévy: suppose that two players A and B play a game n times, and let N_n be the number of games that B loses; then the probability $P(N_n < na^2)$ tends almost certainly to $\frac{2}{\pi} \sin^{-1} a$, for all constants $a \in [0, 1]$.

2. Inequalities for martingales

Let $G_0, \ldots, G_n, \ldots$ be a sequence of independent real-valued integrable random variables. The sequence of random variables $X_n = G_0 + \cdots + G_n$ is called a *martingale* if G_n is orthogonal to every function of $G_0, \ldots, G_{n-1}$. Now let $V_0, \ldots, V_n, \ldots$ be a sequence of random variables taking only the values 0 and 1, where V_n is a function of $G_0, \ldots, G_{n-1}$, and put $Y_n = V_0 G_0 + \cdots + V_n G_n$. Then the sequence (Y_n) is also a martingale, and for each $c > 0$, there is an inequality $cP\left(\sup_n |Y_n| \geqslant c\right) \leqslant K \sup_n E(|X_n|)$, where K is an absolute constant.

3. Trajectories of processes

Let $T = \mathbf{R}$. The *trajectories* of a process $(X_t)_{t \in T}$ are the mappings $t \mapsto X_t(\omega)$ for $\omega \in \Omega$. The probabilistic study of these trajectories consists in determining whether they have a given property $\boldsymbol{P}$ (of functions defined on $\mathbf{R}$ with values in $\mathbf{R}^k$) almost surely, i.e., whether the set of $\omega \in \Omega$ such that the function $t \mapsto X_t(\omega)$ does not possess $\boldsymbol{P}$ has probability zero.

A typical example is the study of *random Fourier series*. Let (A_n) be a sequence of independent complex-valued random variables; the question is whether the series $\sum_{n=-\infty}^{+\infty} A_n e^{nit}$ is almost surely continuous, or satisfies a Lipschitz condition almost surely, or is almost surely nondifferentiable almost everywhere, etc. A general theorem due to Steinhaus is the following one. Suppose that the random variables A_n are "rotation invariant," i.e., that A_n and $A_n e^{i\alpha}$ have the same distribution for all $\alpha \in \mathbf{R}$. Then, for a very general class of properties $\boldsymbol{P}$ (including those mentioned above), either the series $\sum_n A_n e^{nit}$ has the property $\boldsymbol{P}$ almost surely, or it has the property "not $\boldsymbol{P}$" almost surely (B 200).

As a particular case of such series, we should mention *Brownian motion* for its historical importance: this is the series $\sum_{n=-\infty}^{+\infty} n^{-1} Z_n e^{nit}$, where $Z_n = X_n + iY_n$, and X_n, Y_n are independent real-valued random variables each having the *normal* (or *Gaussian*) distribution, i.e., the measure on $\mathbf{R}$ whose density with respect to Lebesgue measure is the function

$$x \mapsto (2\pi)^{-1/2} \int_{-\infty}^{x} e^{-y^2/2} \, dy.$$

The series can be shown to be continuous almost surely and to satisfy almost surely a Hölder condition of exponent $<1/2$, but not to satisfy almost surely a Hölder condition of exponent $>1/2$. Up to normalization, Brownian motion is the only process $(X_t)_{0 \leqslant t \leqslant 2\pi}$ with almost surely continuous trajectories, such that the distributions of the X_t are normal and the $X_t - X_s$ are independent for two disjoint intervals $[s, t[$ (B 161).

More generally, let $(X_t)_{t \in \mathbf{R}}$ be a process such that all the X_t have normal distribution (but are no longer necessarily independent), and consider whether there exists for each $t \in \mathbf{R}$ a random variable X'_t that is equal to X_t almost everywhere and such that for the new process (X'_t) the trajectories are bounded, or continuous. The answer depends on the *covariance* of the process, namely, the function $\Gamma(s, t) = E(X_s X_t)$ on $T \times T$, which defines a metric $d(s, t) = \|X_s - X_t\|_2 = (\Gamma(t, t) + \Gamma(s, s) - 2\Gamma(s, t))^{1/2}$ on T, and the conditions are expressed in terms of the geometrical properties of the metric space so defined (B 470).

4. Generalized processes

A process $(X_t)_{t\in T}$ may be considered as a random variable $\omega \mapsto (X_t(\omega))_{t\in T}$ with values in the product $\mathbf{R}^T$, but there are several possible definitions for the notion of probability on a σ-algebra of sets in $\mathbf{R}^T$, which lead to difficulties when T is uncountable. Following an idea of Gelfand, a more satisfactory theory is obtained by replacing $\mathbf{R}^T$ by the *dual* E′ of a suitable locally convex space E. A subset H_A of the algebraic dual E^* of E is said to be *cylindrical* if it consists of the vectors $x^* \in E^*$ that satisfy a relation of the form $(\langle h_1, x^*\rangle, \ldots, \langle h_p, x^*\rangle) \in A$, where the h_j $(1 \leqslant j \leqslant p)$ belong to E, the integer p is arbitrary and A is a Borel set in $\mathbf{R}^p$. The question is whether there exists a probability measure P on the σ-algebra $\mathscr{C}$ of intersections of cylindrical sets with E′. A necessary condition is that for given $h_j \in E$, the function $A \mapsto m_{h_1 \cdots h_p}(A) = P(H_A \cap E')$ should be a probability measure on $\mathbf{R}^p$ (called the *margin* of P corresponding to (h_j)). When E is a direct limit of Fréchet spaces E_n, Prokhorov has given a necessary and sufficient condition for given margins to correspond to a probability measure P: for each $\varepsilon > 0$, there should exist a neighborhood U of 0 in some E_n such that

$$m_{h_1 \cdots h_p}(J^p) \geqslant 1 - \varepsilon$$

for all p and all choices of $h_j \in U$ $(1 \leqslant j \leqslant p)$, where J^p is the unit cube in $\mathbf{R}^p$. When E is in addition a nuclear space (**C** III) there is a condition of another nature (Minlos). A complex-valued function Φ on E is said to be of *positive type* if it is continuous on each finite-dimensional subspace of E and if $\sum_{i,j} c_i \bar{c}_j \Phi(h_i - h_j) \geqslant 0$ for all $h_i \in E$ and $c_i \in \mathbf{C}$ $(1 \leqslant i \leqslant n$, n arbitrary). Given such a function satisfying $\Phi(0) = 1$, there exists a probability measure P on the σ-algebra $\mathscr{C}$ such that $\Phi(h) = \int_{E'} e^{i\langle h, x'\rangle}\, dP(x')$ (B 272, 311; LN 360, 379).

5. Random variables with values in locally compact groups

Another generalization is to consider random variables with values in a locally compact group G, in relation to the extension to G of the classical notion of a harmonic function on $\mathbf{R}^n$. Suppose that we are given a probability measure μ on G such that, if m is a right Haar measure on G, there exists an integer $n > 0$ for which μ^n (the convolution of n measures equal to μ) is a measure with base m. A real-valued function f on G is then said to be *μ-harmonic* if it is a bounded Borel function such that $f(s) = \int_G f(st)\, d\mu(t)$

for all $s \in G$. It can be shown that this definition is equivalent to the following probabilistic definition: if (X_n) is a sequence of random variables with values in G, all having as distribution the measure μ, and if $X_{n-1}^{-1}X_n$ is independent of $X_0, \ldots, X_{n-1}$ for all n, then the sequence of real-valued random variables $(f(X_n))$ is a martingale. This is an example of the close relations between probability theory, potential theory, and second-order elliptic equations, which enrich all three theories (B 370; LN 26, 77, 451; [121]).

6. Connections with the natural sciences

For a long time, the applications of the calculus of probabilities to the natural sciences were limited to statistics and the calculation of observational errors; but since the middle of the 19th century, first classical statistical mechanics (B 431, 480) and then in modern times quantum mechanics have put the notion of probability at the center of their methods.

7. The originators

The main ideas in probability theory are due to the following mathematicians: Jacques Bernoulli (1654–1705), A. De Moivre (1667–1754), P. Laplace (1749–1827), P. Tchebichev (1821–1894), A. Markov (1856–1922), E. Borel (1871–1956), N. Wiener (1894–1964), P. Lévy (1886–1971), A. Kolmogorov, A. Khintchine (1894–1959), J. Doob, W. Feller (1907–1970), G. Hunt, D. Poisson (1781–1840).

The following have also contributed substantially to these theories: E. Andersen, E. Azencott, L. Bachelier (1870–1946), Bawly, S. Bernstein (1880–1968), D. Blackwell, S. Bochner, J. Bretagnolle, D. Burkholder, P. Cartier, S. Chatterji, K. Chung, H. Cramer, D. D'Acunha-Castelle, D. Darling, B. de Finetti, C. Dellacherie, W. Döblin (1915–1940), M. Donsker, L. Dubins, R. Dudley, A. Dvoretzky, E. Dynkin, P. Erdös, C. Esseen, X. Fernique, R. Fortet, H. Furstenberg, M. Fréchet (1878–1973), I. Gelfand, R. Getoor, B. Gnedenko, R. Gundy, K. Ito, M. Kac, J. P. Kahane, H. Kesten, H. Kunita, L. Le Cam, A. Liapounov (1857–1918), J. Lindeberg, Ju. Linnik (1915–1972), Z. Lomnicki, M. Loève (1907–1979), P. Malliavin, P. A. Meyer, H. McKean, R. Minlos, G. Mokobodzki, E. Mourier, J. Neveu, R. Paley (1907–1933), V. V. Petrov, F. Pollaczek, G. Pólya, Ju. Prokhorov, M. Rao, A. Rényi (1921–1970), R. Salem (1898–1963), N. V. Smirnov, F. Spitzer, H.

Steinhaus (1887–1972), W. Stout, K. Urbanik, J. Ville, R. von Mises, T. Watanabe, J. Wendel, A. Zygmund.

References

B: 161, 200, 241, 272, 311, 370, 431, 470, 480.

LN: 26, 39, 51, 77, 88, 124, 190, 191, 258, 284, 307, 321, 360, 379, 381, 390, 426, 440, 451, 465, 472, 480, 511, 516, 539, 563, 581, 598, 607, 624, 636, 649, 656, 672, 675, 678, 695, 706, 709, 721, 774, 784, 828.

[15], [47], [49], [53], [110], [114], [121].

C I

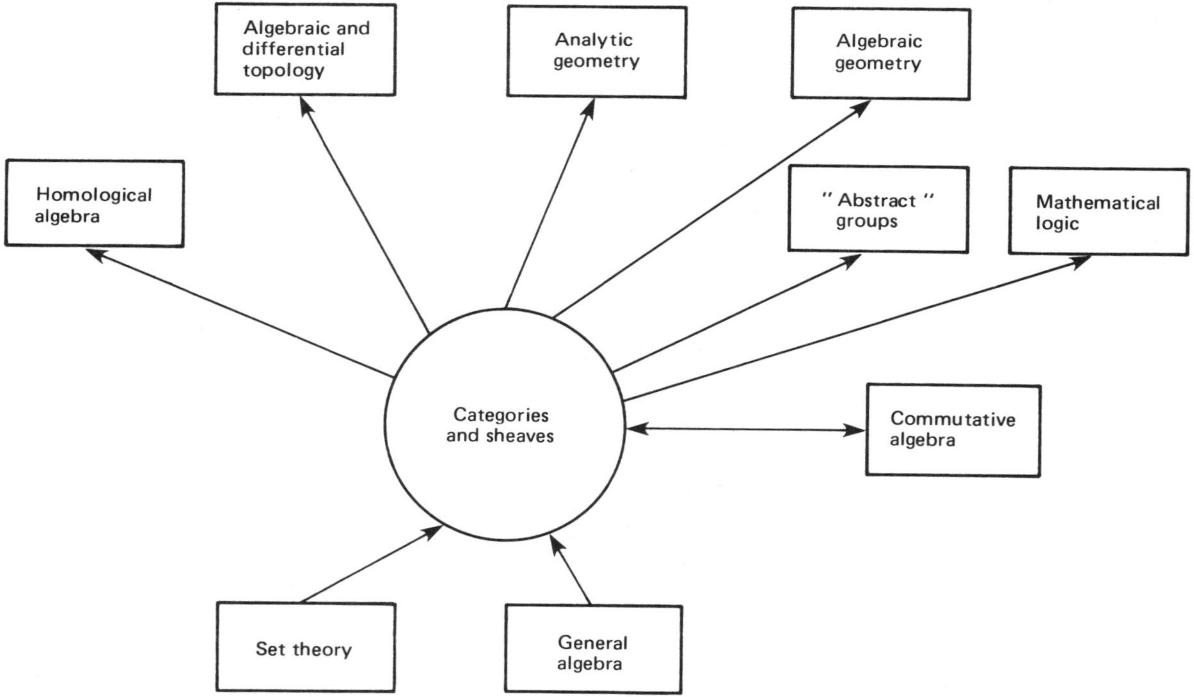
Algebraic and differential topology
Analytic geometry
Algebraic geometry
Homological algebra
" Abstract " groups
Mathematical logic
Categories and sheaves
Commutative algebra
Set theory
General algebra

C I

Categories and sheaves

Through the 19th century and the first half of the 20th century, the observation of similarities in the behavior of various objects encountered in mathematical problems gradually led to the notion of *structure* (for example, the structure of a group, a topological space, a differential manifold). This produced enormous simplifications and economies of thought in the development of many theories, by bringing out the previously hidden "structural" aspects of properties contingent to the theory under consideration.

From 1940 onward, analogies observed between *different* structures and methods of construction that associated with objects having a given structure other objects having a (possibly different) structure gradually led to the formulation of two very general concepts applicable to many structures, namely, those of *morphism* and *functor*. For example, to the notion of group structure there is closely related the notion of a homomorphism of one group into another (which, however, is not mentioned in the axioms of a group); likewise, the notion of a topological structure carries with it the notion of a continuous mapping of one topological space into another (which again does not feature in the axioms of a topological space): these are two examples of morphisms. As examples of functors, we may mention the procedures that associate with a group its commutator subgroup; with two A-modules M, N their tensor product $M \otimes_A N$; with a topological space X its fundamental group $\pi_1(X)$ (**A** I) (in this last case we pass from the structure of a topological space to that of a group). By an effort of abstraction "to the second degree," the systematization of these notions has led to the general theory of *categories*, which in many modern theories (topological algebra, algebraic and differential topology, analytic geometry, algebraic geometry, etc.) performs the very valuable function of a *framework* and a *guide* to the development of the theory.

The "naïve" point of view is that one gathers together into a "category" *all* the objects having the same structure, so that we have for example the category of *all* groups or of *all* topological spaces. There are various ways of avoiding the known "paradoxes" of set theory that are latent in such a concept: the simplest way is to allow only objects that belong to a given "sufficiently large" set, and this is no impediment in the majority of applications.

1. Categories and functors

A category $\boldsymbol{C}$ consists of a set Ob $\boldsymbol{C}$ (the set of *objects* of $\boldsymbol{C}$) *together with* another set Ar $\boldsymbol{C}$, called the set of *morphisms* (or *arrows*) of $\boldsymbol{C}$, satisfying the following axioms:

(1) To each pair of objects X, Y of $\boldsymbol{C}$ there is associated a subset $\mathrm{Mor}_{\boldsymbol{C}}(X, Y)$ (or simply Mor(X, Y)) of Ar $\boldsymbol{C}$, called the "set of morphisms from X to Y," in such a way that Mor(X, Y) and Mor(X′, Y′) are disjoint if $(X', Y') \neq (X, Y)$.

(2) To each triple of objects X, Y, Z of $\boldsymbol{C}$ there is associated a mapping $(u, v) \mapsto vu$ of $\mathrm{Mor}(X, Y) \times \mathrm{Mor}(Y, Z)$ into Mor(X, Z) such that $w(vu) = (wv)u$ for $u \in \mathrm{Mor}(X, Y)$, $v \in \mathrm{Mor}(Y, Z)$, and $w \in \mathrm{Mor}(Z, T)$.

(3) For each object X of $\boldsymbol{C}$, there exists an element 1_X in Mor(X, X) such that for each object Y of $\boldsymbol{C}$ and each $u \in \mathrm{Mor}(X, Y)$ (resp. each $v \in \mathrm{Mor}(Y, X)$), we have $u = u1_X$ (resp. $v = 1_X v$).

The elements of Mor(X, Y) are often written (as if they were mappings between sets) $u : X \to Y$ or $X \xrightarrow{u} Y$. Instead of writing vu as above, we often write $X \xrightarrow{u} Y \xrightarrow{v} Z$; as in set theory, this enables us to speak of "commutative diagrams" of morphisms.

An element $u \in \mathrm{Mor}(X, Y)$ is called an *isomorphism* if there exists $v \in \mathrm{Mor}(Y, X)$ such that $vu = 1_X$ and $uv = 1_Y$; this element v is then unique, and is denoted by u^{-1}.

The simplest example of a category is the category $\boldsymbol{Ens}$ of "all" sets (meaning: elements of some unspecified "sufficiently large" set), where Mor(X, Y) is the set of all mappings of X into Y. Another elementary example is the category $\boldsymbol{Gr}$ of "all" groups, in which Mor(X, Y) is the set of homomorphisms of X into Y. In both these examples, the objects of the category are effectively sets, and the morphisms are mappings; but it is essential to note that *this is not the general case* (see later).

A *functor* (or *covariant functor*) $F : \boldsymbol{C} \to \boldsymbol{C}'$ from a category $\boldsymbol{C}$ to a category $\boldsymbol{C}'$ consists of *two* mappings Ob $\boldsymbol{C} \to$ Ob $\boldsymbol{C}'$ and Ar $\boldsymbol{C} \to$ Ar $\boldsymbol{C}'$, both denoted by F, such that

(1) For X, Y objects of $\boldsymbol{C}$, we have $F(\mathrm{Mor}(X, Y)) \subset \mathrm{Mor}(F(X), F(Y))$.

(2) For each object X of $\boldsymbol{C}$, $F(1_X) = 1_{F(X)}$.

(3) For two morphisms $X \xrightarrow{u} Y \xrightarrow{v} Z$ in $\boldsymbol{C}$, $F(vu) = F(v)F(u)$.

It is clear that the composition of two functors is a functor. An example of a functor is the *forgetful functor* $\boldsymbol{Gr} \to \boldsymbol{Ens}$, which sends each group G to the underlying set G and each group homomorphism $G \to H$ to the same homomorphism considered as a mapping between sets (there are many similar examples of "forgetful functors").

By abuse of notation, a functor is often written $X \mapsto F(X)$, i.e., by indicating only the mapping $\text{Ob}\ \boldsymbol{C} \to \text{Ob}\ \boldsymbol{C}'$, provided that there is no ambiguity about the mapping $\text{Ar}\ \boldsymbol{C} \to \text{Ar}\ \boldsymbol{C}'$.

The notion of a *multifunctor* on several categories $\boldsymbol{C}_1, \boldsymbol{C}_2, \ldots$ with values in a category $\boldsymbol{C}'$ is defined in the same way. For example, if to each pair of sets X, Y we associate their product $X \times Y$, and to each pair of mappings $X \xrightarrow{u} X'$, $Y \xrightarrow{v} Y'$ the mapping $X \times Y \xrightarrow{u \times v} X' \times Y'$, we have a *bifunctor* from the categories ***Ens***, ***Ens*** to ***Ens***.

A category $\boldsymbol{C}'$ is said to be a *subcategory* of a category $\boldsymbol{C}$ if $\text{Ob}\ \boldsymbol{C}'$ is a subset of $\text{Ob}\ \boldsymbol{C}$ and if, for each pair of objects X', Y' of $\boldsymbol{C}'$, $\text{Mor}_{\boldsymbol{C}'}(X', Y')$ is a subset of $\text{Mor}_{\boldsymbol{C}}(X', Y')$, the composition mapping

$$\text{Mor}_{\boldsymbol{C}'}(X', Y') \times \text{Mor}_{\boldsymbol{C}'}(Y', Z') \to \text{Mor}_{\boldsymbol{C}'}(X', Z')$$

is the restriction of

$$\text{Mor}_{\boldsymbol{C}}(X', Y') \times \text{Mor}_{\boldsymbol{C}}(Y', Z') \to \text{Mor}_{\boldsymbol{C}}(X', Z'),$$

and the identity morphisms $1_{X'}$ are the same relative to $\boldsymbol{C}$ and $\boldsymbol{C}'$, for each $X' \in \text{Ob}\ \boldsymbol{C}'$. A subcategory $\boldsymbol{C}'$ of $\boldsymbol{C}$ is said to be *full* if

$$\text{Mor}_{\boldsymbol{C}'}(X', Y') = \text{Mor}_{\boldsymbol{C}}(X', Y')$$

for each pair of objects X', Y' of $\boldsymbol{C}'$. For example, in the category of groups ***Gr***, the abelian groups (with the same morphisms) form a full subcategory ***Ab***.

If $F : \boldsymbol{C} \to \boldsymbol{C}'$ is a functor, $F(\text{Ob}\ \boldsymbol{C})$ and $F(\text{Ar}\ \boldsymbol{C})$ are respectively the set of objects and the set of morphisms of a subcategory $F(\boldsymbol{C})$ of $\boldsymbol{C}'$. The functor F is said to be *faithful* if the mapping $F : \text{Ar}\ \boldsymbol{C} \to \text{Ar}\ \boldsymbol{C}'$ is injective, and *fully faithful* if for each pair of objects X, Y of $\boldsymbol{C}$ the restriction

$$\text{Mor}_{\boldsymbol{C}}(X, Y) \to \text{Mor}_{\boldsymbol{C}'}(F(X), F(Y))$$

of F is bijective. In this case, $F(\boldsymbol{C})$ is a full subcategory of $\boldsymbol{C}'$; if in addition there exists, for each object X' of $\boldsymbol{C}'$, an object X of $\boldsymbol{C}$ and an isomorphism $F(X) \xrightarrow{\sim} X'$, then F is said to be an *equivalence* of categories. There then exists an equivalence $G : \boldsymbol{C}' \to \boldsymbol{C}$, and the categories $\boldsymbol{C}$ and $\boldsymbol{C}'$ are said to be *equivalent*. Usually there is no need to distinguish between equivalent categories. For example, the category of finite-dimensional vector spaces over a field K (with linear mappings as the morphisms) is equivalent to the full subcategory consisting of the vector spaces K^n ($n \in \mathbf{N}$).

Opposite categories; contravariant functors. To each category $\boldsymbol{C}$ there is canonically associated another category $\boldsymbol{C}^0$, called the *opposite* (or *dual*) of $\boldsymbol{C}$. It is defined as follows: we take $\mathrm{Ob}\,\boldsymbol{C}^0 = \mathrm{Ob}\,\boldsymbol{C}$ and $\mathrm{Ar}\,\boldsymbol{C}^0 = \mathrm{Ar}\,\boldsymbol{C}$, but for X, Y in $\mathrm{Ob}\,\boldsymbol{C}$ we define $\mathrm{Mor}_{\boldsymbol{C}^0}(\mathrm{X}, \mathrm{Y}) = \mathrm{Mor}_{\boldsymbol{C}}(\mathrm{Y}, \mathrm{X})$, and if

$$u \in \mathrm{Mor}_{\boldsymbol{C}^0}(\mathrm{X}, \mathrm{Y}),\ v \in \mathrm{Mor}_{\boldsymbol{C}^0}(\mathrm{Y}, \mathrm{Z}),$$

the "composition" $v * u$ in $\boldsymbol{C}^0$ is $uv \in \mathrm{Mor}_{\boldsymbol{C}^0}(\mathrm{X}, \mathrm{Z}) = \mathrm{Mor}_{\boldsymbol{C}}(\mathrm{Z}, \mathrm{X})$. The identity morphisms 1_{X} are the same in $\boldsymbol{C}^0$ as in $\boldsymbol{C}$. In other words, we pass from $\boldsymbol{C}$ to $\boldsymbol{C}^0$ by "reversing the arrows," and we have $(\boldsymbol{C}^0)^0 = \boldsymbol{C}$. The notion of the opposite category does not arise naturally in the applications of category theory, but it serves to express in a simple and concise fashion certain properties of morphisms or of functors. For example, a *contravariant functor* from a category $\boldsymbol{C}$ to a category $\boldsymbol{C}'$ may be defined as a (covariant) functor from $\boldsymbol{C}^0$ to $\boldsymbol{C}'$ (or from $\boldsymbol{C}$ to $\boldsymbol{C}'^0$); to define it without recourse to opposite categories, we must replace the axioms (1) and (3) for functors by $\mathrm{F}(\mathrm{Mor}(\mathrm{X}, \mathrm{Y})) \subset \mathrm{Mor}(\mathrm{F}(\mathrm{Y}), \mathrm{F}(\mathrm{X}))$ and $\mathrm{F}(vu) = \mathrm{F}(u)\mathrm{F}(v)$. A *duality* is an equivalence between a category $\boldsymbol{C}$ and the opposite of a category $\boldsymbol{C}'$. For example, if $\boldsymbol{C}$ is the category of locally compact abelian groups (the morphisms being the continuous homomorphisms), the Pontrjagin functor that takes each group $\mathrm{G} \in \mathrm{Ob}\,\boldsymbol{C}$ to its dual $\hat{\mathrm{G}}$ (**B** IV), and each homomorphism $u : \mathrm{G} \to \mathrm{H}$ to its transpose ${}^t u : \hat{\mathrm{H}} \to \hat{\mathrm{G}}$ (defined by $\langle {}^t u(\hat{y}), x\rangle = \langle \hat{y}, u(x)\rangle$) is an equivalence of $\boldsymbol{C}$ with $\boldsymbol{C}^0$.

Functorial morphisms. If $\boldsymbol{C}, \boldsymbol{C}'$ are two categories, we define a new category $\boldsymbol{Funct}(\boldsymbol{C}, \boldsymbol{C}')$, the "category of functors from $\boldsymbol{C}$ to $\boldsymbol{C}'$," as follows. The set $\mathrm{Ob}(\boldsymbol{Funct}(\boldsymbol{C}, \boldsymbol{C}'))$ is the set of functors $\boldsymbol{C} \to \boldsymbol{C}'$, and it remains to define $\mathrm{Ar}(\boldsymbol{Funct}(\boldsymbol{C}, \boldsymbol{C}'))$, in other words to define the notion of a morphism $\xi : \mathrm{F} \to \mathrm{G}$, where F and G are functors from $\boldsymbol{C}$ to $\boldsymbol{C}'$. Such a morphism is called a *functorial morphism* or *natural transformation*, and is by definition a mapping $\xi : \mathrm{Ob}\,\boldsymbol{C} \to \mathrm{Ar}\,\boldsymbol{C}'$ such that, for each object X of $\boldsymbol{C}$, $\xi(\mathrm{X})$ belongs to $\mathrm{Mor}(\mathrm{F}(\mathrm{X}), \mathrm{G}(\mathrm{X}))$ and such that for each morphism $u : \mathrm{X} \to \mathrm{Y}$ in $\boldsymbol{C}$, the diagram of morphisms in $\boldsymbol{C}'$

$$\begin{array}{ccc} \mathrm{F}(\mathrm{X}) & \xrightarrow{\mathrm{F}(u)} & \mathrm{F}(\mathrm{Y}) \\ {\scriptstyle \xi(\mathrm{X})}\downarrow & & \downarrow{\scriptstyle \xi(\mathrm{Y})} \\ \mathrm{G}(\mathrm{X}) & \xrightarrow[\mathrm{G}(u)]{} & \mathrm{G}(\mathrm{Y}) \end{array}$$

is commutative. Two functorial morphisms $\xi : \mathrm{F} \to \mathrm{G}$, $\eta : \mathrm{G} \to \mathrm{H}$ are composed according to the rule $(\eta\xi)(\mathrm{X}) = \eta(\mathrm{X})\xi(\mathrm{X})$ for each $\mathrm{X} \in \mathrm{Ob}\,\boldsymbol{C}$, and the morphism 1_{F} is such that $1_{\mathrm{F}}(\mathrm{X}) = 1_{\mathrm{F}(\mathrm{X})}$.

2. Representable functors

One of the most important notions in the applications of category theory is that of a *representable functor*. In order to define it we shall first define, for any category $\boldsymbol{C}$, a canonical covariant functor $\boldsymbol{h} : \boldsymbol{C} \to \boldsymbol{Funct}(\boldsymbol{C}^0, \boldsymbol{Ens})$ as follows. For each object X of $\boldsymbol{C}$, $\boldsymbol{h}_X : \boldsymbol{C}^0 \to \boldsymbol{Ens}$ is the functor such that $\boldsymbol{h}_X(Y) = \text{Mor}(Y, X)$ for $Y \in \text{Ob}\, \boldsymbol{C}$ and, for $u \in \text{Mor}(Y, Z)$, $\boldsymbol{h}_X(u)$ is the mapping $v \mapsto vu$ of $\boldsymbol{h}_X(Z) = \text{Mor}(Z, X)$ into $\boldsymbol{h}_X(Y) = \text{Mor}(Y, X)$. For each morphism $w : X \to X'$ in $\boldsymbol{C}$, $\boldsymbol{h}_w : \boldsymbol{h}_X \to \boldsymbol{h}_{X'}$ is the functorial morphism such that $\boldsymbol{h}_w(Y)$, for $Y \in \text{Ob}\, \boldsymbol{C}$, is the mapping $v \mapsto wv$ of $\boldsymbol{h}_X(Y) = \text{Mor}(Y, X)$ into $\boldsymbol{h}_{X'}(Y) = \text{Mor}(Y, X')$. The morphism w is said to be a *monomorphism* if $\boldsymbol{h}_w(Y)$ is an *injective* mapping for each $Y \in \text{Ob}\, \boldsymbol{C}$.

Consider now an arbitrary contravariant functor $F : \boldsymbol{C}^0 \to \boldsymbol{Ens}$, an object X of $\boldsymbol{C}$, and the set F(X). For each element $x \in F(X)$, and each morphism $v : Y \to X$ in $\boldsymbol{C}$, $F(v)$ is a mapping $F(X) \to F(Y)$ and therefore $(F(v))(x)$ is an element of F(Y). We have thus defined a mapping $v \mapsto (F(v))(x)$ of $\boldsymbol{h}_X(Y)$ into F(Y); if we denote this mapping by $\beta(x)(Y)$, then $\beta(x) : \boldsymbol{h}_X \to F$ is a functorial morphism, and so finally we have a canonical mapping

$$\beta : F(X) \to \text{Mor}(\boldsymbol{h}_X, F).$$

It is easily verified that this mapping is *bijective* (Yoneda's lemma). If in particular we take $F = \boldsymbol{h}_{X'}$, where X′ is another object in $\boldsymbol{C}$, the mapping $\beta : \text{Mor}(X, X') \to \text{Mor}(\boldsymbol{h}_X, \boldsymbol{h}_{X'})$ is just the mapping $w \mapsto \boldsymbol{h}_w$ defined above. It follows that the canonical functor $\boldsymbol{h} : \boldsymbol{C} \to \boldsymbol{Funct}(\boldsymbol{C}^0, \boldsymbol{Ens})$ is *fully faithful*. This fact has the following very useful consequence for morphisms in $\boldsymbol{C}$: in order to prove, for example, that a diagram of morphisms is commutative, it is enough to prove that the diagram of *mappings* which are the images of these morphisms under $w \mapsto \boldsymbol{h}_w$ is commutative, and this is often much easier.

The functor F is said to be *representable* if there exists $X \in \text{Ob}\, \boldsymbol{C}$ and an element $x \in F(X)$ such that $\beta(x) : \boldsymbol{h}_X \to F$ is an *isomorphism* of functors, i.e., such that for each object Y of $\boldsymbol{C}$ the mapping $v \mapsto (F(v))(x)$ of Mor(Y, X) into F(Y) is *bijective*; the pair (X, x) (or, by abuse of language, the object X) is then said to *represent* the functor F.† If (X', x') is a second pair representing F, there is a unique isomorphism $w : X \xrightarrow{\sim} X'$ such that $x = F(w)(x')$.

---

† This notion includes as particular cases various notions of "universal objects" introduced prior to the advent of category theory. For example, let $\boldsymbol{C}'$ be the category of connected differential manifolds with base points, $\boldsymbol{C}$ the full subcategory of simply connected differential manifolds with base points. Let $V \in \text{Ob}\, \boldsymbol{C}'$ and let $F : \boldsymbol{C}^0 \to \boldsymbol{Ens}$ be the functor defined by $F(X) = \text{Mor}_{\boldsymbol{C}'}(X, V)$ for $X \in \text{Ob}\, \boldsymbol{C}$. This functor is representable by the pair $(\tilde{V}, p)$ where $\tilde{V}$ is a *universal covering* of V (with base point) and $p : \tilde{V} \to V$ the canonical projection [D, Chapter 16].

Examples: final objects, products, kernels, inverse limits. Let $\boldsymbol{C}$ be a category, $\{a\}$ a set consisting of a single element. Define a contravariant functor $F : \boldsymbol{C}^0 \to \boldsymbol{Ens}$ by taking $F(X) = \{a\}$ for all objects X in $\boldsymbol{C}$, and $F(u)$ to be the unique mapping $\{a\} \to \{a\}$ for all morphisms u in $\boldsymbol{C}$. To say that this functor F is representable means that there exists an object e in $\boldsymbol{C}$ such that $\text{Mor}(Y, e)$ is a one-element set for all $Y \in \text{Ob}\, \boldsymbol{C}$. Such an object e is called a *final object* in $\boldsymbol{C}$ (when it exists); any two final objects are isomorphic. In the category $\boldsymbol{Ens}$, the final objects are the one-element sets.

Now let X and Y be two objects in $\boldsymbol{C}$, and consider the contravariant functor $F : \boldsymbol{C}^0 \to \boldsymbol{Ens}$ such that $F(T) = \text{Mor}(T, X) \times \text{Mor}(T, Y)$ for each $T \in \text{Ob}\, \boldsymbol{C}$, and for each morphism $v : T \to T'$, $F(v)$ is the mapping

$$(f', g') \mapsto (f'v, g'v)$$

from $F(T')$ to $F(T)$. This functor is representable if there exists an object Z in $\boldsymbol{C}$ and morphisms $p_1 : Z \to X$, $p_2 : Z \to Y$ such that the mapping

$$v \mapsto (p_1 v, p_2 v)$$

is an isomorphism of functors $\text{Mor}(T, Z) \xrightarrow{\sim} \text{Mor}(T, X) \times \text{Mor}(T, Y)$. If such a triple (Z, p_1, p_2) exists, it is determined up to a unique isomorphism; Z is called the *product* of X and Y in $\boldsymbol{C}$, and p_1, p_2 are respectively the *first* and *second projections* of Z. Usually the product Z is denoted by $X \times Y$.

The product of several objects in $\boldsymbol{C}$ (when it exists) is defined in the same way. An example of a category in which products do not in general exist is the category of fields (a subcategory of the category of rings, where products *do* exist).

A more general (and still more important) notion is that of a *fiber product*. Given three sets E, F, G and two mappings $\varphi : E \to G$, $\psi : F \to G$, the fiber product $E \times_G F$ (relative to φ and ψ) is the subset of the cartesian product $E \times F$ consisting of the pairs (x, y) such that $\varphi(x) = \psi(y)$. In an arbitrary category $\boldsymbol{C}$ we consider likewise, for two morphisms $\varphi : X \to S$, $\psi : X \to S$, the functor

$$T \mapsto \text{Mor}(T, X) \times_{\text{Mor}(T, S)} \text{Mor}(T, Y),$$

where the right-hand side is the fiber product relative to the mappings $\boldsymbol{h}_\varphi(T)$ and $\boldsymbol{h}_\psi(T)$. If this functor is representable, there exists an object $X \times_S Y$ in $\boldsymbol{C}$ (called the fiber product of X and Y relative to φ and ψ) and two "projection" morphisms $p_1 : X \times_S Y \to X$, $p_2 : X \times_S Y \to Y$ such that each pair of morphisms $u : T \to X$, $v : T \to Y$ that satisfy the condition $\varphi u = \psi v$ *factorize* through a unique morphism $w : T \to X \times_S Y$ such that $p_1 w = u$ and $p_2 w = v$.

Products and fiber products are particular cases of the general notion of *inverse limit*. Let I be an ordered set, and consider an *inverse system* in the category ***Ens***, i.e., a family $(E_\alpha)_{\alpha \in I}$ of sets and a family $(\varphi_{\alpha\beta})$ of mappings $\varphi_{\alpha\beta} : E_\beta \to E_\alpha$ defined only for pairs (α, β) such that $\alpha \leqslant \beta$, and satisfying the conditions $\varphi_{\alpha\alpha} = \text{Id.}$ and $\varphi_{\alpha\beta} \circ \varphi_{\beta\gamma} = \varphi_{\alpha\gamma}$ for $\alpha \leqslant \beta \leqslant \gamma$. The inverse limit of the family (E_α) with respect to the mappings $\varphi_{\alpha\beta}$ is the subset E of the product $\prod_{\alpha \in I} E_\alpha = G$ consisting of the families $x = (x_\alpha)$ such that $x_\alpha = \varphi_{\alpha\beta}(x_\beta)$ for $\alpha \leqslant \beta$; it is denoted by $\varprojlim(E_\alpha, \varphi_{\alpha\beta})$ or simply by $\varprojlim E_\alpha$. If (f_α) is a family of mappings $f_\alpha : F \to E_\alpha$ such that $f_\alpha = \varphi_{\alpha\beta} \circ f_\beta$ whenever $\alpha \leqslant \beta$, there exists a unique mapping $f : F \to \varprojlim E_\alpha$ such that $f_\alpha = \text{pr}_\alpha \circ f$. In order to define inverse limits in a category $\boldsymbol{C}$, let (X_α) be a family of objects of $\boldsymbol{C}$ and $(u_{\alpha\beta})$ a family of morphisms $u_{\alpha\beta} : X_\beta \to X_\alpha$ for $\alpha \leqslant \beta$ with $u_{\alpha\alpha} = 1_{X_\alpha}$ and $u_{\alpha\beta} u_{\beta\gamma} = u_{\alpha\gamma}$ for $\alpha \leqslant \beta \leqslant \gamma$, and consider the functor

$$F(T) = \varprojlim(\text{Mor}(T, X_\alpha))$$

constructed as above from the mappings $\text{Mor}(T, X_\beta) \to \text{Mor}(T, X_\alpha)$ induced canonically by the $u_{\alpha\beta}$ for $\alpha \leqslant \beta$; we have then merely to repeat the definitions given above (when F is representable).

If E, F are sets and $u_1 : E \to F$, $u_2 : E \to F$ are two mappings, the *kernel* (or *coincidence set*) of u_1 and u_2 is the subset $\text{Ker}(u_1, u_2)$ of E consisting of the $x \in E$ such that $u_1(x) = u_2(x)$. A diagram of mappings

$$N \xrightarrow{j} E \underset{u_2}{\overset{u_1}{\rightrightarrows}} F$$

is said to be *exact* if j is injective and $j(N) = \text{Ker}(u_1, u_2)$.

Now let X, Y be two objects of a category $\boldsymbol{C}$, and $u_1 : X \to Y$, $u_2 : X \to Y$ two morphisms in $\boldsymbol{C}$. This time we define a functor F such that $F(T) = \text{Ker}(\boldsymbol{h}_{u_1}(T), \boldsymbol{h}_{u_2}(T))$ for each object T in $\boldsymbol{C}$, and for each morphism $v : T \to T'$, $F(v)$ is the mapping $F(T') \to F(T)$ that is the restriction of $\boldsymbol{h}_X(v)$ to $F(T')$ (the image of this restriction may be verified to be contained in F(T)). This functor is representable if there exists an object N in $\boldsymbol{C}$ and a morphism $j : N \to X$ such that the mapping $v \mapsto jv$ is an isomorphism of functors $\text{Mor}(T, N) \xrightarrow{\sim} \text{Ker}(\boldsymbol{h}_{u_1}(T), \boldsymbol{h}_{u_2}(T))$; this is equivalent to saying that the diagram of sets and mappings

$$\text{Mor}(T, N) \xrightarrow[\boldsymbol{h}_j(T)]{} \text{Mor}(T, X) \underset{\boldsymbol{h}_{u_2}(T)}{\overset{\boldsymbol{h}_{u_1}(T)}{\rightrightarrows}} \text{Mor}(T, Y)$$

is *exact* for each $T \in \text{Ob}\, \boldsymbol{C}$, and we express this fact by saying that the diagram of *morphisms*

$$N \xrightarrow{j} X \underset{u_2}{\overset{u_1}{\rightrightarrows}} Y$$

is *exact*; the morphism j is a monomorphism, and we write $N = \text{Ker}(u_1, u_2)$ and call it the *kernel* of the morphisms u_1, u_2.

If all fiber products exist in $\boldsymbol{C}$, then so also do kernels.

Dual notions. All the above definitions may be applied to the opposite category $\boldsymbol{C}^0$ of $\boldsymbol{C}$, and each therefore gives rise to a new notion when interpreted in terms of objects and morphisms in $\boldsymbol{C}$. Thus we have a *canonical contravariant functor* $\boldsymbol{h}^0 : \boldsymbol{C}^0 \to \boldsymbol{Funct}(\boldsymbol{C}, \boldsymbol{Ens})$ that is fully faithful, and defined by: (1) for $Y \in \text{Ob } \boldsymbol{C}$, $\boldsymbol{h}_X^0(Y) = \text{Mor}(X, Y)$, and for $u \in \text{Mor}(Y, Z)$, $\boldsymbol{h}_X^0(u)$ is the mapping $v \mapsto uv$ of $\text{Mor}(X, Y)$ into $\text{Mor}(X, Z)$; (2) for a morphism $w : X \to X'$ in $\boldsymbol{C}$, $\boldsymbol{h}_w^0 : \boldsymbol{h}_{X'}^0 \to \boldsymbol{h}_X^0$ is the functorial morphism such that $\boldsymbol{h}_w^0(Y)$ is the mapping $v \mapsto vw$ of $\text{Mor}(X', Y)$ into $\text{Mor}(X, Y)$. A morphism $w : X \to X'$ is called an *epimorphism* if $\boldsymbol{h}_w^0(Y)$ is *surjective* for all $Y \in \text{Ob } \boldsymbol{C}$.

Corresponding to the notion of a final object of $\boldsymbol{C}^0$ is that of an *initial object* of $\boldsymbol{C}$: this is an object e such that $\text{Mor}(e, X)$ is a one-element set for all $X \in \text{Ob } \boldsymbol{C}$. In the category $\boldsymbol{Ens}$, the empty set $\varnothing$ is an initial object; in the category of rings with identity, $\mathbf{Z}$ is an initial object; in the category $\boldsymbol{Alg}_k$ of algebras (with identity element) over a field k (the morphisms being homomorphisms of k-algebras that map identity element to identity element), k is an initial object.

To the notion of *product* in $\boldsymbol{C}^0$ corresponds that of *sum* (or *coproduct*) in $\boldsymbol{C}$: if X, Y are two objects of $\boldsymbol{C}$, their sum $X \amalg Y$ is an object of $\boldsymbol{C}$ together with two morphisms $j_1 : X \to X \amalg Y$, $j_2 : Y \to X \amalg Y$ such that $v \mapsto (vj_1, vj_2)$ is an isomorphism of functors

$$\text{Mor}(X \amalg Y, T) \simeq \text{Mor}(X, T) \times \text{Mor}(Y, T).$$

For example, in the category $\boldsymbol{Alg}_k$, the "sum" of two k-algebras A, B is their *tensor product* $A \otimes_k B$, together with the two canonical injections $x \mapsto x \otimes 1$ and $y \mapsto 1 \otimes y$.

The notion corresponding to inverse limit is *direct limit*. For an ordered set I, consider a *direct system* in the category $\boldsymbol{Ens}$, i.e., a family $(E_\alpha)_{\alpha \in I}$ of sets and a family $(\varphi_{\beta\alpha})$ of mappings $\varphi_{\beta\alpha} : E_\alpha \to E_\beta$ defined only for $\alpha \leqslant \beta$ and such that $\varphi_{\alpha\alpha} = \text{Id.}$ and $\varphi_{\gamma\beta} \circ \varphi_{\beta\alpha} = \varphi_{\gamma\alpha}$ when $\alpha \leqslant \beta \leqslant \gamma$. Let G be the disjoint union of the E_α, and let R be the smallest equivalence relation on G whose graph contains all pairs (x_α, x_β) such that $\alpha \leqslant \beta$ and $x_\beta = \varphi_{\beta\alpha}(x_\alpha)$. Then the direct limit of the E_α relative to the mappings $\varphi_{\beta\alpha}$ is defined to be G/R, and is denoted by $\varinjlim(E_\alpha, \varphi_{\beta\alpha})$ or simply $\varinjlim E_\alpha$. Let φ_α denote the restriction to E_α of the canonical mapping $G \to G/R$; if (f_α) is any family of mappings $f_\alpha : E_\alpha \to F$ of the E_α into a set F such that $f_\alpha = f_\beta \circ \varphi_{\beta\alpha}$ whenever $\alpha \leqslant \beta$, then there exists a unique mapping $f : \varinjlim E_\alpha \to F$ such that $f_\alpha = f \circ \varphi_\alpha$ for all $\alpha \in I$. For arbitrary categories, we proceed in the usual way.

Finally, to the notion of a kernel in $\boldsymbol{C}^0$ there corresponds that of *cokernel* in $\boldsymbol{C}$: given two morphisms $X \overset{u_1}{\underset{u_2}{\rightrightarrows}} Y$, this is an object $K = \text{Coker}(u_1, u_2)$ together with an epimorphism $p : Y \to K$ such that the diagram of mappings

$$\text{Mor}(K, T) \xrightarrow[\boldsymbol{h}_p^0(T)]{} \text{Mor}(Y, T) \overset{\boldsymbol{h}_{u_1}^0(T)}{\underset{\boldsymbol{h}_{u_2}^0(T)}{\rightrightarrows}} \text{Mor}(X, T)$$

is exact for all $T \in Ob(\boldsymbol{C})$, in which case the diagram of *morphisms* $X \underset{u_2}{\overset{u_1}{\rightrightarrows}} Y \xrightarrow{p} K$ is said to be *exact*.

Adjoint functors. Let $\boldsymbol{C}$, $\boldsymbol{C}'$ be two categories and let $F : \boldsymbol{C} \to \boldsymbol{C}'$ be a covariant functor. For each object X' of $\boldsymbol{C}'$, the composition $\boldsymbol{h}_{X'} \circ F$ is a contravariant functor $\boldsymbol{C}^0 \to \boldsymbol{Ens}$. If it is *representable* by a pair $(Y, \sigma_{X'})$, where $Y \in Ob\, \boldsymbol{C}$ and $\sigma_{X'} : F(Y) \to X'$ is a morphism in $\boldsymbol{C}'$, and if for each morphism $u : T \to Y$ we denote by $u^{\#}$ the composition $F(T) \xrightarrow{F(u)} F(Y) \xrightarrow{\sigma_{X'}} X'$, then the functorial isomorphism $\boldsymbol{h}_Y \simeq \boldsymbol{h}_{X'} \circ F$ is explicitly the bijection $u \mapsto u^{\#}$ of $Mor_{\boldsymbol{C}}(T, Y)$ onto $Mor_{\boldsymbol{C}'}(F(T), X')$ for all $T \in Ob\, \boldsymbol{C}$. We denote the inverse bijection by $u' \mapsto u'^{\flat}$.

Suppose now that for *each* X', $\boldsymbol{h}_{X'} \circ F$ is representable by a pair that we shall denote by $(F^{ad}(X'), \sigma_{X'})$. We can then define a *functor* $F^{ad} : \boldsymbol{C}' \to \boldsymbol{C}$: to define $F^{ad}(u')$ for a morphism $u' : X' \to Y'$, we consider the composite morphism

$$F(F^{ad}(X')) \xrightarrow{\sigma_{X'}} X' \xrightarrow{u'} Y'$$

and define $F^{ad}(u') = (u'\sigma_{X'})^{\flat} : F^{ad}(X') \to F^{ad}(Y')$. The functor F^{ad} so defined is called the *right adjoint* of F, and the bijection $u \mapsto u^{\#}$ then defines an *isomorphism of bifunctors* (in T and X′)

$$Mor_{\boldsymbol{C}}(T, F^{ad}(X')) \simeq Mor_{\boldsymbol{C}'}(F(T), X').$$

By applying these notions to $\boldsymbol{C}^0$ and $\boldsymbol{C}'^0$ we have the notion of a *left adjoint functor* ${}^{ad}F : \boldsymbol{C}' \to \boldsymbol{C}$ of F. If F^{ad} exists, so does ${}^{ad}(F^{ad}) = F$; and likewise if ${}^{ad}F$ exists, then so also does $({}^{ad}F)^{ad} = F$; in this case we say simply that F and $F' = F^{ad}$ are *adjoints*.

Adjoint functors occur in all parts of mathematics. For example, the forgetful functor $\boldsymbol{Gr} \to \boldsymbol{Ens}$ has a left adjoint F such that F(T), for any set T, is the *free group* F(T) generated by T (**B** III). In the category $\boldsymbol{Mod}_A$ of modules over a commutative ring A, for each A-module E the functor $F \mapsto E \otimes_A F$ is a left adjoint of the functor $G \mapsto Hom_A(E, G)$: this simply expresses the classical isomorphism of bifunctors

$$Hom_A(E \otimes_A F, G) \simeq Hom_A(F, Hom_A(E, G)).$$

Algebraic structures on categories. The canonical functor $\boldsymbol{h}$ enables us to define the notion of an (internal) *law of composition* on an object of an arbitrary category. If F, F′ are two functors $\boldsymbol{C}^0 \to \boldsymbol{Ens}$, their product $F \times F'$ in the category $\boldsymbol{Funct}(\boldsymbol{C}^0, \boldsymbol{Ens})$ is defined and given by the formulas

$$(F \times F')(Y) = F(Y) \times F'(Y), \qquad (F \times F')(u) = F(u) \times F'(u)$$

for $Y \in \text{Ob}\, \boldsymbol{C}$ and $u \in \text{Ar}\, \boldsymbol{C}$. If now X is an object in $\boldsymbol{C}$, an internal law of composition on X is by definition a *functorial morphism* $\gamma_X : \boldsymbol{h}_X \times \boldsymbol{h}_X \to \boldsymbol{h}_X$. In other words, for each object Y of $\boldsymbol{C}$, $\gamma_X(Y)$ is a law of composition on $\boldsymbol{h}_X(Y)$, subject to the condition that, for each morphism $u : Y \to Z$, $\boldsymbol{h}_X(u)$ is a *homomorphism* of $\boldsymbol{h}_X(Z)$ into $\boldsymbol{h}_X(Y)$ relative to the laws of composition $\gamma_X(Z)$ and $\gamma_X(Y)$. If $\gamma_X(Y)$ is a group law for each object Y of $\boldsymbol{C}$, we say that X together with the law γ_X is a ***C**-group* (or a *group-object in **C***). Other algebraic structures on objects of $\boldsymbol{C}$ (rings, modules, etc.) are defined in the same way.

(For more details on representable functors, see C 1960–61 and [69].)

3. Abelian categories

A category $\boldsymbol{C}$ is said to be *additive* if it has the following properties:

(1) For each pair of objects X, Y in $\boldsymbol{C}$, Mor(X, Y) is endowed with an abelian group structure (generally written additively), such that composition of morphisms is bilinear, i.e., for $f, g \in \text{Mor}(X, Y)$, we have

$$(f + g)u = fu + gu, \qquad v(f + g) = vf + vg.$$

(2) $\boldsymbol{C}$ has a final object A, which is also an initial object, so that $\text{Mor}(A, A) = \{0\}$. It is usually denoted by 0.

(3) Each pair of objects X, Y in $\boldsymbol{C}$ has a product in $\boldsymbol{C}$; then it also has a sum, which is isomorphic to the product.

A category $\boldsymbol{C}$ is said to be *abelian* if it is additive and has the following supplementary properties:

(4) For each morphism $f : X \to Y$, the morphisms f and 0 have a kernel and a cokernel, so that there is an exact sequence

$$N \xrightarrow{j} X \underset{0}{\overset{f}{\rightrightarrows}} Y \xrightarrow{p} K.$$

We put $j = \text{Ker}(f)$ and $p = \text{Coker}(f)$ (we also write $N = \text{Ker}(f)$ and $K = \text{Coker}(f)$); N is a *subobject* of X and K is a *quotient object* of Y.

(5) Every monomorphism is of the form Ker(f) and every epimorphism of the form Coker(f).

The prototype example of an abelian category is the category $\boldsymbol{Mod}_A$ of left A-modules over an arbitrary associative ring (with identity) A, where addition in $\text{Hom}_A(X, Y)$ is defined in the usual way. The category of abelian topological groups (the morphisms being the continuous homomorphisms) is additive but not abelian. The opposite of an abelian category is abelian.

The classical notions of elementary linear algebra can be transported to abelian categories. For example, any morphism $f : X \to Y$ factors canonically into $X \xrightarrow{\text{Coker}(\text{Ker}(f))} I \xrightarrow{\text{Ker}(\text{Coker}(f))} Y$; the object I is called the *image* of f, denoted by $\text{Im}(f)$. A sequence $X \xrightarrow{f} Y \xrightarrow{g} Z$ is said to be *exact* if

$$\text{Im}(f) = \text{Ker}(g).$$

A functor $F: \boldsymbol{C} \to \boldsymbol{C}'$ between additive categories is said to be *additive* if $F(u + v) = F(u) + F(v)$ for any two morphisms $u, v \in \text{Mor}(X, Y)$, X and Y being arbitrary objects of $\boldsymbol{C}$. When $\boldsymbol{C}$ and $\boldsymbol{C}'$ are abelian categories, an additive functor $F: \boldsymbol{C} \to \boldsymbol{C}'$ is called *left exact* (resp. *right exact*) if for each exact sequence $0 \to X \to Y \to Z$ (resp. $X \to Y \to Z \to 0$) the sequence $0 \to F(X) \to F(Y) \to F(Z)$ (resp. $F(X) \to F(Y) \to F(Z) \to 0$) is exact; F is said to be *exact* if it is both left exact and right exact, in which case for any exact sequence $X \to Y \to Z$ the sequence $F(X) \to F(Y) \to F(Z)$ is exact.

For example, in the category $\boldsymbol{Mod}_A$, for each right A-module F the functor $E \mapsto E \otimes_A F$ is right exact, but not (in general) left exact.

For any abelian category $\boldsymbol{C}$ and any object X in $\boldsymbol{C}$, the functor

$$Y \mapsto \text{Mor}(X, Y)$$

is a left exact additive functor $\boldsymbol{C} \to \boldsymbol{Ab}$. If this functor is exact, X is said to be a *projective* object of $\boldsymbol{C}$. This means that if $p: Y \to Z$ is an epimorphism, any morphism $f: X \to Z$ can be written $f = pg$, where $g: X \to Y$ is a morphism (f can be "lifted" to g). Likewise, the functor $Y \mapsto \text{Mor}(Y, X)$ is a left exact additive functor $\boldsymbol{C}^0 \to \boldsymbol{Ab}$; if it is exact, X is said to be an *injective* object in $\boldsymbol{C}$. This means that if $j: Y \to Z$ is a monomorphism, every morphism $f: Y \to X$ can be written $f = gj$, where $g: Z \to X$ is a morphism (f can be "extended" to g).

The study of the category $\boldsymbol{Mod}_A$ for some types of algebras A over an algebraically closed field has made possible the first substantial progress in the classification of these algebras beyond the semisimple ones (B 444, 545; LN 488, 831, 832).

4. Sheaves and ringed spaces

Given a topological space X, a *presheaf of sets* on X is a mapping $\mathscr{F}: U \mapsto \mathscr{F}(U)$ of the set of nonempty open subsets U of X into a set of sets, subject to the following condition: to each pair of nonempty open sets U, V in X such that $U \supset V$ there corresponds a *restriction* mapping $\rho_{VU}: \mathscr{F}(U) \to \mathscr{F}(V)$ such that, if $U \supset V \supset W$ are three nonempty open sets, we have $\rho_{WU} = \rho_{WV} \circ \rho_{VU}$. The presheaf $\mathscr{F}$ is called a *sheaf* if in addition, for each covering (U_α) of an open set U by nonempty open sets U_α contained in U, and each family (s_α) of elements $s_\alpha \in \mathscr{F}(U_\alpha)$ such that $\rho_{U_{\alpha\beta}U_\alpha} s_\alpha = \rho_{U_{\alpha\beta}U_\beta} s_\beta$ for each pair α, β such that $U_{\alpha\beta} = U_\alpha \cap U_\beta$ is nonempty, there exists a unique $s \in \mathscr{F}(\mathrm{U})$ such that $\rho_{\mathrm{U}_\alpha \mathrm{U}} s = s_\alpha$ for all indices α. This condition may also be expressed as follows: if we define three mappings

$$r = (\rho_{\mathrm{U}_\alpha \mathrm{U}}) : \mathscr{F}(\mathrm{U}) \to \prod_\alpha \mathscr{F}(\mathrm{U}_\alpha),$$

$$r' : \prod_\alpha \mathscr{F}(\mathrm{U}_\alpha) \to \prod_{(\alpha, \beta)} \mathscr{F}(\mathrm{U}_{\alpha\beta})$$

such that $\mathrm{pr}_{\alpha\beta} \circ r' = \rho_{\mathrm{U}_{\alpha\beta}\mathrm{U}_\alpha} \circ \mathrm{pr}_\alpha$, and

$$r'' : \prod_\alpha \mathscr{F}(\mathrm{U}_\alpha) \to \prod_{(\alpha, \beta)} \mathscr{F}(\mathrm{U}_{\alpha\beta})$$

such that $\mathrm{pr}_{\alpha\beta} \circ r'' = \rho_{\mathrm{U}_{\alpha\beta}\mathrm{U}_\beta} \circ \mathrm{pr}_\beta$, then the above condition means that the diagram

$$\mathscr{F}(\mathrm{U}) \xrightarrow{r} \prod_\alpha \mathscr{F}(\mathrm{U}_\alpha) \underset{r''}{\overset{r'}{\rightrightarrows}} \prod_{(\alpha, \beta)} \mathscr{F}(\mathrm{U}_{\alpha\beta}) \tag{1}$$

is *exact*.

If in these definitions we replace the sets $\mathscr{F}(\mathrm{U})$ by groups (resp. rings) and the mappings ρ_{VU} by homomorphisms, we have the definitions of a presheaf or sheaf of groups (resp. rings). More generally, we may define a *presheaf with values in a category* $\boldsymbol{C}$ by replacing the $\mathscr{F}(\mathrm{U})$ by objects of $\boldsymbol{C}$ and the ρ_{VU} by morphisms of $\boldsymbol{C}$. The notion of a *sheaf* is then generalized as follows: $\mathscr{F}$ is a sheaf in $\boldsymbol{C}$ if, for each object T of $\boldsymbol{C}$, $\mathrm{U} \mapsto \mathrm{Mor}(\mathrm{T}, \mathscr{F}(\mathrm{U}))$ is a sheaf of sets. If U is a nonempty open set in X, $\mathscr{F}(\mathrm{U})$ is called the *object of sections* of $\mathscr{F}$ over U, and is also written $\Gamma(\mathrm{U}, \mathscr{F})$.

The presheaves (resp. sheaves) on X with values in $\boldsymbol{C}$ themselves form a *category*: a morphism $f : \mathscr{F} \to \mathscr{G}$ is by definition a mapping $\mathrm{U} \mapsto f_\mathrm{U}$ of the set of nonempty open subsets of X into Ar $\boldsymbol{C}$ such that $f_\mathrm{U} \in \mathrm{Mor}(\mathscr{F}(\mathrm{U}), \mathscr{G}(\mathrm{U}))$ and such that, whenever $\mathrm{U} \supset \mathrm{V}$ are nonempty open sets, the diagram of morphisms

$$\begin{array}{ccc} \mathscr{F}(\mathrm{U}) & \xrightarrow{f_\mathrm{U}} & \mathscr{G}(\mathrm{U}) \\ {\scriptstyle \rho_{\mathrm{VU}}}\downarrow & & \downarrow{\scriptstyle \rho_{\mathrm{VU}}} \\ \mathscr{F}(\mathrm{V}) & \xrightarrow[f_\mathrm{V}]{} & \mathscr{G}(\mathrm{V}) \end{array}$$

is commutative.

A most important notion in all questions concerning manifolds (topological, differential, holomorphic, algebraic, etc.) is that of a *ringed space*: this is a pair $(\mathrm{X}, \mathscr{O}_\mathrm{X})$ consisting of a topological space X and a *sheaf of commutative rings* $\mathscr{O}_\mathrm{X}$ on X. With a ringed space there is associated a category of sheaves, called $\mathscr{O}_\mathrm{X}$-Modules: these are sheaves $\mathscr{F}$ such that, for every nonempty open set U in X, the set $\mathscr{F}(\mathrm{U})$ carries an $\mathscr{O}_\mathrm{X}(\mathrm{U})$-module structure, that is to say, an external law of composition $\mathscr{O}_\mathrm{X}(\mathrm{U}) \times \mathscr{F}(\mathrm{U}) \to \mathscr{F}(\mathrm{U})$

satisfying the module axioms; in addition we require that for each pair $U \supset V$ of nonempty open sets, the diagram

$$\begin{array}{ccc} \mathcal{O}_X(U) \times \mathcal{F}(U) & \to & \mathcal{F}(U) \\ \downarrow & & \downarrow \\ \mathcal{O}_X(V) \times \mathcal{F}(V) & \to & \mathcal{F}(V) \end{array}$$

(in which the vertical arrows are restriction mappings) should be commutative. A homomorphism $f : \mathcal{F} \to \mathcal{G}$ of $\mathcal{O}_X$-Modules is a morphism of sheaves of abelian groups such that for each nonempty open set U the mapping $f_U : \mathcal{F}(U) \to \mathcal{G}(U)$ is a homomorphism of $\mathcal{O}_X(U)$-modules. The category so defined is *abelian*, and the whole of module theory can be transposed to this category—the notions of sub-$\mathcal{O}_X$-Module, the sum $\mathcal{F} + \mathcal{G}$ of two sub-$\mathcal{O}_X$-Modules, the quotient $\mathcal{O}_X$-Module of an $\mathcal{O}_X$-Module $\mathcal{F}$ by a sub-$\mathcal{O}_X$-Module $\mathcal{G}$, the tensor product $\mathcal{F} \otimes_{\mathcal{O}_X} \mathcal{G}$ of two $\mathcal{O}_X$-Modules, the $\mathcal{O}_X$-Module of homomorphisms $\mathcal{H}om_{\mathcal{O}_X}(\mathcal{F}, \mathcal{G})$, the exterior powers $\bigwedge^p \mathcal{F}$ of an $\mathcal{O}_X$-Module, etc. In a sense, the theory of $\mathcal{O}_X$-Modules is "localized" linear algebra.

For each open subset Y of a topological space X, the *restriction* $\mathcal{F} \mid Y$ of a sheaf $\mathcal{F}$ on X is defined by the $\mathcal{F}(U)$, where U runs through the nonempty open sets contained in Y. If $(X, \mathcal{O}_X)$ is a ringed space, $(Y, \mathcal{O}_X \mid Y)$ is a ringed space, said to be *induced* by $(X, \mathcal{O}_X)$ on Y; if $\mathcal{F}$ is an $\mathcal{O}_X$-Module, $\mathcal{F} \mid Y$ is an $(\mathcal{O}_X \mid Y)$-Module.

As in linear algebra, *finiteness* conditions play a large role in the theory of $\mathcal{O}_X$-Modules. An $\mathcal{O}_X$-Module $\mathcal{F}$ is said to be *of finite type* if each point $x \in X$ has an open neighborhood Y such that $\mathcal{F} \mid Y$ is a quotient of an $(\mathcal{O}_X \mid Y)$-Module of the form $(\mathcal{O}_X \mid Y)^n$. It is said to be *coherent* if it is of finite type and if for each open $Y \subset X$, each integer n and each homomorphism $u : \mathcal{O}_X^n \mid Y \to \mathcal{F} \mid Y$, the kernel of u is of finite type. The most important case is that in which $\mathcal{O}_X$ itself is coherent: in that case the notion of a coherent $\mathcal{O}_X$-Module generalizes that of a finitely generated module over a Noetherian ring.

For sheaves of groups or rings on X, an important notion is that of the *stalk* at a point: if $\mathcal{F}$ is a sheaf of groups or rings on X and if $x \in X$, the open neighborhoods of x in X form a directed set with respect to the relation $U \supset V$, and the groups (resp. rings) $\mathcal{F}(U)$ form a direct system (indexed by this directed set) with respect to the homomorphisms $\rho_{VU} : \mathcal{F}(U) \to \mathcal{F}(V)$; the stalk $\mathcal{F}_x$ of $\mathcal{F}$ at x is the direct limit of this direct system.

The notion of sheaf thus appears as the proper mathematical formulation of the vague idea of a "family of objects having the same structure" that "varies as a function of a parameter." The notion of a "section" over X then corresponds to the passage from "local" properties of the family to "global" properties (cf. **B** I).

Direct and inverse images of sheaves. Let X, Y be two topological spaces, $\psi : X \to Y$ a continuous mapping, and let $\mathscr{F}$ be a presheaf on X with values in a category $\boldsymbol{C}$. For each open $U \subset Y$, put $\mathscr{G}(U) = \mathscr{F}(\psi^{-1}(U))$, and if $V \subset U$ is another open set contained in U, let $\rho_{VU} : \mathscr{F}(\psi^{-1}(U)) \to \mathscr{F}(\psi^{-1}(V))$ be the restriction morphism. It is immediately verified that the $\mathscr{G}(U)$ and the ρ_{VU} define a presheaf *on* Y with values in $\boldsymbol{C}$; this presheaf is called the *direct image of* $\mathscr{F}$ *under* ψ and is denoted by $\psi_*(\mathscr{F})$. If $\mathscr{F}$ is a sheaf, so is $\psi_*(\mathscr{F})$.

Now let $\mathscr{G}$ be a *presheaf* on Y with values in $\boldsymbol{C}$. Then

$$\mathscr{F} \mapsto \mathrm{Hom}_Y(\mathscr{G}, \psi_*(\mathscr{F}))$$

(morphisms of presheaves) is a covariant functor from the category of $\boldsymbol{C}$-valued *sheaves* on X to the category ***Ens***; if this functor is *representable* by a sheaf on X with values in $\boldsymbol{C}$, the representing sheaf is called the *inverse image* of $\mathscr{G}$ by ψ, and denoted by $\psi^{-1}(\mathscr{G})$. If $\boldsymbol{C}$ is the category of sets, the category of groups or the category of rings, then $\psi^{-1}(\mathscr{G})$ exists for *every* presheaf $\mathscr{G}$ on Y with values in $\boldsymbol{C}$, and $\mathscr{G} \mapsto \psi^{-1}(\mathscr{G})$ is the *left adjoint* functor of the functor $\mathscr{F} \mapsto \psi_*(\mathscr{F})$ (considered as taking its values in the category of presheaves on X with values in $\boldsymbol{C}$). If (for such a category $\boldsymbol{C}$) we take in particular $Y = X$ and $\psi = 1_X$, then for each $\boldsymbol{C}$-valued presheaf $\mathscr{F}$ its inverse image is a $\boldsymbol{C}$-valued sheaf, called the *associated sheaf* of the presheaf $\mathscr{F}$.

Morphisms of ringed spaces. Given two ringed spaces $(X, \mathscr{O}_X)$ and $(Y, \mathscr{O}_Y)$, a *morphism* of $(X, \mathscr{O}_X)$ into $(Y, \mathscr{O}_Y)$ is a *pair* (ψ, θ) consisting of a continuous mapping $\psi : X \to Y$ and a homomorphism (in the opposite direction!) $\theta : \mathscr{O}_Y \to \psi_*(\mathscr{O}_X)$ of sheaves of rings. This apparently strange definition is justified by the theory of schemes (**A** IX), where it is quite natural.† In this way the ringed spaces form a category; this is a very important typical example of a category in which the objects are *not* sets and the morphisms are *not* (set-theoretic) mappings.

(For more details on sheaves and ringed spaces, see [69]).

5. Sites and topoi

The definition of a sheaf of sets on a topological space X may be interpreted as follows. Let ***Ouv***$_X$ denote the category in which the objects are the open subsets of X, and for two open sets U, V in X, Mor(U, V) is empty unless $U \subset V$, in which case it is the set whose only element is the canonical injection of U into V; the composition

$$\mathrm{Mor}(U, V) \times \mathrm{Mor}(V, W) \to \mathrm{Mor}(U, W)$$

† When $\mathscr{O}_X$ (resp. $\mathscr{O}_Y$) is a sheaf of germs of *functions* on X (resp. Y), one may remark that a mapping ψ from X to Y defines a mapping from functions on Y to functions on X, by composition with ψ.

is the composition of the canonical injections when $U \subset V \subset W$ (the only case in which all three sets are nonempty). Then a presheaf of sets on X is just a *contravariant functor* $\mathscr{F}: \boldsymbol{Ouv}_X^0 \to \boldsymbol{Ens}$.

It is therefore clear how the notion of a presheaf of sets should be generalized: the generalization is simply any contravariant functor $\boldsymbol{C}^0 \to \boldsymbol{Ens}$. But to be able to define *sheaves* in this generality, i.e., to have a condition analogous to (1), we require in the category $\boldsymbol{C}$ a notion that generalizes that of an "open covering." This is provided by the highly original concept of a *Grothendieck topology* (or *pretopology*) $\mathscr{T}$ on a category $\boldsymbol{C}$. For this it is necessary to assume that fiber products exist in $\boldsymbol{C}$ (in the category $\boldsymbol{Ouv}_X$, the fiber product $U \times_W V$, where $U \subset W$ and $V \subset W$, is just the intersection $U \cap V$). A topology $\mathscr{T}$ is then a pair (Cat $\mathscr{T}$, Cov $\mathscr{T}$) where Cat $\mathscr{T} = \boldsymbol{C}$ and Cov $\mathscr{T}$ is a set of *families of morphisms* $(U_i \to U)_{i \in I}$ in $\boldsymbol{C}$ satisfying the following conditions:

(i) For each isomorphism $\phi \in \operatorname{Ar} \boldsymbol{C}$, $\{\phi\}$ belongs to Cov $\mathscr{T}$.

(ii) If $(U_i \to U)_{i \in I}$ and, for each $i \in I$, $(U_{ij} \to U_i)_{j \in K_i}$ belong to Cov $\mathscr{T}$, then the family $(U_{ij} \to U_i \to U)_{i \in I,\, j \in K_i}$ of composite morphisms belongs to Cov $\mathscr{T}$.

(iii) If $(U_i \to U)_{i \in I}$ belongs to Cov $\mathscr{T}$ and if $V \to U$ is any morphism, then the family $(U_i \times_U V \to V)_{i \in I}$ obtained by "base change" belongs to Cov $\mathscr{T}$.

The condition (1) is then generalized to any functor $\mathscr{F}: \boldsymbol{C}^0 \to \boldsymbol{Ens}$ by requiring the *exactness* of the sequence

$$\mathscr{F}(U) \to \prod_{i \in I} \mathscr{F}(U_i) \rightrightarrows \prod_{(i,j) \in I \times I} \mathscr{F}(U_i \times_U U_j) \tag{2}$$

for all families $(U_i \to U)_{i \in I}$ in Cov $\mathscr{T}$. The elements of Cov $\mathscr{T}$ are called the *covering families* for the topology $\mathscr{T}$. A category $\boldsymbol{C}$ endowed with a topology is called a *site*.

Since presheaves are now functors, there is automatically a notion of morphisms of presheaves, so that the presheaves on $\boldsymbol{C}$ form a category $\hat{\boldsymbol{C}}$, and the sheaves on $\boldsymbol{C}$ (relative to a topology $\mathscr{T}$) a full subcategory $\tilde{\boldsymbol{C}}_{\mathscr{T}}$. Categories equivalent to categories of the form $\tilde{\boldsymbol{C}}_{\mathscr{T}}$ are called *topoi*; they can be characterized by intrinsic properties that do not depend on the category $\boldsymbol{C}$ that occurs in the definition above. Topoi also occur in mathematical logic (LN 274, 455).

The essential fact is that the forgetful functor $\tilde{\boldsymbol{C}}_{\mathscr{T}} \to \hat{\boldsymbol{C}}$ has a *left adjoint* $a: \hat{\boldsymbol{C}} \to \tilde{\boldsymbol{C}}_{\mathscr{T}}$; this enables us to define the *associated sheaf* $a\mathscr{F}$ of any presheaf $\mathscr{F}$, generalizing the notion described above under the same name. The theory of topoi then follows the theory of sheaves on a topological space; we may also consider sheaves with values in a category, the most important case being that of sheaves with values in ***Ab***. The culmination of this theory, which is capital for applications to algebraic geometry (**A** IX), is the possibility of developing a cohomology theory for sheaves on a site, with values in ***Ab*** (**B** I).

(For more details on sites and topoi, see B 256; LN 269, 274; [7], [209]).

6. Connections with the natural sciences

None at present.

7. The originators

The main ideas of the theory of categories and the theory of sheaves are due to the following mathematicians: S. Eilenberg, S. MacLane, J. Leray, D. Buchsbaum, H. Cartan, J. P. Serre, A. Grothendieck, D. Kan.

The following have also contributed substantially to these theories: M. Artin, J. Bénabou, C. Ehresmann (1905–1979), P. Freyd, P. Gabriel, J. Giraud, R. Godement, A. Heller, P. Hilton, P. Huber, G. Kelly, F. Lawvere, S. Lubkin, B. Mazur, B. Mitchell, K. Rowe, J. L. Verdier, N. Yoneda.

References

B: 256, 444, 513, 545.
LN: 269, 274, 445, 456, 488, 651, 753, 831, 832.
[7], [69], [209].

C II

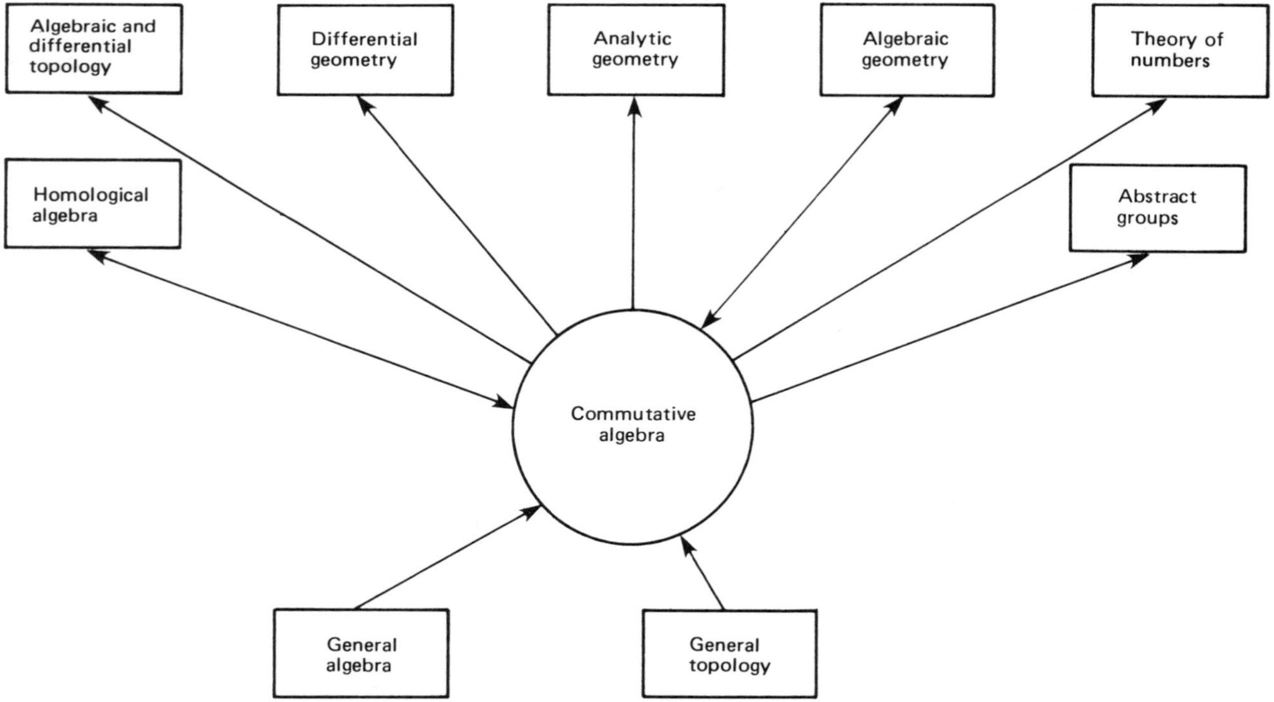
Algebraic and differential topology
Differential geometry
Analytic geometry
Algebraic geometry
Theory of numbers
Homological algebra
Abstract groups
Commutative algebra
General algebra
General topology

C II

Commutative algebra

Commutative algebra is the study of commutative rings and of modules over such rings; it has developed from problems about rings and ideals that arise in number theory and algebraic geometry. The "linearization" of the theory, that is to say, its enlargement by considering not only ideals but arbitrary modules, came later; and still more recently this has allowed the use of all the resources of homological algebra (**B** I), which has become an essential tool in almost all problems of commutative algebra.

There is no precise dividing line between commutative algebra, algebraic geometry, and number theory nowadays. Algebraic geometry relies ultimately on arguments of a purely algebraic nature, devoid of geometric content; but conversely, since the theory of schemes (**A** IX) enables one to give a geometrical form to every situation in commutative algebra, it may be regarded as encompassing the latter as a particular case. This is not merely a question of classification; presenting a problem in a geometrical form often suggests methods of solution that would not be apparent from its algebraic aspect (see below, also SAMS XXIX (Lipman)).

On the other hand, "arithmetical" problems (in the wide sense of the word) can be regarded as problems of commutative algebra relating to *particular* rings and modules, whereas in general commutative algebra or algebraic geometry the objects under study are not subject to such restrictive hypotheses: for example, the ground field may be an *unspecified* field of characteristic p in algebraic geometry, whereas in number theory it will be a *finite* field. But the distinction is not clearcut, and there are questions in algebraic geometry in which the method is first to reduce to the case of very particular rings or fields, and then to pass to more general cases.

1. The principal notions

The notions currently in use in the applications of commutative algebra may be grouped under several broad headings.

Localization and globalization (B22). When considering rational functions on $\mathbf{C}$ in a neighborhood of a point $a \in \mathbf{C}$, it is natural to distinguish those that have no pole at the point a; they form a ring intermediate between the ring of polynomials $\mathbf{C}[z]$ and the field of rational functions $\mathbf{C}(z)$, namely, the ring of fractions $P(z)/Q(z)$, where P and Q are polynomials such that $Q(a) \neq 0$. This ring is the *localization* of $\mathbf{C}[z]$ at the point a. This construction can be immediately generalized to any integral domain A with field of fractions K: if S is any *nonempty* subset of A *closed under multiplication* and not containing 0, the *localization* $S^{-1}A$ of A with respect to S is the subring of K consisting of all $s^{-1}a$ with $s \in S$ and $a \in A$. But one can go further, starting with *any* ring A and *any* multiplicatively stable subset S of A, by considering the relation on the set $S \times A$ between (s, a) and (s', a') defined as follows: "there exists $s'' \in S$ such that $s''(s'a - sa') = 0$"; it is easily verified that this is an equivalence relation and that the quotient of $S \times A$ by this relation is a ring. The class of (s, a) is denoted by a/s, even if s is a zero-divisor.

The most important cases are those in which S consists of the powers t^n $(n \geqslant 0)$ of an element $t \in A$, in which case the ring $S^{-1}A$ is denoted by A_t, and that in which S is the complement of a prime ideal $\mathfrak{p}$ of A (the fact that this complement is multiplicatively closed may be taken as the definition of a prime ideal); the ring $S^{-1}A$ in this case is denoted by $A_{\mathfrak{p}}$. There is a (not necessarily injective) canonical homomorphism $a \mapsto a/1$ of A into $A_{\mathfrak{p}}$. The mapping $\mathfrak{q} \mapsto \mathfrak{q}A_{\mathfrak{p}}$ of the set of prime ideals of A into the set of ideals of $A_{\mathfrak{p}}$ is such that $\mathfrak{q}A_{\mathfrak{p}} = A_{\mathfrak{p}}$ unless $\mathfrak{q} \subset \mathfrak{p}$, and it maps the set of prime ideals $\mathfrak{q} \subset \mathfrak{p}$ bijectively onto the set of all prime ideals in $A_{\mathfrak{p}}$: in other words, the passage from A to $A_{\mathfrak{p}}$ "kills off" the prime ideals not contained in $\mathfrak{p}$. In particular, $A_{\mathfrak{p}}$ has a *unique maximal ideal* $\mathfrak{p}A_{\mathfrak{p}}$. A ring with this property is called a *local ring*, and $A_{\mathfrak{p}}$ is called the *localization* (or local ring) of A at $\mathfrak{p}$. The field $A_{\mathfrak{p}}/\mathfrak{p}A_{\mathfrak{p}}$ is the field of fractions of $A/\mathfrak{p}$, called the *residue field* of $A_{\mathfrak{p}}$. The process of localization does not lose much information about the ring A: for example, if A is an integral domain, the fields of fractions of A and $A_{\mathfrak{p}}$ are the same; but it permits operations (see later) which, from a geometrical point of view, provide information about the "neighborhood" of $\mathfrak{p}$ in Spec(A) (**A** IX).

On the other hand, many properties of A or of A-modules are true if they are true for $A_{\mathfrak{m}}$ or the modules obtained by tensoring with $A_{\mathfrak{m}}$, as $\mathfrak{m}$ runs through the set of maximal ideals of A: this is the elementary aspect of "passage from local to global." For example, if M and N are two A-modules, an A-homomorphism $u: M \to N$ is injective (resp. surjective) if and only if each $A_{\mathfrak{m}}$-homomorphism $u \otimes 1 : M \otimes_A A_{\mathfrak{m}} \to N \otimes_A A_{\mathfrak{m}}$ is injective (resp. surjective). The canonical mapping $A \to \prod_{\mathfrak{m}} A_{\mathfrak{m}}$ that sends $x \in A$ to the family $(x_{\mathfrak{m}})$, where $x_{\mathfrak{m}}$ is the image $x/1$ of x in $A_{\mathfrak{m}}$, is injective.

Finiteness conditions. There are few important results in commutative algebra that do not require some "finiteness" condition on the modules or rings involved. For an A-module M, the simplest finiteness condition is that of being *finitely generated* (or *of finite type*), or equivalently of the existence of an exact sequence $A^m \to M \to 0$ for some positive integer m; if there exists an exact sequence $A^n \to A^m \to M \to 0$, the module M is said to be *finitely presented.* A submodule of a finitely generated module need not be finitely generated, in general. The rings A for which every submodule of a finitely generated module is finitely generated are therefore of great importance: they are called *Noetherian* rings. In a Noetherian ring A, every ideal is finitely generated, and every finitely generated module is finitely presented. All localizations $S^{-1}A$ and all quotient rings $A/\mathfrak{a}$ of Noetherian rings are Noetherian; but a subring of a Noetherian ring need not be Noetherian.

Coming next to algebras, a commutative A-algebra B is said to be *finitely generated* (or *of finite type*) if it is generated *as an algebra* by a finite number of elements, or equivalently if it is a quotient of a polynomial algebra $A[T_1, \ldots, T_n]$. If B is isomorphic to $A[T_1, \ldots, T_n]/\mathfrak{a}$ and the ideal $\mathfrak{a}$ is finitely generated, B is said to be a *finitely presented* A-algebra. If A is Noetherian, so is every finitely generated A-algebra, and every finitely generated A-algebra is finitely presented.

A stricter finiteness condition for A-algebras is that the A-algebra B should be finitely generated as an A-*module*, in which case B is called a *finite* A-algebra. An A-algebra B is said to be *integral* (and the elements $x \in B$ are said to be *integral* over A) if, for each $x \in B$, the subalgebra $A[x]$ generated by x is finite, or equivalently if each $x \in B$ satisfies an equation of the form $x^m + a_1x^{m-1} + \cdots + a_m = 0$, where the a_j belong to A.

Linear algebra over rings. Over a field, every module is free, and the functors Hom and ⊗ are exact (**C** I). This is not so over an arbitrary ring, and homological algebra is indispensable for treating problems of linear algebra. Hence the injective modules, and even more the projective modules (**C** I) play an important part; one of the most useful properties of the latter is that a submodule N of a module M such that M/N is projective is a direct summand, so that in particular every projective module P is a direct summand of a free module.

For certain types of rings, it can be proved that projective modules are in fact free modules. For example, if A is a local ring, every finitely presented projective module is free. Over a principal ideal domain, every finitely generated projective module is free. Recently it has been proved that if $A = k[T_1, \ldots, T_n]$ is a polynomial ring over a field, every finitely generated projective module is free (B 484; LN 635).

Still more important is the role played by the *flat* A-modules (**B** I), i.e., the modules E for which the functor $M \mapsto M \otimes_A E$ is exact. Projective modules are flat, and conversely finitely presented flat modules are projective (but in general a finitely generated flat module need not be projective). A fundamental fact is that any localization $S^{-1}A$ of a ring A is a *flat* A-module.

Graduations and filtrations. An abelian group G is *graded* if it is a direct sum $\bigoplus_{n=0}^{\infty} G_n$ of subgroups, which constitute the *graduation*; the elements of G_n are said to be *homogeneous of degree n*. A commutative ring A is *graded* if the additive group of A carries a graduation $(A_n)_{n \geqslant 0}$ such that

$$A_m A_n \subset A_{m+n},$$

with the identity element belonging to A_0. An A-module M is *graded* if its additive group carries a graduation (M_n) such that $A_p M_q \subset M_{p+q}$. The prototype example of graded rings is given by the polynomial rings $R[T_1, \ldots, T_m]$ over a commutative ring R, where A_n is the set of homogeneous polynomials of degree *n*. The usefulness of graded rings and modules is that in many circumstances they allow the use of arguments by induction on the degree of homogeneous elements.

A (decreasing) *filtration* on a group G is a decreasing sequence (G_n) of *normal* subgroups of G. A (decreasing) *filtration* on a commutative ring A (resp. on an A-module M) is a decreasing sequence (A_n) of ideals of A (resp. a decreasing sequence (M_n) of submodules of M) such that $A_p A_q \subset A_{p+q}$ (resp. $A_p M_q \subset M_{p+q}$). A typical example of a filtration of a ring is provided by the powers $\mathfrak{J}^n$ of an ideal; the $\mathfrak{J}^n M$ then form a filtration of any A-module M. These filtrations are called *$\mathfrak{J}$-adic*.

From a filtered ring A (resp. a filtered A-module M), we can construct canonically a *graded ring* (resp. a *graded module* over this ring): let

$$\mathrm{gr}_p(A) = A_p/A_{p+1}$$

and $\mathrm{gr}_p(M) = M_p/M_{p+1}$, and define a canonical action of $\mathrm{gr}_p(A)$ on $\mathrm{gr}_q(M)$ mapping $\mathrm{gr}_p(A) \times \mathrm{gr}_q(M)$ into $\mathrm{gr}_{p+q}(M)$ by passing to quotients; then form the direct sum $\mathrm{gr}_\bullet(A) = \bigoplus_{p=0}^{\infty} \mathrm{gr}_p(A)$ $\left(\text{resp. } \mathrm{gr}_\bullet(M) = \bigoplus_{p=0}^{\infty} \mathrm{gr}_p(M)\right)$. Under certain conditions on the filtrations it is possible to "lift" properties of $\mathrm{gr}_\bullet(M)$ to properties of M, for example to prove that M is finitely generated by showing that this is true of $\mathrm{gr}_\bullet(M)$.

Topologies and completions. A filtration (G_n) on a group G determines a topology compatible with the group structure of G, for which the G_n form a fundamental system of neighborhoods of the identity element. For example, let L be a Galois extension of a field K, the union of an increasing sequence (L_n) of finite Galois extensions; then the Galois group Gal(L/K) is endowed with a topology for which the normal subgroups $\mathrm{Gal}(L/L_n)$ form a fundamental system of neighborhoods of the identity element. The group Gal (L/K) so topologized is called the *topological Galois group* of L/K; it is compact, metrizable, and totally disconnected.

Likewise, if (A_n) is a filtration on a commutative ring A, the A_n form a fundamental system of neighborhoods of 0 for a topology compatible with the ring structure of A. If $A_\infty = \bigcap_n A_n$, the quotient A/A_∞ is a *metrizable* topological ring, the completion $\hat{A}$ of which is called the (*Hausdorff*) *completion* of A; the closures in $\hat{A}$ of the A_n/A_∞ form a fundamental system of neighborhoods of 0. Moreover, the ring A may be canonically identified with the inverse limit (**C** I) $\varprojlim A/A_n$.

The typical example is the case where $A_n = \mathfrak{J}^n$, the nth power of an ideal $\mathfrak{J}$: the corresponding topology is called the $\mathfrak{J}$-*adic* topology. Suppose for simplicity that $\bigcap_n \mathfrak{J}^n = \{0\}$; then, if $\mathfrak{J}$ is *finitely generated*, the closure $\overline{\mathfrak{J}^n}$ of $\mathfrak{J}^n$ in $\hat{A}$ is equal to $(\overline{\mathfrak{J}})^n$ and also to $\mathfrak{J}^n\hat{A}$ (it should be observed that these assertions may be false if $\mathfrak{J}$ is not finitely generated). If we take $A = R[T_1, \ldots, T_n]$ and $\mathfrak{J}$ to be the (finitely generated) ideal generated by $T_1, \ldots, T_n$, then the completion $\hat{A}$ is denoted by $R[[T_1, \ldots, T_n]]$, and its elements are called *formal power series* in n indeterminates over R; they may be written as series $\sum_\alpha c_\alpha T^\alpha$ (where $T^\alpha = T_1^{\alpha_1} \cdots T_n^{\alpha_n}$ for $\alpha = (\alpha_1, \ldots, \alpha_n) \in \mathbf{N}^n$), which converge for the topology on $\hat{A}$. If R is an integral domain, so also is $R[[T_1, \ldots, T_n]]$. If R is a field k, the field of fractions of the integral domain $k[[T_1, \ldots, T_n]]$ is denoted by $k((T_1, \ldots, T_n))$ and is called the *field of formal power series* in n indeterminates over k.

The most important case in applications is where A is a *Noetherian local* ring with maximal ideal $\mathfrak{m}$; then we have $\bigcap_n \mathfrak{m}^n = \{0\}$. The completion $\hat{A}$ of A with respect to the $\mathfrak{m}$-adic topology is again a Noetherian local ring, with maximal ideal $\mathfrak{m}\hat{A}$, and residue field canonically isomorphic to that of A. Moreover, $\hat{A}$ is a flat A-module, and more precisely is *faithfully flat* (i.e., every prime ideal of A is the intersection of A with a prime ideal of $\hat{A}$). We remark also that in that case, for every finitely generated A-module M, the $\mathfrak{m}$-adic topology on M is Hausdorff, and for each submodule N of M, the $\mathfrak{m}$-adic topology on N is induced by the $\mathfrak{m}$-adic topology on M.

Complete Noetherian local rings (i.e., such that $\hat{A} = A$) have a much simpler structure than general Noetherian local rings (see later); so there is a "loss" of structure in passing from a Noetherian local ring A to its completion. But the process of completion brings to light properties of A not otherwise visible; for example, it can happen that A is an integral domain but that $\hat{A}$ has zero divisors or even nilpotent elements $\neq 0$. An example of the former possibility is provided by the local ring of the double point of a plane cubic curve having a double point with distinct tangents; A is an integral domain, but $\hat{A}$ has two distinct minimal prime ideals, corresponding to the two "branches" of the curve.

Dimension. The (Krull) *dimension* of a ring A is defined to be the least upper bound dim(A) of integers n such that there exists a "chain" of $n + 1$ distinct prime ideals $\mathfrak{p}_0 \subset \mathfrak{p}_1 \subset \cdots \subset \mathfrak{p}_n$. Geometrically this corresponds to a strictly decreasing sequence of $n + 1$ closed subschemes of Spec(A) (**A** IX) and therefore corresponds reasonably well to intuition. It is clear that dim(A) is the least upper bound of the $\dim(A_\mathfrak{p})$ for all prime ideals $\mathfrak{p}$. If A is Noetherian, the numbers $\dim(A_\mathfrak{p})$ are all finite, but it can still happen that $\dim(A) = +\infty$. Also for a Noetherian ring A we have $\dim(A[T]) = \dim(A) + 1$ (but this can be false for non-Noetherian rings).

If A is a Noetherian local ring, we have $\dim(\hat{A}) = \dim A$, and if B is a finite A-algebra, dim B = dim A. For Noetherian local rings, there is another interpretation of dimension: for each integer $n \geqslant 1$, the A-module $A/\mathfrak{m}^n$ has finite length $\chi(n)$, and there exists an integer n_0 such that for $n \geqslant n_0$ the function $n \mapsto \chi(n)$ coincides with a *polynomial* in n, called the *Hilbert–Samuel polynomial* of A (necessarily unique); the degree of this polynomial is the dimension of A (see **A** IX). It should be remarked that two maximal chains of prime ideals of A are not necessarily of equal length (LN 647).

If A is a finitely generated algebra over a field k and an integral domain, for each maximal ideal $\mathfrak{m}$ of A the local ring $A_\mathfrak{m}$ has the same dimension, equal to the transcendence degree over k of the field of fractions of A [40]. But a Noetherian local ring can have dimension $\geqslant 1$ without containing a field: the typical example is provided by the local rings $\mathbf{Z}_{p\mathbf{Z}}$ of $\mathbf{Z}$ for all prime numbers p, which have dimension 1, so that $\dim(\mathbf{Z}) = 1$.

If $\mathfrak{m}$ is the maximal ideal of a Noetherian local ring A of dimension d, the minimal number of generators of $\mathfrak{m}$ is always $\geqslant d$. If it is equal to d, the local ring A is called *regular*; if $k = A/\mathfrak{m}$ is the residue field, an equivalent condition is that the k-vector space $\mathfrak{m}/\mathfrak{m}^2$ has dimension d. An important property of regular local rings, from the cohomological point of view, is that every finitely generated A-module M has a projective resolution (**B** I)

$$0 \to L_d \to L_{d-1} \to \cdots \to L_0 \to M \to 0$$

(Hilbert's syzygy theorem); in fact (Serre) this property characterizes regular local rings of dimension d. A Noetherian local ring A is regular if and only if $\hat{A}$ is regular, and every localization $A_\mathfrak{p}$ of A is also regular. A (nonlocal) Noetherian ring A is said to be regular if $A_\mathfrak{m}$ is regular for each maximal ideal $\mathfrak{m}$ of A. If A is regular, so are the polynomial ring A[T] and the power series ring A[[T]].

Integral closure. If A is an integral domain, K its field of fractions, the *integral closure* of A is the A-algebra $A' \subset K$ consisting of all $x \in K$ that are integral over A. If A is Noetherian, A′ need not be Noetherian. The integral domain A is said to be *integrally closed* if $A' = A$; in that case, every localization $S^{-1}A$ of A is also integrally closed, and conversely if $A_{\mathfrak{m}}$ is integrally closed for each maximal ideal $\mathfrak{m}$ of A, then A is integrally closed. If A is integrally closed, so is the polynomial ring A[T]. A regular local ring is an integrally closed integral domain.

Excellent rings. Fields, the ring **Z** of rational integers, and complete Noetherian local rings all belong to the category of *excellent* Noetherian rings [70], which have remarkable *permanence* properties: if A is excellent, so is every localization $S^{-1}A$ and every finitely generated A-algebra. If A is an excellent local ring, for A to be *reduced* (i.e., to have no nilpotent element $\neq 0$), it is necessary and sufficient that $\hat{A}$ should be reduced; for A to be an integrally closed integral domain, it is necessary and sufficient that $\hat{A}$ have the same properties; and if A is an excellent integral domain, its integral closure A′ is a finite A-algebra.

Henselian rings. Let A be a local ring. If B is a finite A-algebra, it has only a *finite* number of maximal ideals, each of which has as inverse image in A the unique maximal ideal of A. The ring A is said to be *Henselian* if every finite A-algebra is a *product* of local rings: this is an algebraic analog of the property of simple connectivity for a topological space (every finite covering of a simply connected space has its connected components homeomorphic to the space itself), and it is the reason for the importance of Henselian rings in algebraic geometry (LN 169). Every complete Noetherian local ring is Henselian; but there are interesting non-Noetherian Henselian rings, for example, the ring of germs of continuous real-valued functions at a point of a topological space. For each local ring A, there exists a ring ${}^hA$, called the *Henselization* of A, which is "universal" in the sense that every homomorphism $A \to B$ of A into a Henselian ring that maps the maximal ideal of A into the maximal ideal of B factorizes as $A \to {}^hA \to B$. When A is Noetherian, passing from A to ${}^hA$ "destroys" less structure than the passage from A to $\hat{A}$: for example, if A is an integral domain, there is a canonical one–one correspondence between the maximal ideals of the integral closure A′ and the minimal prime ideals of ${}^hA$ (which is not always true with ${}^hA$ replaced by $\hat{A}$, unless A is excellent).

Valuations and absolute values. The structure of a Noetherian local ring of dimension 1 can be extremely complicated (as one sees by considering singularities of algebraic curves) (LN 327). But integrally closed local domains of dimension 1 are regular local rings, and are the simplest examples of *valuation rings.* A valuation ring V is an integral domain such that, if K is its field of fractions, every element $x \in K - V$ satisfies $x^{-1} \in V$. An equivalent definition is that $V^{\times} = V \cap K^{\times}$ is the set of $x \in K^{\times}$ such that $v(x) \geqslant 0$, where v is a *valuation* on $K^{\times}$ (the multiplicative group of K), that is to say, a mapping of $K^{\times}$ into a totally ordered abelian group Γ (written additively) such that $v(xy) = v(x) + v(y)$ and $v(x + y) \geqslant \inf(v(x), v(y))$ if $x + y \neq 0$. Every valuation ring V is a local ring, whose maximal ideal $\mathfrak{m}$ is the set of $x \in V$ such that $v(x) > 0$ or $x = 0$, and the ideals of V are totally ordered by inclusion. If $V \neq K$, then V is Noetherian if and only if $v(K^{\times})$ is isomorphic to $\mathbf{Z}$, in which case the valuation v is said to be *discrete*, and V is a *discrete valuation ring*; these are precisely the regular Noetherian local rings of dimension 1. When v is discrete we may assume that $\Gamma = v(K^{\times}) = \mathbf{Z}$; if $\pi \in V$ is an element such that $v(\pi) = 1$ (a "uniformizing parameter" of V), the *only ideals* $\neq 0$ in V are the principal ideals (π^n), $n \geqslant 0$ (so that V is a principal ideal domain).

If E is an extension field of K, every valuation v on K can be extended to a valuation on E. If E/K is a finite algebraic extension, of degree n, a *discrete* valuation v on K has a *finite* number $m \leqslant n$ of extensions to valuations v_j of E. The group $v_j(E^{\times})$ may be strictly larger than $v(K^{\times})$; if $v_j(E^{\times}) = v(K)$, the valuation v_j is said to be *unramified* over v.

When the group Γ of a valuation v is a subgroup of $\mathbf{R}$ (in which case v is called a *real* valuation), the notion of valuation may be presented in another way. Choose $a \in \mathbf{R}$ such that $0 < a < 1$, and put $|x|_v = a^{v(x)}$ for $x \neq 0$, and $|0|_v = 0$; then we have $|xy|_v = |x|_v |y|_v$ and $|x + y|_v \leqslant \sup(|x|_v, |y|_v)$ for all x, y in K, also $|x|_v > 0$ unless $x = 0$. A function $x \mapsto |x|_v$ with these three properties is called an *ultrametric absolute value* on K.

More generally, an *absolute value* on a field K is a mapping $x \mapsto \|x\|$ of K into $\mathbf{R}_+$ such that (i) $\|x\| \geqslant 0$, and $\|x\| = 0$ if and only if $x = 0$; (ii) $\|xy\| = \|x\| \cdot \|y\|$; (iii) $\|x + y\| \leqslant \|x\| + \|y\|$ for all $x, y \in K$. It can be shown that either $\|x\|$ is an ultrametric absolute value, or else there exists an isomorphism j of K onto a *subfield* of $\mathbf{C}$ such that $\|x\| = |j(x)|^{\rho}$ with $0 < \rho < 1$, in which case $\|x\|$ is called an *archimedean* absolute value.

A field endowed with an absolute value $\|x\|$ is called a *valued* field. On such a field K, the function $d(x, y) = \|x - y\|$ is a metric, with respect to which the metric space K can be completed. The functions $(x, y) \mapsto x + y$ and $(x, y) \mapsto xy$ extend by continuity to $\hat{K} \times \hat{K}$, and define a field structure on the completion $\hat{K}$, and the continuous extension of the absolute value of K is an absolute value on $\hat{K}$. If this absolute value is not ultrametric, then $\hat{K}$

is isomorphic to either **R** or **C**. If v is a discrete valuation, the valuation ring $\hat{V}$ in $\hat{K}$ is the completion of the Noetherian local ring V.

One of the prototype examples of a valued field is the field **Q** of rational numbers: fix a prime number p, and for $x \in \mathbf{Q}^{\times}$ let $v_p(x)$ be the exponent (positive or negative) of p in the factorization of x into prime factors; then v_p is a valuation on **Q**, called the *p-adic* valuation, and $|x|_p = p^{-v_p(x)}$ is an absolute value on **Q**, called the *p-adic* absolute value. The completion $\mathbf{Q}_p$ of **Q** for this absolute value is the *field of p-adic numbers*, and the closure $\mathbf{Z}_p$ of **Z** in $\mathbf{Q}_p$ is the *ring of p-adic integers*; it is a complete discrete valuation ring, namely, the completion of the local ring $\mathbf{Z}_{p\mathbf{Z}}$, and its residue field is the prime field $\mathbf{F}_p = \mathbf{Z}/p\mathbf{Z}$.

A valued field K is called a *local field* if it is locally compact and not discrete. The only connected local fields are **R** and **C**; the others are totally disconnected, and are complete with respect to an ultrametric absolute value with finite residue field; more precisely, they are finite algebraic extensions of either $\mathbf{Q}_p$ or $\mathbf{F}_p[[T]]$ for some prime number p.

Structure of complete Noetherian local rings. Discrete valuation rings may be divided into two types, according as their residue field k and their field of fractions K have the same characteristic, or different characteristics (in which case k has characteristic $p > 0$ and K has characteristic 0). For *every* field k of characteristic $p > 0$, there exists a complete discrete valuation ring W_k (called the *ring of Witt vectors* over k) whose field of fractions has characteristic 0, whose residue field is isomorphic to k, and for which p is a uniformizing parameter. (If $k = \mathbf{F}_p$, then W_k is isomorphic to $\mathbf{Z}_p$). There is then the following general structure theorem for *any* complete Noetherian local ring A with residue field k: if A contains a field isomorphic to k, it is isomorphic to a quotient of $k[[T_1, \ldots, T_n]]$; if not, it is isomorphic to a quotient of $W_k[[T_1, \ldots, T_n]]$. If moreover A is an integral domain, then it is a finite B-algebra, where B is either $k[[T_1, \ldots, T_n]]$ or $W_k[[T_1, \ldots, T_n]$ (I. Cohen's theorems).

If A is *regular* and contains a field isomorphic to k, it is isomorphic to $k[[T_1, \ldots, T_n]]$. Geometrically, this means that the completions of the local rings of simple points of *all* algebraic varieties over k of dimension n are isomorphic, in striking contrast to the local rings themselves.

2. Problems of field theory

Quasi-algebraically closed fields. A fundamental theorem of Hilbert (the "Nullstellensatz") is that if k is an algebraically closed field, and $f \in k[T_1, \ldots, T_n]$ is a nonconstant *homogeneous* polynomial over k, then there exists a point $(t_1, \ldots, t_n) \in k^n$, distinct from 0, such that $f(t_1, \ldots, t_n) = 0$.

If k is a *finite* field, this assertion is still true provided that the *degree* d of f is $<n$ (Chevalley–Warning theorem). A field k is said to have the *property* C_i if the above assertion is true whenever $n > d^i$, and a field which has the property C_1 is called *quasi-algebraically closed*; one of the important properties of these fields is that their Brauer groups (**B** I) are trivial. Every finite extension of a C_1-field is C_1. If K is complete with respect to a discrete valuation, with algebraically closed residue field, then K is C_1. If k is a finite field, the field of formal power series $k((T))$ is C_2; but there exist prime numbers p such that the p-adic field $\mathbf{Q}_p$ is not C_2 (B 70, 299).

Subextensions of a pure transcendental extension. If k is a field, an extension field E of k is called *finitely generated* if it is generated (as a *field*, not as a ring) by k and a finite number of elements of E; in that case, every subextension $L \subset E$ is also a finitely generated extension of k, and if L and E have the same transcendence degree over k, then E is a *finite* algebraic extension of L (i.e., $[E:L] < +\infty$). When $E = k(T_1, \ldots, T_n)$ is a pure transcendental extension, it may be asked whether each subextension $L \subset E$ of transcendence degree n over k is also a pure transcendental extension. This is true when $k = \mathbf{C}$ and $n = 1$ or 2 (Lüroth, Castelnuovo), but it is only recently that counter examples have been constructed for $n = 3$ (B 402). These examples have been obtained by geometrical means, by defining a projective algebraic variety X of dimension 3 whose field of rational functions $L = R(X)$ is a subfield of $\mathbf{C}(T_1, T_2, T_3)$, and showing that certain invariants attached to X, which depend only on R(X), are different from those for $\mathbf{P}_3(\mathbf{C})$ (SAMS XXIX (Hartshorne)).

A related problem arises from elementary Galois theory. If k is a field, the symmetric group $\mathfrak{S}_n$ acts on the field $E = k(T_1, \ldots, T_n)$ by permuting the T_j, and the fixed subfield K is a pure transcendental extension of k (generated by the "elementary symmetric functions" of the T_j) such that E is a Galois extension of K with Galois group $\mathfrak{S}_n$. Now let G be an arbitrary subgroup of $\mathfrak{S}_n$, and let $L = E^G$ be the subfield of E fixed by G (so that $K \subset L \subset E$, and E is a Galois extension of L with Galois group G): the question is whether L is necessarily a pure transcendental extension of k (E. Noether's conjecture). A counter example has recently been obtained, with $k = \mathbf{Q}$, $n = 47$, and G cyclic of order n (B 372); the proof uses K-theory (**B** I). Still more recently, necessary and sufficient conditions have been found for L to be a pure transcendental extension of k (B 445).

The importance of Noether's conjecture is that in cases where it is true (with $k = \mathbf{Q}$) it is possible to construct Galois extensions of $\mathbf{Q}$ with Galois group G (it is unknown whether such extensions exist for *every* finite group G): if $L = \mathbf{Q}(u_1, \ldots, u_n)$ where the u_j are algebraically independent over $\mathbf{Q}$, it is enough to replace the u_j by suitably chosen rational numbers t_j in the coefficients of the minimal polynomial of an element $\theta \in E$ such that $E =$

$L(\theta)$; Hilbert's irreducibility theorem (B 201) shows that these choices can be made in such a way that the polynomial remains irreducible over **Q** and the corresponding extension of **Q** has the desired property.

Hilbert's 14th problem. This is a question of the same type as the preceding ones. Let $E = k(T_1, \ldots, T_n)$ and $R = k[T_1, \ldots, T_n]$, which is obviously a finitely generated k-algebra; the question is whether, for each intermediate field $k \subset L \subset E$, the *k-algebra* $R \cap L$ is finitely generated. This is true for $n = 1$ and $n = 2$ (B 99), by interpreting the question as a problem of algebraic geometry, and using the theory of divisors (**A** IX); but Nagata's counter-example mentioned à propos of invariant theory (**A** IX) (which also is of geometrical origin) proves that the answer is negative in general.

3. Connections with the natural sciences

None at present.

4. The originators

The main ideas in commutative algebra are due to the following mathematicians: R. Dedekind (1831–1916), D. Hilbert (1862–1943), K. Hensel (1861–1941), E. Lasker (1868–1941), E. Steinitz (1871–1928), E. Noether (1882–1935), W. Krull (1899–1970), O. Zariski, E. Witt, M. Nagata, I. Cohen (1917–1955), P. Samuel, J. P. Serre, A. Grothendieck.

The following have also contributed substantially to this theory: S. Abhyankar, Y. Akizuki, A. Andreotti (1924–1980), E. Artin (1898–1962), M. Auslander, H. Bass, J. Bertin (1939–1978), D. Buchsbaum. C. Chevalley, V. Danilov, M. Deuring, K. Dörge, B. Eckmann, D. Eisenbud, D. Ferrand, R. Fossum, W. Franz, F. Grell, P. Griffith, R. Hartshorne, H. Hasse (1899–1979), J. Herzog, M. Hochster, G. Horrocks, I. Kaplansky, E. Kunz, J. Kürschak (1864–1933), S. Lang, D. Lazard, H. Lenstra, J. Lipman, F. Macaulay (1862–1937), E. Matlis, Y. Mori, D. Mumford, M. Murthy, D. Northcott, A. Ogus, A. Ostrowski, C. Peskine, H. Prüfer (1896–1934), D. Quillen, L. Ratliff, M. Raynaud, J. Roberts, P. Salmon, G. Scheja, F. K. Schmidt, A. Schöpf, A. Seidenberg, A. Suslin, R. Swan, L. Szpiro, O. Teichmüller (1913–1943), J. Towber, A. Uzkov, P. Vaserstein, V. Voskresenski, B. L. van der Waerden.

References

B: 22, 70, 99, 175, 201, 299, 372, 402, 484.
LN: 169, 327, 635, 647.
SAMS: XXIX.
[40], [70].

C III

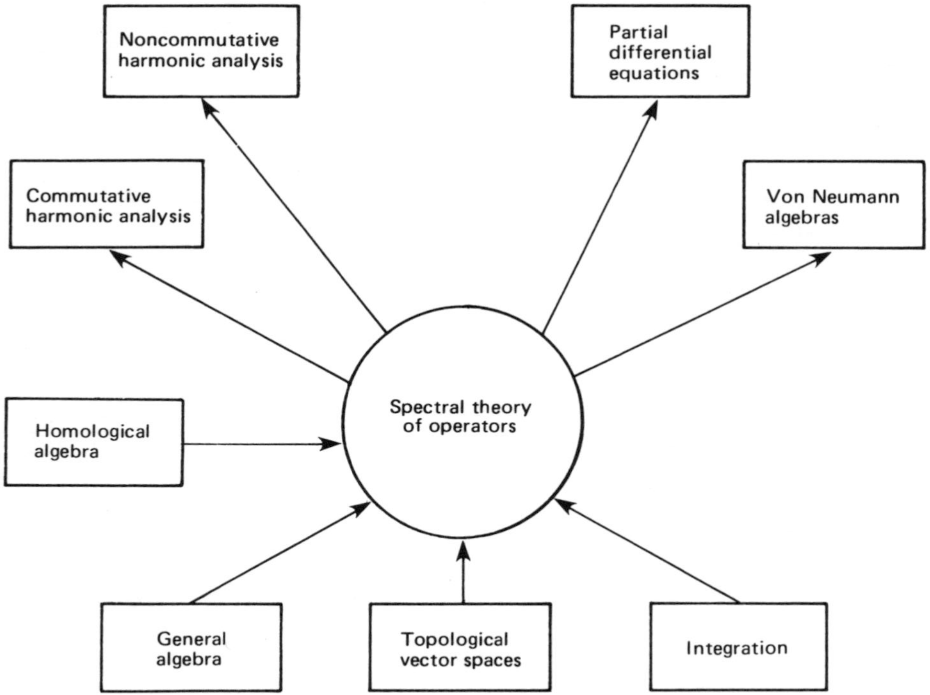
Noncommutative harmonic analysis
Partial differential equations
Commutative harmonic analysis
Von Neumann algebras
Spectral theory of operators
Homological algebra
General algebra
Topological vector spaces
Integration

C III

Spectral theory of operators

Spectral theory grew out of problems of solving *linear equations*. With the development of linear algebra in the 19th century it became understood that the solution of linear systems of equations with the same number of unknowns as equations, i.e., in vector notation, $A \cdot x = y$ (where A is an endomorphism of a finite-dimensional vector space E over a field K, y is a given vector in E, and x is the unknown vector) is governed by the similarity invariants of A. The simplest case is that where K is *algebraically closed*; in that case, the matrix of A (relative to a suitably chosen basis of E) is a diagonal array of *Jordan matrices*

$$\begin{pmatrix} \lambda_j & 0 & 0 & \cdots & 0 & 0 \\ 1 & \lambda_j & 0 & \cdots & 0 & 0 \\ 0 & 1 & \lambda_j & \cdots & 0 & 0 \\ \vdots & \vdots & \vdots & \ddots & \vdots & \vdots \\ 0 & 0 & 0 & \cdots & \lambda_j & 0 \\ 0 & 0 & 0 & \cdots & 1 & \lambda_j \end{pmatrix},$$

where $\lambda_j \in$ K (possibly with several blocks in the diagonal array corresponding to the same λ_j). Once such a basis of E has been determined, the solution of $A \cdot x = y$ is a trivial matter. The λ_j are the *eigenvalues* of A, namely, the roots of the characteristic equation $\det(A - \lambda I) = 0$; the multiplicity of each eigenvalue λ_j is the sum of the orders of the corresponding Jordan matrices, and the number of these matrices is the dimension of the *eigenspace* $\mathrm{E}(\lambda_j)$ corresponding to λ_j, namely, the set of vectors $x \in$ E such that $A \cdot x = \lambda_j x$ (the *eigenvectors* of A corresponding to the eigenvalue λ_j).

There are two methods which lead to this result. The first (called the Weyr–Fitting method) is to consider, for each eigenvalue λ_j, the endomorphism $A_j = A - \lambda_j I$ and its *iterates* A_j^k ($k = 1, 2, \ldots$), and to show that there is a least integer m_j such that for $k \geqslant m_j$ all the endomorphisms A_j^k have the same kernel $\mathrm{N}(\lambda_j)$ and the same image $\mathrm{F}(\lambda_j)$; E is the direct sum of $N(\lambda_j)$ and $F(\lambda_j)$, the restriction of A_j to $N(\lambda_j)$ is nilpotent, and its restriction to $F(\lambda_j)$ is bijective. Relative to a suitable basis of $N(\lambda_j)$, the matrix of the restriction of A to $N(\lambda_j)$ is the diagonal array of Jordan matrices corresponding to the eigenvalue λ_j. The same method is then applied to the restriction of A to $F(\lambda_j)$ (which does not have λ_j as an eigenvalue) and the proof is then concluded by induction on the dimension of E.

The second method (which works for *any* field K) is to consider the *commutative subalgebra* A of the K-algebra End(E) generated by the identity I and the endomorphism A. The algebra A may be regarded as a quotient of the algebra K[X] of polynomials in one indeterminate over K: the mapping $K[X] \to A$, which takes a polynomial $\sum_{k=0}^{m} a_k X^k$ to the endomorphism

$$a_0 I + a_1 A + \cdots + a_m A^m$$

of E, is surjective. This fact can also be interpreted by saying that E is a K[X]-*module* (or that K[X] *acts* on E) by the law of composition

$$\left(\sum_{k=0}^{m} a_k X^k\right) \cdot z = \sum_{k=0}^{m} a_k (A^k \cdot z)$$

for $z \in E$. One then uses the particular fact that K[X] is a *principal ideal domain* and that the structure of finitely generated modules over such a ring is completely elucidated by the theory of invariant factors [D, Chapter 21, Appendix].

An important particular case is that in which K is algebraically closed and all the Jordan matrices of A are of order 1; this means that if A is identified with its matrix relative to some basis of E, there exists an invertible matrix P such that PAP^{-1} is a *diagonal* matrix. If $K = \mathbf{C}$, an equivalent condition is that A is a *normal* endomorphism, i.e., such that $A^*A = AA^*$, where A^* is the adjoint of A. Suppose more particularly that A has a diagonal matrix $\mathrm{diag}(\lambda_1, \ldots, \lambda_n)$ where the $\lambda_k \in \mathbf{C}$ are all *distinct*, and let $S \subset \mathbf{C}$ be the set $\{\lambda_1, \ldots, \lambda_n\}$ (called the *spectrum* of A). Then E may be interpreted as the set $\mathbf{C}^S$ of all complex-valued *functions* $\lambda_j \mapsto z_j$ $(1 \leqslant j \leqslant n)$ on the discrete space S, and A as the operator of *multiplication* of these functions by the "identity" function, the restriction to S of the identity mapping $z \mapsto z$ of $\mathbf{C}$.

When A has an arbitrary diagonal matrix whose elements are no longer all distinct, the set $S \subset \mathbf{C}$ of these elements is still called the spectrum of A, and E and A may be described as follows. There exists a decreasing sequence $(S_j)_{1 \leqslant j \leqslant r}$ of nonempty subsets of S, and E may be identified with the direct sum of the spaces $\mathbf{C}^{S_j}$ (the space of all mappings of S_j into $\mathbf{C}$); A stabilizes each of the $\mathbf{C}^{S_j}$ and its restriction to each $\mathbf{C}^{S_j}$ is multiplication by the "identity" function.

Spectral operator theory consists of generalizations of these results to (usually infinite-dimensional) *function spaces*; but here the type of operators to which the previous methods can be generalized will depend on the method under consideration.

1. Riesz–Fredholm theory

The typical case in which the Weyr–Fitting method can be generalized is that of a *normed* (not necessarily complete) complex vector space E and a linear operator $A : \mathrm{E} \to \mathrm{E}$ that is *compact*, i.e., maps each bounded subset of E to a relatively compact subset (this condition implies that A is continuous). The simplest example is that first considered by Fredholm, where $\mathrm{E} = \mathscr{C}_{\mathbf{C}}([0, 1])$ is the Banach space of continuous complex-valued functions defined on the interval $[0, 1]$ and A is the integral operator defined by

$$(A \cdot f)(t) = \int_0^1 \mathrm{K}(s, t) f(s)\, ds,$$

where K is a continuous function on $[0, 1] \times [0, 1]$, called the *kernel* of A.

For an arbitrary compact operator A, the eigenvalues of A form an at most denumerable set, which may however be empty, as is the case for the Volterra operator defined on $\mathscr{C}_{\mathbf{C}}([0, 1])$ by

$$(A \cdot f)(t) = \int_0^t \mathrm{K}(s, t) f(s)\, ds,$$

where the kernel K is continuous for $0 \leqslant s \leqslant t \leqslant 1$. The eigenvalues are isolated in $\mathbf{C}$, and if they form an infinite set S we have $0 \in \bar{\mathrm{S}}$ (although 0 may not be an eigenvalue). For each eigenvalue $\lambda \neq 0$, the spaces $\mathrm{N}(\lambda)$, $\mathrm{F}(\lambda)$, and $\mathrm{E}(\lambda)$ are defined as in the finite-dimensional case and enjoy the same properties (and the restriction of $A - \lambda I$ to $\mathrm{F}(\lambda)$ is bicontinuous). If λ, μ are distinct eigenvalues, we have $\mathrm{N}(\lambda) \subset \mathrm{F}(\mu)$; but the example of Volterra operators shows that in general the (direct) sum of the $\mathrm{N}(\lambda)$ is not even dense in E. However, if E is complete, it can be shown that there always exist closed subspaces F of E, other than 0 and E, which are stable under A (even when A has no eigenvalues) (B 85, 549; [5]).

Refinements and generalizations. In elementary linear algebra [D, Appendix], if E and F are finite-dimensional vector spaces over a field K, there is a canonical isomorphism of vector spaces $\mathrm{E}^* \otimes \mathrm{F} \xrightarrow{\sim} \mathrm{Hom}(\mathrm{E}, \mathrm{F})$ that maps a tensor product $x^* \otimes y$ to the linear mapping $x \mapsto \langle x, x^* \rangle y$. Moreover, the space $\mathrm{B}(\mathrm{E}, \mathrm{F})$ of bilinear forms on $\mathrm{E} \times \mathrm{F}$ is the dual of $\mathrm{E} \otimes \mathrm{F}$, and is isomorphic to $\mathrm{E}^* \otimes \mathrm{F}^*$.

In the theory of topological vector spaces, these relations can be extended in various ways. Clearly one should consider only continuous linear mappings, and hence replace the algebraic duals E*, F* by the topological duals E′, F′. Also, in order to obtain results of use in applications, it is necessary to endow the algebraic tensor products E ⊗ F with "natural" topologies, and then to *complete* them with respect to these topologies (even if E, F are themselves complete). For example, if E and F are Banach spaces, a norm on E ⊗ F may be defined by the condition that $\|u\|$ is the greatest lower bound of the sums $\sum_j \|x_j\| \cdot \|y_j\|$, taken over all expressions $u = \sum_j x_j \otimes y_j$ with $x_j \in \mathrm{E}$ and $y_j \in \mathrm{F}$. By completing the normed space so defined we obtain the so-called projective tensor product of E and F, denoted by $\mathrm{E} \mathbin{\hat{\otimes}} \mathrm{F}$.

There is thus a general theory of *topological tensor products* and their relations with certain types of continuous linear mappings (B 65, 211, 386). This theory has in particular brought to light a new class of locally convex topological vector spaces, the *nuclear spaces* ([68 *bis*], [141 *bis*]), which possess remarkable stability properties; they have acquired an importance comparable with that of Banach spaces, and in particular they play a large role in measure theory on infinite-dimensional spaces (LN 56).

The theory of topological tensor products has also drawn attention to certain particular types of compact linear mappings, examples of which had previously been encountered in the theory of Hilbert spaces.

A continuous operator U on a separable Hilbert space H is said to be a *Hilbert–Schmidt* operator if, for each Hilbert basis (a_n) of H, the sum $\sum_n \|U \cdot a_n\|^2$ is finite; this condition implies that U is a compact operator. If U is self-adjoint, an equivalent condition is that the sequence (λ_n) of its eigenvalues (all of which are real) satisfies $\sum_n \lambda_n^2 < +\infty$. Products $T = UV$ of two Hilbert–Schmidt operators are called operators *of trace class*; they are the operators for which a *trace* can be defined as for operators of finite rank, by the same formula $\mathrm{Tr}(T) = \sum_n (T \cdot a_n | a_n)$ (where (a_n) is any Hilbert basis of H). The self-adjoint operators of trace class are those for which $\sum_n |\lambda_n| < +\infty$, where as before (λ_n) is the sequence of eigenvalues. These notions can be generalized in various ways to Banach spaces, and indeed to arbitrary locally convex spaces; for some of these particular types of compact operators, a theory of "determinants" can be developed, and applied to linear equations, on the model of Fredholm's original memoir (B 91, 386).

These operators, on a Banach space E, have the property that they can be approximated, relative to the norm on $\mathscr{L}(\mathrm{E})$, by operators of *finite* rank.

For a long time, it was an open question whether this property was valid for all compact operators on any Banach space; only in 1973 was a counter-example found to this conjecture (B 433).

We mention finally a class of linear mappings that has recently acquired great importance (**A** V): these are the mappings $u: \mathrm{E} \to \mathrm{F}$ such that the kernel $\mathrm{Ker}(u)$ is finite dimensional, and the image $\mathrm{Im}(u)$ is closed in F and of finite codimension. They are called *Fredholm* mappings, and may be characterized (when E and F are Banach spaces) by the property that there exists a continuous linear operator $v: \mathrm{F} \to \mathrm{E}$ such that $1_{\mathrm{E}} - vu$ and $1_{\mathrm{F}} - uv$ are compact operators. Such an operator u has an *index*

$$\mathrm{ind}(u) = \dim(\mathrm{Ker}(u)) - \mathrm{codim}(\mathrm{Im}(u)),$$

which has the remarkable invariance property $\mathrm{ind}(u + v) = \mathrm{ind}(u)$ whenever v is a compact operator or has sufficiently small norm.

2. Banach algebras

The idea of considering *polynomials* $p(T)$ in an endomorphism T of a finite-dimensional vector space E can be applied to *any* vector space over **C**; but if E is a topological vector space and T a continuous operator, it is again necessary to "complete" the algebra of polynomials $p(T)$, in order to be able to define "functions of T" $f(T)$ for functions f more general than polynomials. Indeed, the problem of solving the equation $T \cdot x = y$ requires such a generalization, since it comes down to attaching a meaning to $f(T)$ for the rational function $f(\mathrm{X}) = \mathrm{X}^{-1}$.

In the simplest case where E is a Banach space over **C**, the algebra $\mathscr{L}(\mathrm{E})$ of all continuous endomorphisms of E is naturally endowed with a norm $\|T\| = \sup_{\|x\| \leqslant 1} \|T \cdot x\|$, relative to which it is a Banach space and satisfies the relations $\|TU\| \leqslant \|T\| \cdot \|U\|$ and $\|I\| = 1$, where I is the identity. For a Hilbert space E, two other topologies on $\mathscr{L}(\mathrm{E})$ are very useful: the *strong* topology, defined by the semi-norms $p_x(T) = \|T \cdot x\|$ for all $x \in \mathrm{E}$, and the *weak* topology, defined by the semi-norms $p_{x,y}(T) = |(T \cdot x \mid y)|$ for all $x, y \in \mathrm{E}$.

A natural idea is therefore to consider the *closed* subalgebra of $\mathscr{L}(\mathrm{E})$ (for the norm topology) which is the closure of the set of operators $p(T)$. But for this purpose, it is better to proceed in a more abstract and axiomatic manner, by defining generally a *normed algebra* to be a **C**-algebra A (not necessarily commutative), endowed with a structure of a normed vector space, with the inequality $\|uv\| \leqslant \|u\| \cdot \|v\|$ for the product, and the relation $\|e\| = 1$ if A has an identity element e. If A is complete with respect to its norm, it is called a *Banach algebra*.

For a Banach algebra A with identity element e, the fundamental notion at the basis of the theory is that of the *spectrum* of an element $u \in \mathrm{A}$: this is the set $\mathrm{Sp}(u)$ of complex numbers ζ such that $u - \zeta e$ has no inverse in A. The set $\mathrm{Sp}(u)$ is always compact and nonempty, and is contained in the disk $|\zeta| \leqslant \|u\|$. If $\mathrm{A} = \mathscr{L}(\mathrm{E})$, where E is a Banach space, the spectrum $\mathrm{Sp}(T)$ of $T \in \mathscr{L}(\mathrm{E})$ contains all the eigenvalues of T, but in general contains other numbers as well. For example, if T is compact and E is infinite dimensional, $\mathrm{Sp}(T)$ consists of the eigenvalues of T, together with 0; if E is a Hilbert space and (a_n) is a Hilbert basis of E, the "shift operator" T defined by $T \cdot a_n = a_{n+1}$ for all n has the disk $|\zeta| \leqslant 1$ as spectrum, but has no eigenvalues. In general, the *continuous spectrum* of T is defined to be the set of $\zeta \in \mathbf{C}$ that are not eigenvalues but are such that the operator $T - \zeta I$ has dense image in E, and $(T - \zeta I)^{-1}$ is not continuous on this image; and the *residual spectrum* of T is the set of ζ that are not eigenvalues but are such that $\mathrm{Im}(T - \zeta I)$ is not dense in E. In the example of the shift operator, the continuous spectrum is the circle $|\zeta| = 1$ and the residual spectrum is the open disk $|\zeta| < 1$.

By definition, the function $\zeta \mapsto (u - \zeta e)^{-1}$ is defined on the open set $\mathbf{C} - \mathrm{Sp}(u)$, and may be shown to be analytic; Cauchy's theory therefore allows us to define $f(u) \in \mathrm{A}$ for any function f that is *analytic* on an open neighborhood of $\mathrm{Sp}(u)$ in $\mathbf{C}$, and $f \mapsto f(u)$ is a homomorphism into A of the algebra of germs of analytic functions defined on neighborhoods of $\mathrm{Sp}(u)$.

To make further progress, it is necessary to impose supplementary hypotheses on A, which may be of two kinds: A is assumed to be either *commutative* or an *algebra with involution.*

If A is a commutative $\mathbf{C}$-algebra with identity element e, a *character* of A is by definition any homomorphism χ of A into $\mathbf{C}$ such that $\chi(e) = 1$. If A is a Banach algebra, every character χ is a continuous linear form on A such that $|\chi(x)| \leqslant \|x\|$. The set $\mathbf{X}(\mathrm{A})$ of characters of A is therefore contained in the unit ball $\|x'\| \leqslant 1$ in the dual A′ of the Banach space A; moreover, $\mathbf{X}(\mathrm{A})$ is *compact* for the weak topology of A′. For each $x \in \mathrm{A}$, the mapping $\chi \mapsto \chi(x)$ of $\mathbf{X}(\mathrm{A})$ into $\mathbf{C}$ is denoted by $\mathscr{G}x$ and is called the *Gelfand transform* of x. The mapping $x \mapsto \mathscr{G}x$ is a continuous homomorphism of the Banach algebra A into the Banach algebra $\mathscr{C}_{\mathbf{C}}(\mathbf{X}(\mathrm{A}))$ of continuous functions on $\mathbf{X}(\mathrm{A})$, such that $\|\mathscr{G}x\| \leqslant \|x\|$ for all $x \in \mathrm{A}$, and $\mathscr{G}e = 1$. The compact space $\mathbf{X}(\mathrm{A})$ is called the *spectrum* of A: this terminology is justified by the fact that for each $x \in \mathrm{A}$ the set of values of the continuous function $\mathscr{G}x$ on $\mathbf{X}(\mathrm{A})$ is just $\mathrm{Sp}(x)$. If moreover $x_0 \in \mathrm{A}$ is such that the algebra generated by e and x_0 is dense in A, then the mapping $\chi \mapsto \chi(x_0)$ is a homeomorphism of $\mathbf{X}(\mathrm{A})$ onto $\mathrm{Sp}(x_0)$, so that in this situation $\mathbf{X}(\mathrm{A})$ is identified with a compact subset of $\mathbf{C}$. The prototype example of a commutative Banach algebra is the algebra $\mathscr{C}_{\mathbf{C}}(\mathrm{K})$ for a compact space K. The characters of this algebra are the Dirac measures $\varepsilon_t : x \mapsto x(t)$ for each point $t \in \mathrm{K}$, and $t \mapsto \varepsilon_t$ is a homeomorphism of K onto $\mathbf{X}(\mathscr{C}_{\mathbf{C}}(\mathrm{K}))$. The Banach subalgebras of the algebras $\mathscr{C}_{\mathbf{C}}(\mathrm{K})$ have been much studied; they are closely connected with certain questions in the theory of holomorphic functions (BAMS 79 (Gamelin, Sarason), LN 1, 75, 121; [59], [109], [151]).

In a commutative Banach algebra A it is possible to define, for any number of elements $x_1, \ldots, x_n$ in A, an element $f(x_1, \ldots, x_n)$ where f is a holomorphic function having the following property: if $\mathrm{Sp}(x_1, \ldots, x_n)$ is the image of $\mathbf{X}(\mathrm{A})$ in $\mathbf{C}^n$ under the mapping $\chi \mapsto (\chi(x_1), \ldots, \chi(x_n))$ (called the "simultaneous spectrum" of $x_1, \ldots, x_n$), then f must be holomorphic on a neighborhood of this compact subset of $\mathbf{C}^n$. The existence and the properties of $f(x_1, \ldots, x_n)$ depend on the theory of holomorphic functions of several complex variables (**A** VIII), and can be extended to commutative topological algebras more general than Banach algebras (B 125; LN 164, 230).

In general, the Gelfand transformation $x \mapsto \mathscr{G}x$ is neither injective nor surjective; it is only in the context of the theory of algebras with involution that we possess a criterion for isometry of A and $\mathscr{C}_{\mathbf{C}}(\mathbf{X}(\mathrm{A}))$ (see later). An *involution* on a C-algebra A is a bijection $x \mapsto x^*$ of A onto itself such that $(x^*)^* = x$, $(x + y)^* = x^* + y^*$, $(xy)^* = y^*x^*$ and $(\lambda x)^* = \bar{\lambda} x^*$ for $\lambda \in \mathbf{C}$; these conditions imply that $e^* = e$ if e is the identity element, and $(x^{-1})^* = (x^*)^{-1}$. A *Banach algebra with involution* is a Banach algebra A endowed with an involution such that $\|x^*\| = \|x\|$, and a C*-*algebra* is a Banach algebra with involution in which $\|x\|^2 = \|x^*x\|$.

Typical examples of Banach algebras with involution are first of all the algebra $\mathscr{L}(\mathrm{E})$ of continuous operators on a Hilbert space E; here T^* is the adjoint of T, defined by the identity $(T \cdot x \mid y) = (x \mid T^* \cdot y)$ for all $x, y \in \mathrm{E}$; $\mathscr{L}(\mathrm{E})$ is a C*-algebra. Next, when E is an infinite-dimensional Hilbert space, the Hilbert–Schmidt operators form a subalgebra $\mathscr{L}_2(\mathrm{E})$ of $\mathscr{L}(\mathrm{E})$, stable under the involution $T \mapsto T^*$; we put a *different* norm $\|T\|_2$ on $\mathscr{L}_2(\mathrm{E})$, defined by $\|T_2\|^2 = \sum_n \|T \cdot a_n\|^2$, where (a_n) is any Hilbert basis of E; then $\mathscr{L}_2(\mathrm{E})$ is a Banach algebra with involution, but is not a C*-algebra. A third fundamental example is the algebra (with respect to convolution) of bounded complex measures on a locally compact group G (the dual of the space of continuous functions on G which vanish at infinity); with the dual space norm and the involution defined by $\mu^*(f) = \overline{\mu(f^*)}$, where $f^*(s) = \overline{f(s^{-1})}$, this is a Banach algebra with involution, but not in general a C*-algebra.

The *commutative* C*-algebras with identity element are characterized by the Gelfand–Naimark theorem: the Gelfand transformation is an *isometric isomorphism* of such an algebra A onto $\mathscr{C}_{\mathbf{C}}(\mathbf{X}(\mathrm{A}))$. If A contains an element x_0 such that the subalgebra generated by e, x_0, and x_0^* is dense in A, then the mapping $\chi \mapsto \chi(x_0)$ is a homeomorphism of $\mathbf{X}(\mathrm{A})$ onto $\mathrm{Sp}(x_0) \subset \mathbf{C}$.

The theory of not necessarily commutative algebras with involution is dominated by the idea of a (unitary) *representation* of an algebra A, that is to say, an algebra homomorphism $s \mapsto U(s)$ of A into the algebra $\mathscr{L}(\mathrm{E})$ of continuous operators on a Hilbert space E, subject to the supplementary condition $U(s^*) = (U(s))^*$, and transforming the identity element (when it exists) into the identity operator. This notion generalizes that of a character for commutative algebras, and a knowledge of the representations of A provides information on the structure of this algebra.

If U is a representation of A in $\mathscr{L}(\mathrm{E})$, the Hilbert space E may be expressed (not uniquely) as a Hilbert sum of closed subspaces E_α, each of which is stable under the operators $U(s)$, $s \in \mathrm{A}$ and also contains an element x_α such that the $U(s) \cdot x_\alpha$ generate a dense vector subspace of E_α. The representation U is said to be the *Hilbert sum* of its subrepresentations $s \mapsto U(s)|\mathrm{E}_\alpha$, each of which is *topologically cyclic* (or *monogenic*) with x_α as *totalizing vector*.

To a representation U admitting a totalizing vector $x_0 \in \mathrm{E}$ we associate the *linear form* f_{x_0} on A defined by $f_{x_0}(s) = (U(s) \cdot x_0 | x_0)$, which has the property that $f_{x_0}(s^*s) \geqslant 0$ for all $s \in \mathrm{A}$. A linear form f on A with this property is said to be *positive*. From such an f we derive a bilinear form

$$(s, t) \mapsto g(s, t) = f(t^*s),$$

which is *Hermitian* and *positive* (i.e., $g(s, s) \geqslant 0$) and also satisfies the relation $g(st, u) = g(t, s^*u)$. Such a bilinear form is called a *positive Hilbert form*. Conversely, if g is any positive Hilbert form on A, the set $\mathfrak{n}$ of elements $s \in \mathrm{A}$ such that $g(s, s) = 0$ is a left ideal in A; if $\pi : \mathrm{A} \to \mathrm{A}/\mathfrak{n}$ is the canonical mapping, $\mathrm{A}/\mathfrak{n}$ carries a unique structure of a pre-Hilbert space such that $(\pi(s)|\pi(t)) = g(s, t)$ for all $s, t \in \mathrm{A}$. Let E be the completion of the pre-Hilbert space $\mathrm{A}/\mathfrak{n}$; then each $s \in \mathrm{A}$ induces an endomorphism $\pi(t) \mapsto \pi(st)$ of the vector space $\mathrm{A}/\mathfrak{n}$, and if g satisfies the additional condition:

(U) For each $s \in \mathrm{A}$, there exists a number $\mathrm{M}_s \geqslant 0$ such that

$$g(st, st) \leqslant \mathrm{M}_s g(t, t)$$

for all $t \in \mathrm{A}$,

then the endomorphism $\pi(t) \mapsto \pi(st)$ of $\mathrm{A}/\mathfrak{n}$ extends to a continuous endomorphism $x \mapsto V(s) \cdot x$ of E, and $s \mapsto V(s)$ is a representation of A.

The study of positive Hilbert forms is therefore basic to the study of representations of algebras. The most important of these forms are *bitraces*, i.e., positive Hilbert forms g that in addition satisfy $g(y^*, x^*) = g(x, y)$; for a bitrace g, the ideal $\mathfrak{n}$ is two-sided and $\mathrm{A}/\mathfrak{n}$ is an algebra with involution (obtained by passing to the quotient from the involution $s \mapsto s^*$ on A).

We are thus led to study algebras with involution of the form $A/\mathfrak{n}$; the most important are the *Hilbert algebras*. A Hilbert algebra $\mathfrak{A}$ is by definition endowed with a scalar product $(x|y)$ with respect to which it is a pre-Hilbert space, and which also satisfies the following axioms:

(I) $(xy|z) = (y|x^*z)$, or equivalently $(x|y)$ is a positive Hilbert form;
(II) this form satisfies condition (U);
(III) the products xy generate a dense vector subspace of A;
(IV) $(y^*|x^*) = (x|y)$, i.e., $(x|y)$ is a bitrace.

As a typical example of a Hilbert algebra, we mention the algebra $\mathscr{L}_2(E)$ of Hilbert–Schmidt operators on a Hilbert space E, with the scalar product $(T|U) = \sum_n (T \cdot a_n | U \cdot a_n)$, where (a_n) is a Hilbert basis of E. Another example is the algebra $\mathscr{K}(G)$ of continuous functions with compact support on a unimodular locally compact group G, with convolution as multiplication, the involution being defined by $f^*(s) = \overline{f(s^{-1})}$, and the scalar product induced by the scalar product on $L^2(G)$. Hilbert algebras play a large part in harmonic analysis (**B** IV) and the theory of von Neumann algebras (**B** V) (see [D, Chapter 15] and [45]).

Recently, applications of homological algebra (and in particular K-theory) to the theory of C*-algebras have substantially enriched that theory (LN 725, [227]).

3. Hilbert–von Neumann spectral theory

The theory of Banach algebras with involution can be applied to the study of a *normal* operator $N \in \mathscr{L}(E)$ on a Hilbert space E (i.e., satisfying $N^*N = NN^*$) by considering the closed subalgebra A of $\mathscr{L}(E)$ generated by 1_E, N, and N^*. The most important normal operators are the *self-adjoint* operators ($N = N^*$). For such an operator, $(N \cdot x|x)$ is real for all $x \in E$, and N is said to be *positive* if $(N \cdot x|x) \geqslant 0$ for all $x \in E$. The spectrum of a self-adjoint (resp. positive self-adjoint) operator is contained in $\mathbf{R}$ (resp. $\mathbf{R}_+$).

From the Gelfand–Naimark theorem we obtain an isometric isomorphism of $\mathscr{C}_{\mathbf{C}}(\mathrm{Sp}(N))$ onto A, which we denote by $f \mapsto f(N)$; this notation is justified by the fact that $(f + g)(N) = f(N) + g(N)$, $(fg)(N) = f(N)g(N)$, $\bar{f}(N) = f(N)^*$. The image of the identity mapping $\zeta \mapsto \zeta$ of $\mathrm{Sp}(N)$ onto itself is N, and for each function $f \in \mathscr{C}_{\mathbf{C}}(\mathrm{Sp}(N))$ we have $\|f(N)\| = \sup_{\zeta \in \mathrm{Sp}(N)} |f(\zeta)|$. In this way the idea of a "function of N" is extended to all *continuous* functions on $\mathrm{Sp}(N)$, not merely to functions analytic on a neighborhood of $\mathrm{Sp}(N)$. In fact, it is possible to go further and define $f(N)$ when f is assumed only to be bounded and universally measurable on $\mathrm{Sp}(N)$; for example, if $X \subset \mathrm{Sp}(N)$ is a universally measurable set, $\varphi_X(N)$ is an orthogonal projection on a closed subspace of E.

These results may be made more precise by use of the theory of integration. There exists a positive measure μ on the compact space $\mathrm{Sp}(N)$, with support $\mathrm{Sp}(N)$, and a (finite or infinite) decreasing sequence (S_k) of universally measurable subsets of $\mathrm{S}_1 = \mathrm{Sp}(N)$ with the following properties: there exists an isomorphism T of the Hilbert space E onto the *Hilbert sum* F of the spaces $\mathrm{L}^2(\mathrm{S}_k, \mu_k)$ (where μ_k is the measure induced by μ on S_k) such that the operator TNT^{-1} leaves invariant each of the subspaces $\mathrm{L}^2(\mathrm{S}_k, \mu_k)$ and the restriction of TNT^{-1} to each of these subspaces is *multiplication by* ζ on each function $\zeta \mapsto f(\zeta)$ in this subspace. This is the exact analog of the reduction to *diagonal* form of a normal endomorphism of a finite-dimensional space, and the isomorphism T above is therefore called a *diagonalization* of N. This result can be presented in a more elegant and more general form by making use of the notion of "continuous sum" or "direct integral" of Hilbert spaces (**B** 19, 25; [45]).

This notion of diagonalization may be generalized by replacing multiplication by ζ by multiplication by a measurable function $\Phi(\zeta)$, and the space $\mathrm{Sp}(N)$ by a more general locally compact space. The typical example of diagonalization is Fourier transformation (**B** IV). Let G be a locally compact abelian group and let $g \in \mathrm{L}^1(\mathrm{G}) \cap \mathrm{L}^2(\mathrm{G})$; then convolution by g is a *normal* operator $N : f \mapsto g * f$ on $\mathrm{L}^2(\mathrm{G})$, and the Fourier transform $\mathscr{F} : \mathrm{L}^2(\mathrm{G}) \simeq \mathrm{L}^2(\hat{\mathrm{G}})$ is a diagonalization such that $\mathscr{F}N\mathscr{F}^{-1}$ is multiplication by the function $\mathscr{F}g$. In fact this result does not depend on the presence of a group structure, and can be generalized to a whole class of integral operators, called *Carleman operators* (**B** 102; LN 33). In the example above, the spectrum of N is the closure in $\mathbf{C}$ of the set of values $\mathscr{F}g(\hat{x})$ for $\hat{x} \in \hat{\mathrm{G}}$, and there are no eigenvalues unless $\hat{\mathrm{G}}$ is discrete (and therefore G compact). Nevertheless, each character $\hat{x}$ is such that $g * \hat{x} = \mathscr{F}g(\hat{x}) \cdot \hat{x}$, so that one is tempted to regard $\hat{x}$ as an "eigenvector" for the "eigenvalue" $\mathscr{F}g(\hat{x}) \in \mathbf{C}$; but in general $\hat{x}$ does not belong to $\mathrm{L}^2(\mathrm{G})$. It is called a "generalized eigenvector," and there is an analogous situation for all Carleman operators.

The importance of the spectral theory of normal operators (due to Hilbert) lies in its applications to differential operators. However, a differential operator on $\mathbf{R}$, for example, is not defined on all of $\mathrm{L}^2(\mathbf{R})$ but only on the set of differentiable functions f such that f and f' lie in $\mathrm{L}^2(\mathbf{R})$. Hence it is necessary to begin by generalizing the theory to operators which are not everywhere defined and not continuous. The operators T that arise in applications are defined on a dense subspace $\mathrm{dom}(T)$ (the "domain" of T) of a Hilbert space E, and are such that their graph

$$\Gamma(T) = \{(x, T \cdot x) : x \in \mathrm{dom}(T)\}$$

is *closed* in E × E. Such an operator has an *adjoint* T^* which is such that $\mathrm{dom}(T^*)$ is the set of $y \in \mathrm{E}$ for which the mapping $x \mapsto (T \cdot x | y)$ is a continuous linear form on dom(T); it then extends to a continuous linear form on E, which can be written $x \mapsto (x|T^* \cdot y)$ for a unique vector $T^* \cdot y$, thus defining T^*; dom(T^*) is dense in E, the graph of T^* is closed, and finally $T^{**} = T$.

An operator N of this type is said to be *normal* if dom(N) = dom(N^*) and if N^*N and NN^* have the same domain and are equal on this domain. The theory of such operators can be reduced to the theory of continuous normal operators: if E is separable, it is the Hilbert sum of subspaces E_n contained in dom(N) and stable under N and N^*, the restriction of N to E_n being a *continuous* normal operator. This result enables the spectral theory of Hilbert to be extended to all normal operators; the most important case is that of the *self-adjoint* operators A, such that $A = A^*$; the spectrum of such an operator is a subset of the *real axis* **R**.

However, the majority of differential operators and their generalizations, pseudodifferential operators (**A** V), which arise in applications, are not self-adjoint, but have a weaker property: the closure of the graph of the operator is the graph of an operator H with dense domain dom(H) $\subset$ dom(H^*), H^* being an *extension* of H (so that $(H \cdot x|y) = (x|H \cdot y)$ for $x, y \in$ dom(H)). Such an operator H is called *Hermitian*. For example, if $E = L^2(I)$, where I is an open interval in **R**, the operator H whose graph is the closure of the graph of id/dx is Hermitian. It can then be shown (von Neumann) that dom (H^*) is the direct sum of dom(H) and two eigenspaces E_+, E_-, where E_+ (resp. E_-) is the set of $x \in$ dom(H^*) such that $H^* \cdot x = ix$ (resp. $H^* \cdot x = -ix$); the dimensions m, n of E_+ and E_- (which may be finite or infinite) are called the *defects* of H. For H to be extendable to a self-adjoint operator, it is necessary and sufficient that $m = n$; if $m = n > 0$, there are in general an infinite number of such extensions A such that

$$\text{dom}(H) \subset \text{dom}(A) \subset \text{dom}(H^*),$$

with dom(H) of codimension n in dom(A), and dom(A) of codimension n in dom(H^*), and A is the restriction of H^* to dom(A). In the example of a differential operator considered above, we have $m = n = 1$ if I is bounded; $m = 1$ and $n = 0$ if I is bounded above but not below; $m = 0$ and $n = 1$ if I is bounded below but not above; and finally $m = n = 0$ if I = **R**.

The application of this theory to differential operators on an interval $I \subset \mathbf{R}$ that, like id/dx above, are restrictions of Hermitian operators (they are called "formally self-adjoint") constitutes *Weyl–Kodaira theory*, and generalizes the classical Sturm–Liouville theory for second-order differential equations on a compact interval. It leads to a classification of the various "boundary-value problems" for these operators, and to a deeper study of their spectra (B 65; LN 448; BAMS 79 (Devinatz); [D, Chapter 23]). Generalizations to differential operators on $\mathbf{R}^n$ for $n \geqslant 2$ give rise to much more arduous problems (**A** V).

4. Connections with the natural sciences

Spectral theory of differential operators, integral operators, and their generalizations has always played a prime part in many physical theories which, by the problems they have raised, have contributed in an essential way to the development of this discipline. This role has increased considerably with the advent of quantum theories, in which new and difficult problems continually arise (B 388, 418; LN 313, 433, 650; [146]).

5. The originators

The principal ideas of the spectral theory of operators are due to the following mathematicians: C. Sturm (1803–1855), J. Liouville (1809–1882), H. Schwarz (1843–1921), H. Poincaré (1854–1912), I. Fredholm (1866–1927), D. Hilbert (1862–1943), H. Weyl (1885–1955), F. Riesz (1880–1956), T. Carleman (1892–1949), J. von Neumann (1903–1957), M. Stone, I. Gelfand, K. Kodaira, A. Grothendieck.

The following have also contributed substantially to this theory: N. Ahiezer, W. Ambrose, R. Arens, N. Aronszajn (1908–1980), J. Berezanskii, A. Beurling, M. Birman, H. Brézis, B. Brodskii, L. Brown, J. Calkin, L. Coburn, R. Courant (1888–1972), J. Dixmier, R. Douglas, S. Drury, N. Dunford, P. Enflo, P. Eymard, Ky Fan, P. Fillmore, C. Foias, K. Friedrichs, B. Fuglede, M. Fukamiya, I. Glazman, J. Glimm, R. Godement, I. Gohberg, J. Gram (1850–1916), A. Guichardet, P. Halmos, H. Hamburger (1889–1956), P. Hartman, E. Hellinger (1883–1950), H. Helson, E. Hille (1894–1980), A. Jaffe, R. Kadison, I. Kaplansky, T. Kato, M. Krein, S. Kuroda, N. Levinson, B. Levitan, M. Livsič, F. Mautner, E. Nelson, M. Neumark, M. Nikolskii, R. Pallu de la Barrière, C. Pearcy, R. Phillips, J. Pincus, A. Povzner, V. Ptak, H. Reiter, F. Rellich, C. Rickart, A. Ruston, R. Schatten, J. Schauder (1896–1943), E. Schmidt (1876–1959), I. Schur (1875–1941), J. Schwartz, I. Segal, G. Silov (1917–1974), B. Simon, K. Smith, W. Stinespring, B. Sz-Nagy, J. Tamarkin (1888–1946), J. Taylor, E. Titchmarsh (1899–1963), O. Toeplitz (1881–1940), L. Waelbroeck, Alex. Weinstein (1897–1979), J. Wermer, A. Wightman, A. Wintner (1903–1958), K. Yosida, M. Karoubi, V. Lomonossov.

References

B: 19, 25, 65, 85, 91, 102, 125, 211, 386, 388, 418, 433, 496, 501, 549.
LN: 1, 33, 56, 75, 121, 164, 230, 313, 345, 433, 448, 575, 582, 650, 666, 693, 725, 735.
BAMS: 79 (Gamelin, Sarason, Devinatz).
Astérisque: 11, 55.
[5], [45], [59], [68 *bis*], [109], [141 *bis*], [146], [151], [200], [225], [227].

Bibliography

[B] The exposés of the Séminaire Bourbaki have been published in yearly volumes:
Nos. 1–346 by Benjamin, New York.
Nos. 347–560 in *Lecture Notes in Mathematics*, Nos. 179, 180, 244, 317, 383, 431, 514, 567, 677, 710, 770, 842, Springer-Verlag, Berlin and New York.

[C] *Séminaire H. Cartan*, 1948–1964. Secrétariat mathématique, 11, rue Pierre-Curie, Paris 5e.

[D] J. Dieudonné, *Éléments d'Analyse*, Vols. 1–9, Gauthier-Villars, Paris, 1963–1982. (English translation: *Treatise on Analysis*, Vols. 1–6, Academic Press, New York, 1960–1978.)

*

* *

[1] R. Abraham, "Foundations of Mechanics," Benjamin, New York, 1967.

[2] R. Abraham and J. Robbin, "Transversal Mappings and Flows," Benjamin, New York, 1967.

[2 *bis*] J. F. Adams, "Algebraic Topology: A Student's Guide" (London Math. Soc. Lecture Notes series, No. 4), Cambridge Univ. Press, Cambridge, England, 1972.

[3] S. Agmon, "Lectures on Elliptic Boundary Value Problems," Van Nostrand-Reinhold, Princeton, New Jersey, 1966.

[4] V. Arnold and A. Avez, "Théorie ergodique des systèmes dynamiques," Gauthier-Villars, Paris, 1967.

[5] N. Aronszajn and K. Smith, Invariant subspaces of completely continuous operators, *Ann. of Math.* **60**, 345–350 (1954).

[6] E. Artin and J. Tate, "Class Field Theory," Institute of Advanced Study, mimeograph.

[7] M. Artin, "Grothendieck Topologies," Harvard University, mimeograph, 1962.

[8] L. Auslander, L. Green, and F. Hahn, "Flows on Homogeneous Spaces," Ann. of Math. Studies No. 53, Princeton Univ. Press, Princeton, New Jersey, 1963.

[9] W. Baily, "Introductory Lectures on Automorphic Forms," Publ. Math. Soc. of Japan, No. 12, Princeton Univ. Press, Princeton, New Jersey, 1963.

[9 *bis*] A. Baker, "Transcendental Number Theory," Cambridge Univ. Press, Cambridge, England, 1975.

[10] H. Bass, "Algebraic *K*-Theory," Benjamin, New York, 1968.

[11] R. Beals, A general calculus of pseudodifferential operators, *Duke Math. J.* **42**, 1–42 (1975).

[12] H. Behnke and P. Thullen, "Theorie der Funktionen mehrerer komplexer Veränderlichen," 2nd ed., Ergebnisse der Math., No. 51, Springer-Verlag, Berlin and New York, 1970.

[13] P. Bernat *et al.*, "Représentations des groupes de Lie résolubles," Monogr. Soc. Math. de France, No. 4, Dunod, Paris, 1972.

[14] L. Bers, Uniformization, moduli and Kleinian groups, *Bull. London Math. Soc.* **4**, 257–300 (1972).

[15] P. Billingsley, "Convergence of Probability Measures," Wiley, New York, 1968.

[16] P. Billingsley, "Ergodic Theory and Information," Wiley, New York, 1965.

[17] A. Borel, Les fonctions automorphes de plusieurs variables complexes, *Bull. Soc. Math. France* **80**, 167–182 (1952).

[18] A. Borel, "Linear Algebraic Groups," Benjamin, New York, 1969.

[19] A. Borel, "Introduction aux groupes arithmétiques," Hermann, Paris, 1969.

[20] A. Borel *et al.*, "Seminar on Transformation Groups," Ann. of Math. Studies, No. 46, Princeton Univ. Press, Princeton, New Jersey, 1960.

[21] A. Borel and J. P. Serre, Le théorème de Riemann–Roch, *Bull. Soc. Math. France*, **86**, 97–136 (1958).

[22] A Borel and J. Tits, Groupes réductifs, *Publ. Math. I.H.E.S.*, No. 27, p. 55–148 (1958) and Compléments..., ibid., No. 41, p. 253–276 (1972).

[23] N. Bourbaki, "Eléments de Mathématique, Livre I: Théorie des ensembles," Hermann, Paris, 1954–1956.

[24] N. Bourbaki, "Éléments de Mathématique: Algèbre commutative," Hermann, Paris, 1961–1965.

[25] N. Bourbaki, "Éléments de Mathématique: Groupes et algèbres de Lie," Hermann, Paris, 1960–1975.

[26] W. Browder, "Surgery on Simply Connected Manifolds," Ergebnisse der Math., No. 65, Springer-Verlag, Berlin and New York, 1972.

[27] H. Cartan, Variétés analytiques complexes et cohomologie, *Coll. sur les fonctions de plusieurs variables*, Bruxelles, 1953, Masson, Paris, 1953.

[28] H. Cartan and S. Eilenberg, "Homological Algebra," Princeton Univ. Press, Princeton, New Jersey, 1956.

[29] R. Carter, "Simple Groups of Lie Type," Wiley, New York, 1972.

[30] J. Cassels, "An Introduction to Diophantine Approximation," Camb. Univ. Tracts No. 45, Cambridge Univ. Press, Cambridge, England, 1957.

[31] J. Cassels and A. Fröhlich (eds.), "Algebraic Number Theory," Academic Press, New York, 1967.

[32] *C.I.M.E., III. Ciclo* 1967, "*Geometry of Homogeneous Bounded Domains*," Cremonese, Rome 1967.

[33] *C.I.M.E., I. Ciclo* 1969, "*Potential Theory*," Cremonese, Rome, 1970.

[34] *C.I.M.E., III. Ciclo* 1975, "*Differential Operators on Manifolds*," Cremonese, Rome, 1975.

[35] J. Chazarain, Opérateurs hyperboliques à caractéristiques de multiplicité constante, *Ann. Inst. Fourier* **24**, (1), 173–202 (1974).

[36] J. Coates and S. Lichtenbaum, On *l*-adic zeta functions, *Ann. of Math.*, **98**, 498–550 (1973).

[37] R. Crowell and R. Fox, "Introduction to Knot Theory," Ginn, Boston, 1963.

[38] M. Demazure and P. Gabriel, "Groupes algébriques," Vol. I, Masson, Paris, 1970.

[39] W. De Melo, Structural stability of diffeomorphisms on 2-manifolds, *Invent, Math.* **21**, 233–246 (1973).

[40] J. Dieudonné, "Cours de géométrie algébrique," Collect. SUP, Vols. 1 and 2, Presses Univ. de France, Paris, 1974.

[41] J. Dieudonné, Algebraic geometry. Fondements de la géométrie algébrique, *Adv. in Math.* **3**, 233–413 (1969).

[42] J. Dieudonné, "Introduction to the Theory of Formal Groups," Dekker, New York, 1973.
[43] J. Dieudonné and J. Carrell, "Invariant Theory, Old and New," Academic Press, New York, 1971.
[44] "Dix exposés sur la cohomologie des schémas," North-Holland, Amsterdam, 1968.
[45] J. Dixmier, "Les algèbres d'opérateurs dans l'espace hilbertien," Gauthier-Villars, Paris, 1957.
[46] J. Dixmier, "Les C*-algèbres et leurs représentations," Gauthier-Villars, Paris, 1964.
[47] J. Doob, "Stochastic Processes," Wiley, New York, 1953.
[48] Dynamical systems, Proc. Symp. Bahia, 1971 (M. Peixoto, ed.), Academic Press, New York, 1973.
[49] E. Dynkin, "Markov Processes," Vols. 1 and 2, Springer-Verlag, Berlin and New York, 1965.
[50] B. Eckmann, "Homotopie et cohomologie," Presses Univ. Montréal, 1965.
[51] J. Eells, "Singularities of Smooth Maps," Gordon & Breach, New York, 1967.
[52] S. Eilenberg and N. Steenrod, "Foundations of Algebraic Topology," Princeton Univ. Press, Princeton, New Jersey, 1952.
[53] W. Feller, "An Introduction to Probability Theory and Its Applications," Vols. 1 and 2, Wiley, New York, 1950–1966.
[54] J. Fogarty, "Invariant Theory," Benjamin, New York, 1969.
[55] R. Fossum, "The divisor class of a Krull domain," Ergebnisse der Math., No. 74, Springer-Verlag, Berlin and New York, 1973.
[56] A. Friedman, "Partial Differential Equations of Parabolic Type," Prentice-Hall, Englewood Cliffs, New Jersey, 1964.
[57] H. Furstenberg, "Stationary Processes and Prediction Theory," Ann. of Math. Studies, No. 44, Princeton Univ. Press, Princeton, New Jersey, 1960.
[58] W. Fulton, Rational equivalence on singular varieties, *Publ. Math. I. H. E. S.*, No. 45, p. 147–167 (1975).
[59] T. Gamelin, "Uniform Algebras," Prentice-Hall, Englewood Cliffs, New Jersey, 1969.
[60] A. Garsia, "Topics on Almost Everywhere Convergence," Markham, Chicago, 1970.
[61] S. Gelbart, "Automorphic Forms on Adele Groups," Ann. of Math. Studies, No. 83, Princeton Univ. Press, Princeton, New Jersey, 1975.
[62] I. Gelfand and S. Fomin, Geodesic flows on manifolds of constant curvature, *Amer. Math. Soc. Transl.* **1**, 49–66 (1955).
[63] I. Gelfand and M. Neumark, "Unitäre Darstellungen der klassischen Gruppen," Akad. Verlag, Berlin, 1957.
[64] I. Gelfand, M. Graev, and I. Pyatetskii-Shapiro, "Representation Theory and Automorphic Functions," Saunders, Philadelphia, Pennsylvania, 1969.
[65] R. Godement, "Topologie algébrique et théorie des faisceaux," Hermann, Paris, 1958.
[66] D. Gorenstein, "Finite Groups," Harper, New York, 1968.
[67] W. Gottschalk and G. Hedlund, "Topological Dynamics," Amer. Math. Soc., Coll. Publ. XXXVI, 1955.
[68] A. Grothendieck, Sur quelques points d'algèbre homologique, *Tôhoku Math. J.* **9**, (2), 119–221 (1957).
[68 *bis*] A. Grothendieck, "Produits tensoriels topologiques et espaces nucléaires," Mem. Amer. Math. Soc., No. 16, 1955.
[69] A. Grothendieck and J. Dieudonné, "Eléments de Géométrie algébrique," Chapter I (2nd edition) Springer-Verlag, Berlin and New York, 1971.
[70] A. Grothendieck and J. Dieudonné, Éléments de Géométrie algébrique, Chap. IV, *Publ. Math. I. H. E. S.*, No. 20 (1964), and No. 24 (1965).

[71] A. Haefliger and V. Poenaru, La classification des immersions combinatoires, *Publ. Math. I. H. E. S.*, No. 23, p. 75–91 (1964).

[72] P. Halmos, "Lectures on Ergodic Theory," Publ. Math. Soc. of Japan, No. 3, 1956.

[73] G. Harder, A Gauss–Bonnet formula for discrete arithmetically defined groups, *Ann. Ec. Norm. Sup* **4** (4), 409–455 (1971).

[74] P. Hartman, "Ordinary Differential Equations," Wiley, New York, 1964.

[75] R Hartshorne, On the De Rham cohomology of algebraic varieties, *Publ. Math. I. H. E. S.*, No. 45, p. 5–99 (1975).

[76] S. Helgason, "Differential Geometry and Symmetric Spaces," Academic Press, New York, 1962.

[77] E. Hille and R. Phillips, "Functional Analysis and Semigroups," Amer. Math. Soc. Coll. Publ. XXXI, 1957.

[78] P. Hilton, "An Introduction to Homotopy Theory," Cambridge Univ. Tracts No. 43, Cambridge Univ. Press, Cambridge, England, 1953.

[79] P. Hilton, G. Mislin, and J. Roitberg, "Localisation of Nilpotent Groups and Spaces," Notas de Mat. No. 55, North-Holland, Amsterdam, 1975.

[80] F. Hirzebruch, "Topological Methods in Algebraic Geometry," Ergebnisse der Math. Neue Folge, Heft 9, 3rd ed., Springer-Verlag, Berlin and New York, 1966.

[81] F. Hirzebruch, Elliptische Differentialoperatoren auf Mannigfaltigkeiten, "Festschrift zur Gedächtnisfeier für K. Weierstrass," pp. 583–608, West Deutscher Verlag, Köln-Opladen, 1966.

[82] L. Hörmander, "Linear Partial Differential Operators," Springer-Verlag, Berlin and New York, 1964.

[83] L. Hörmander, Pseudo-differential operators and non-elliptic boundary problems, *Ann. of Math.* **83**, 129–209 (1966).

[84] L. Hörmander, "An Introduction to Complex Analysis in Several Variables," 2nd ed., North-Holland, Amsterdam, 1973.

[85] L. Hörmander, On the existence and the regularity of solutions of linear pseudo-differential equations, *Enseign. Math.* **17** (2), 99–163 (1971).

[86] J. Hudson, "Piecewise Linear Topology," Benjamin, New York, 1969.

[86 *bis*] J. Humphreys, "Linear Algebraic Groups," Springer-Verlag, Berlin and New York, 1975.

[87] D. Husemoller, "Fibre bundles," McGraw-Hill, New York, 1966.

[88] J. Igusa, "Theta Functions," Springer-Verlag, Berlin and New York, 1972.

[89] E. Ince, "Ordinary Differential Equations," Dover, New York, 1949.

[90] K. Ito and H. McKean, "Diffusion Processes and Their Sample Paths," Springer-Verlag, Berlin and New York, 1965.

[91] K. Iwasawa, "Lectures on p-adic L-Functions," Ann. of Math. Studies, No. 74, Princeton Univ. Press, Princeton, New Jersey, 1972.

[92] K. Iwasawa, On $\mathbf{Z}_l$-extensions of algebraic number fields, *Ann of Math.*, **98**, 246–326 (1973).

[93] K. Jacobs, "Neuere Methoden und Ergebnisse der Ergodentheorie," Ergebnisse der Math., Neue Folge, Heft 29, Springer-Verlag, Berlin and New York, 1960.

[94] J. P. Kahane, "Some Random Series of Functions," Heath, Indianapolis, Indiana, 1968.

[95] J. P. Kahane, "Séries de Fourier absolument convergentes," Ergebnisse der Math., No. 50, Springer-Verlag, Berlin and New York, 1970.

[96] J. P. Kahane and R. Salem, "Ensembles parfaits et séries trigonométriques," Hermann, Paris, 1963.

[97] S. Kleene, "Introduction to Metamathematics," North-Holland, Amsterdam, 1952.

[98] G. Kneebone, "Mathematical Logic," Van Nostrand Reinhold, Princeton, New Jersey, 1963.
[99] S. Kobayashi, "Hyperbolic Manifolds and Holomorphic Functions," Dekker, New York, 1970.
[100] S. Kobayashi and K. Nomizu, "Foundations of Differential Geometry," Vols. 1 and 2, Wiley, Interscience, New York, 1963–1969.
[101] E. Kolchin, "Differential Algebra and Algebraic Groups," Academic Press, New York, 1973.
[102] T. Kubota, "Elementary Theory of Eisenstein Series," Wiley, New York, 1973.
[103] A. Landman, On the Picard–Lefschetz transformations, *Trans. Amer. Math. Soc.* **181**, 89–126 (1973).
[104] S. Lang, "Algebra," Addison-Wesley, Reading, Massachusetts, 1965.
[105] S. Lang, "Algebraic Numbers," Addison-Wesley, Reading, Massachusetts, 1964.
[106] S. Lang, "Diophantine Geometry," Wiley (Interscience), New York, 1962.
[107] S. Lang, "Introduction to Algebraic and Abelian Functions," Addison-Wesley, Reading, Massachusetts, 1972.
[108] S. Lang, "$SL_2(R)$," Addison-Wesley, Reading, Massachusetts, 1975.
[109] G. Leibowitz, "Lectures on Complex Function Algebras," Scott, Foresman, Glenview, 1970.
[110] P. Lévy, "Processus stochastiques et mouvement brownien," Gauthier-Villars, Paris, 1948.
[111] A. Liapounov, "Problème général de la stabilité du mouvement," Ann. of Math. Studies, No. 17, Princeton Univ. Press, Princeton, New Jersey, 1949.
[112] Ju. Linnik, "Ergodic Properties of Algebraic Fields," Ergebnisse der Math., No. 45, Springer-Verlag, Berlin and New York, 1968.
[113] J. Lipman, Rational singularities, *Publ. Math. I. H. E. S.*, No. 36, p. 195–279 (1969).
[114] M. Loève, "Probability Theory," 3rd ed., Van Nostrand Reinhold, Princeton, New Jersey, 1963.
[115] G. Mackey, Ergodic theory and virtual groups, *Math. Ann.* **166**, 187–207 (1966).
[116] G. Mackey, Ergodic theory and its significance for statistical mechanics and probability theory, *Adv. in Math.* **12**, 178–268 (1974).
[117] Ju. Manin, "Cubic forms," North-Holland, Amsterdam, 1974.
[118] B. Malgrange, Équations de Lie, *J. Differential Geom.* **6**, 503–522 (1972); **7**, 117–141 (1972).
[119] J. P. May, "Simplicial Objects in Algebraic Topology," Van Nostrand Reinhold, Princeton, New Jersey, 1967.
[120] E. Mendelson, "Introduction to Mathematical Logic," Van Nostrand Reinhold, Princeton, New Jersey, 1964.
[121] P. A. Meyer, "Probabilités et potentiel," Hermann, Paris, 1966.
[122] Y. Meyer, "Algebraic Numbers and Harmonic Analysis," North-Holland, Amsterdam, 1972.
[123] W. Miller, Lie theory and generalization of hypergeometric functions, *SIAM J. Appl. Math.* **25**, 226–235 (1973).
[124] J. Milnor, "Morse Theory," Ann. of Math. Studies, No. 51, Princeton Univ. Press, Princeton, New Jersey, 1963.
[125] J. Milnor, "Singular Points of Complex Hypersurfaces," Ann. of Math. Studies, No. 61, Princeton Univ. Press, Princeton, New Jersey, 1968.
[126] J. Milnor and J. Stasheff, "Characteristic Classes," Ann. of Math. Studies, No. 76, Princeton Univ. Press, Princeton, New Jersey, 1974.

[127] C. Moore, Group extensions of p-adic and adelic groups, *Publ. Math. I. H. E. S.*, No. 35, p. 5–70 (1968).

[128] D. Mumford, "Introduction to Algebraic Geometry," Harvard Univ., mimeograph.

[129] D. Mumford, "Geometric Invariant Theory," Ergebnisse der Math., Neue Folge, Heft 34, Springer-Verlag, Berlin and New York, 1965.

[130] D. Mumford, "Lectures on Curves on an Algebraic Surface," Ann. of Math. Studies, No. 59, Princeton Univ. Press, Princeton, New Jersey, 1966.

[131] D. Mumford, "Abelian Varieties," Oxford Univ. Press, London and New York, 1970.

[132] M. Nagata, "Local Rings," Wiley (Interscience), New York; 1962.

[133] V. Niemytski and V. Stepanov, "Qualitative Theory of Differential Equations," Princeton Univ. Press, Princeton, New Jersey, 1960.

[134] L. Nirenberg, Lectures on linear partial differential equations, *CBMS Regional Conf. Series in Math.* **17**, 1973, Amer. Math. Soc.

[135] *Proc. 5th Nordic Summer School in Math. Algebraic geometry*, Oslo 1970 (F. Oort, ed.), Wolters-Noordhoff, Groningen, 1972.

[136] D. Northcott, "Ideal Theory," Cambridge Univ. Tracts No. 42, Cambridge Univ. Press, Cambridge, England, 1953.

[137] S. Novikov, The methods of algebraic topology from the view-point of cobordism theories, *Izv. Akad. Nauk SSSR* **31**, 855–961 (1967).

[138] T. O'Meara, "Introduction to Quadratic Forms," Springer-Verlag, Berlin and New York, 1963.

[139] D. Ornstein and B. Weiss, Geodesic flows are Bernoullian, *Israel J. Math.* **14**, 184 (1973).

[140] R. Palais, "Seminar on the Atiyah–Singer Index Theorem," Ann. of Math. Studies, No. 57, Princeton Univ. Press, Princeton, New Jersey, 1965.

[141] R. Penrose, Techniques of differential topology in Relativity, *CBMS Regional Conf. Series in Applied Math.* **7**, 1972.

[141 *bis*] A. Pietsch, "Nuclear Locally Convex Spaces," Springer-Verlag, Berlin and New York, 1972.

[142] I. Pyatetskii-Shapiro, "Automorphic Functions and the Geometry of Classical Domains," Gordon & Breach, New York, 1969.

[143] A. Pliš, A smooth linear elliptic differential equation without any solution in a sphere, *Comm. Pure Appl. Math.* **14**, 599–616 (1961).

[144] M. Postnikov, "The Variational Theory of Geodesics," Saunders, Philadelphia, Pennsylvania, 1967.

[145] L. Pukansky, "Leçons sur la représentation des groupes," Soc. Math. de France, Monograph No. 2, Dunod, Paris, 1967.

[146] M. Reed and B. Simon, "Methods of Modern Mathematical Physics," Vols. 1–4, Academic Press, New York, 1972–1979.

[147] A. Robinson, "Nonstandard Analysis," North-Holland, Amsterdam, 1966.

[148] A. Robinson, Metamathematical problems, *J. Symbolic Logic* **38**, 500 (1973).

[149] B. Rotman and G. Kneebone, "The Theory of Sets and Transfinite Numbers," Oldbourne, London, 1966.

[150] W. Rudin, "Fourier Analysis on Groups," Wiley (Interscience), New York, 1968.

[151] W. Rudin, "Function Theory in Polydiscs," Benjamin, New York, 1969.

[152] H. Seifert and W. Threlfall, "Lehrbuch der Topologie," Teubner, Leipzig and Berlin, 1934.

[153] J. P. Serre, Géométrie algébrique et géométrie analytique, *Ann. Inst. Fourier* **6**, 1–42 (1955).

[154] J. P. Serre, "Groupes algébriques et corps de classes," Hermann, Paris, 1959.

[155] J. P. Serre, "Corps locaux," Hermann, Paris, 1962.

[156] J. P. Serre, "Représentations linéaires des groupes," Hermann, Paris, 1967.
[157] J. P. Serre, "Cours d'arithmétique," (Collect. SUP), Presses Univ. de France, Paris, 1970.
[158] J. P. Serre, Problèmes globaux relatifs aux variétés de Stein, *Coll. sur les fonctions de plusieurs variables, Bruxelles*, 1953, Masson, Paris, 1953.
[159] J. P. Serre, Zeta and L-functions, *Arithmetical algebraic geometry, Conf. at Purdue Univ.*, 1963 (O. Schilling, ed.), pp. 82–92, Harper, New York, 1965.
[160] I. Shafarevich, "Lectures on Minimal Models and Birational Transformations of 2-Dimensional Schemes," Tata Inst. of Fund Research, Bombay, mimeograph, 1966.
[161] I. Shafarevich, "Basic Algebraic Geometry," Springer-Verlag, Berlin and New York, 1974.
[162] I. Shafarevich *et al.*, "Algebraic Surfaces," Proc. Steklov Inst. Math., No. 75, Amer. Math. Soc., 1967.
[163] P. Shields, "The Theory of Bernoulli Shifts," Univ. of Chicago Press, Chicago, Illinois, 1973.
[164] G. Shimura, "Introduction to the Arithmetic Theory of Automorphic Functions," Publ. Math. Soc. of Japan, No. 11, Princeton Univ. Press, Princeton, New Jersey, 1971.
[165] G. Shimura, On canonical models of arithmetic quotients of bounded symmetric domains, *Ann. of Math.* **91**, 144–222 (1970).
[166] G. Shimura and Y. Taniyama, "Complex multiplication of abelian varieties," Publ. Math. Soc. of Japan, No. 6, 1961.
[167] K. Shiraiwa, Manifolds which do not admit Anosov diffeomorphisms, *Nagoya Math. J.* **49**, 111–115 (1973).
[168] C. Siegel, "Vorlesungen über Himmelsmechanik," Springer-Verlag, Berlin and New York, 1956.
[169] Y. Siu, "Techniques of Extensions of Analytic Objects," Dekker, New York, 1974.
[169 *bis*] H. Skoda, Fibrés holomorphes à base et à fibre de Stein, *C. R. Acad. Sci. Paris*, A **284** 1199–1202 (1977).
[170] E. Spanier, "Algebraic Topology," McGraw-Hill, New York, 1966.
[171] N. Steenrod, "The Topology of Fibre Bundles," Princeton Univ. Press, Princeton, New Jersey, 1951.
[171 *bis*] N. Steenrod, Cohomology operations, and obstructions to extending continuous functions, *Adv. in Math.* **8**, 371–416 (1972).
[172] E. Stein, Analytic continuation of group representations, *Adv. in Math.* **4**, 172–207 (1970).
[173] S. Sternberg, "Celestial Mechanics," Vols. 1 and 2, Benjamin, New York, 1969.
[174] R. Stong, "Notes on Cobordism Theory," Princeton Univ. Press, Princeton, New Jersey, 1968.
[175] "Studies in Model Theory," M. Morley, ed., Math. Association of America, 1973.
[176] H. Swinnerton-Dyer, The conjectures of Birch and Swinnerton-Dyer and of Tate, *Proc. Conf. Local Fields at Driebergen*, 1966, pp. 132–157, Springer-Verlag, Berlin and New York, 1967.
[177] Symmetric spaces: Short courses presented at Washington Univ. (W. Boothby and G. Weiss, eds.), Dekker, New York, 1972.
[178] J. Synge, "Relativity: The General Theory," North-Holland, Amsterdam, 1960.
[179] J. Tate, Algebraic cycles and poles of zeta functions, *Arithmetical algebraic geometry, Conf. at Purdue Univ.*, 1963 (O. Schilling, ed.), pp. 93–110, Harper, New York, 1965.
[180] R. Thom, "Stabilité structurale et morphogenèse," Benjamin, New York, 1972.
[181] H. Toda, "Composition Methods in Homotopy Groups of Spheres," Ann. of Math. Studies, No. 49, Princeton Univ. Press, Princeton, New Jersey, 1962.
[182] H. Toda, A survey of homotopy theory, *Adv. in Math.* **10**, 417–455 (1973).

[183] A. Tognoli, Recenti progressi in geometria algebraica, *Boll. Un. Mat. Ital.* **7**, Suppl. Fasc. 1, p. 119 (1973).
[184] F. Treves, "Linear Partial Differential Equations with Constant Coefficients," Gordon & Breach, New York, 1966.
[185] F. Treves, "Basic Linear Partial Differential Equations," Academic Press, New York, 1975.
[186] "Value Distribution Theory," Vols. 1 and 2, (R. Kujala and A. Witter, ed.), Dekker, New York, 1974.
[187] N. Vilenkin, "Fonctions spéciales et théorie de la représentation des groupes," Dunod, Paris, 1969.
[188] C. T. C. Wall, "Surgery on Compact Manifolds," Academic Press, New York, 1970.
[189] N. Wallach, "Harmonic Analysis on Homogeneous Spaces," Dekker, New York, 1973.
[190] G. Warner, "Harmonic Analysis on Semi-simple Groups," Vols. 1 and 2, Springer-Verlag, Berlin and New York, 1972.
[191] A. Weil, "Introduction à l'étude des variétés kähleriennes," Hermann, Paris, 1958.
[192] A. Weil, "Basic Number Theory," Springer-Verlag, Berlin and New York, 1967.
[193] R. Wells, "Differential Analysis on Complex Manifolds," Prentice-Hall, Englewood Cliffs, New Jersey, 1973.
[194] G. Whitehead, Generalized homology theories, *Trans. Amer. Math. Soc.* **102**, 227–283 (1962).
[195] G. Whitehead, Recent advances in homotopy theory, *CBMS Regional Conf. Series in Math.* **5**, Amer. Math. Soc., 1970.
[196] H. Whitney, "Geometric Integration Theory," Princeton Univ. Press, Princeton, New Jersey, 1957.
[197] N. Wiener, Generalized harmonic analysis, *Acta Math.* **55**, 117–258 (1930).
[198] O. Zariski, "Algebraic Surfaces," Ergebnisse der Math., Bd. III, Heft 5, 2nd ed., Springer-Verlag, Berlin and New York, 1970.
[199] O. Zariski, "Introduction to the Problem of Minimal Models in the Theory of Algebraic Surfaces," Publ. Math. Soc. of Japan, No. 4, 1958.

Proceedings of the International Congress of Mathematicians (Stockholm, 1962), Almqvist and Wiksells, Uppsala, 1963.
Actes du Congrès international des mathématiciens (Nice, 1970), Gauthier-Villars, Paris, 3 vols., 1971.
Proceedings of the International Congress of Mathematicians (Vancouver, 1974), 2 vols., Canadian Math. Congress, 1975.

Supplementary Bibliography

[200] J. Benedetto, "Spectral Synthesis," Academic Press, New York, 1975.
[201] J. Cassels, "Rational quadratic forms," (London Math. Soc. Monographs No. 13), Academic Press, New York, 1978.
[202] J. Dixmier, "Algèbres enveloppantes," Gauthier-Villars, Paris, 1974.
[203] "Encyclopedic Dictionary of Mathematics," (S. Iyanaga and Y. Kawada, eds.), MIT Press, Cambridge, Massachusetts, 1977.
[204] M. Golubitsky and V. Guillemin, "Stable Mappings and Their Singularities," Springer-Verlag, Berlin and New York, 1973.
[205] H. Halbertstam and K. Roth, "Sequences I," Oxford Univ. Press, London and New York, 1966.

[206] H. Halberstam and H. Richert, "Sieve Methods," Academic Press, New York, 1974.
[207] R. Hartshorne, "Algebraic Geometry," Springer-Verlag, Berlin and New York, 1977.
[208] M. Hazewinkel, "Formal Groups," Academic Press, New York, 1978.
[209] P. Johnstone, "Topos Theory," Academic Press, New York, 1977.
[210] R. Kirby and L. Siebenmann, "Foundational Essays on Topological Manifolds, Smoothings and Triangulations," Princeton Univ. Press, Princeton, New Jersey, 1977.
[211] I. Kra, "Automorphic Forms and Kleinian Groups," Benjamin, New York, 1972.
[212] S. Lefschetz, "Applications of Algebraic Topology," Springer-Verlag, Berlin and New York, 1975.
[213] Ju. Manin, "A Course in Mathematical Logic," Springer-Verlag, Berlin and New York, 1977.
[214] D. Mumford, "Algebraic Geometry I: Complex Projective Varieties," Springer-Verlag, Berlin and New York, 1976.
[215] H. Richert, "Sieve Methods," Tata Inst. of Fund. Research, Bombay, mimeograph, 1976.
[216] J. Rosser, "Simplified Independence Proofs," Academic Press, New York, 1969.
[217] R. Switzer, "Algebraic Topology: Homotopy and Homology," Springer-Verlag, Berlin and New York, 1975.
[218] M. Taibleson, "Fourier Analysis on Local Fields," Princeton Univ. Press, Princeton, New Jersey, 1975.
[219] J. van Heijenoort, "From Frege to Gödel. A Source Book in Mathematical Logic," Harvard Univ. Press, Cambridge, Massachusetts, 1967.
[220] V. Arnold, "Méthodes mathématiques de la mécanique classique," Ed. Mir, Moscow, 1976.
[221] P. Deligne, La conjecture de Weil, II, *Publ. Math. I.H.E.S.*, No. 52, 138–252 (1980).
[222] P. Griffiths and J. Harris, "Principles of algebraic geometry," Wiley, New York, 1978.
[223] W. Klingenberg, "Lectures on Closed Geodesics," Springer-Verlag, Berlin and New York, 1978.
[224] C. Morawetz, Notes on time decay and scattering for some hyperbolic problems, *CBMS Regional Conf. Series in Applied Math.*, p. 19, 1975.
[225] G. Pedersen, "C*-algebras and their automorphism groups," (London Math. Soc. Monographs No. 14), Academic Press, New York, 1979.
[226] M. Takesaki, "Theory of operator algebras I," Springer-Verlag, Berlin and New York, 1979.
[227] R. Douglas, "C*-algebra extensions and K-homology," Princeton Univ. Press, Princeton, New Jersey, 1980.

Index

The references are either to a chapter in the text, or to the bibliography in the case of a definition not given (or incomplete) in the text.

D

I

J

K

L

U

V

W

Y

Z

Pure and Applied Mathematics

A Series of Monographs and Textbooks

Editors **Samuel Eilenberg and Hyman Bass**

Columbia University, New York

RECENT TITLES

CARL L. DEVITO. Functional Analysis

MICHIEL HAZEWINKEL. Formal Groups and Applications

SIGURDUR HELGASON. Differential Geometry, Lie Groups, and Symmetric Spaces

ROBERT B. BURCKEL. An Introduction to Classical Complex Analysis: Volume 1

JOSEPH J. ROTMAN. An Introduction to Homological Algebra

C. TRUESDELL AND R. G. MUNCASTER. Fundamentals of Maxwell's Kinetic Theory of a Simple Monatomic Gas: Treated as a Branch of Rational Mechanics

BARRY SIMON. Functional Integration and Quantum Physics

GRZEGORZ ROZENBERG AND ARTO SALOMAA. The Mathematical Theory of L Systems.

DAVID KINDERLEHRER and GUIDO STAMPACCHIA. An Introduction to Variational Inequalities and Their Applications.

H. SEIFERT AND W. THRELFALL. A Textbook of Topology; H. SEIFERT. Topology of 3-Dimensional Fibered Spaces

LOUIS HALLE ROWEN. Polynominal Identities in Ring Theory

DONALD W. KAHN. Introduction to Global Analysis

DRAGOS M. CVETKOVIC, MICHAEL DOOB, AND HORST SACHS. Spectra of Graphs

ROBERT M. YOUNG. An Introduction to Nonharmonic Fourier Series

MICHAEL C. IRWIN. Smooth Dynamical Systems

JOHN B. GARNETT. Bounded Analytic Functions

EDUARD PRUGOVEČKI. Quantum Mechanics in Hilbert Space, Second Edition

M. SCOTT OSBORNE AND GARTH WARNER. The Theory of Eisenstein Systems

JEAN DIEUDONNÉ. A Panorama of Pure Mathematics; Translated by I. G. Macdonald

JOSEPH G. ROSENSTEIN. Linear Orderings

IN PREPARATION

K. A. ZHEVLAKOV, A. M. SLIN'KO, I. P. SHESTAKOV, AND A. I. SHIRSHOV. Translated by HARRY SMITH. Rings That Are Nearly Associative

ROBERT B. BURCKEL. An Introduction to Classical Complex Analysis: Volume 2

HOWARD OSBORN. Vector Bundles: Volume 1, Foundations and Stiefel–Whitney Classes

RICHARD V. KADISON AND JOHN R. RINGROSE. Fundamentals of the Theory of Operator Algebras

AVRAHAM FEINTUCH AND RICHARD SAEKS. System Theory: A Hilbert Space Approach

BARRETT O'NEILL. Semi-Riemannian Geometry: With Applications to Relativity

ULF GRENANDER. Mathematical Experiments on the Computer